"*You must climb to the top and then you'll see*"
—*The Tinder-box, p. 370*

THE HARVARD CLASSICS

EDITED BY CHARLES W ELIOT LL D

FOLK-LORE AND FABLE

ÆSOP · GRIMM · ANDERSEN

WITH INTRODUCTIONS AND NOTES

VOLUME 17

P F COLLIER & SON COMPANY
NEW YORK

Designed, Printed, and Bound at
The Collier Press, New York

INTRODUCTORY NOTE

THE HABIT of telling stories is one of the most primitive characteristics of the human race. The most ancient civilizations, the most barbarous savages, of whom we have any knowledge have yielded to investigators clear traces of the possession of this practise. The specimens of their narrative that have been gathered from all the ends of the earth and from the remotest times of which we have written record show traces of purpose, now religious and didactic, now patriotic and political; but behind or beside the purpose one can discern the permanent human delight in the story for its own sake.

The oldest of stories are the myths: not the elaborated and sophisticated tales that one finds in, say, Greek epic and drama, but the myth pure and simple. This is the answer of primitive science to the question of the barbaric child, the explanation of the thunder or the rain, of the origin of man or of fire, of disease or death. The form of such myths is accounted for by the belief known as "animism," which assumed personality in every object and phenomenon, and conceived no distinction in the kind of existence of a man, a dog, a tree, or a stone. Such myths are still told among, e. g., the American Indians, and the assumption just mentioned accounts for such features as the transformation of the same being from a man into a log or a fish, or the marriage of a coyote and a woman. Derived from this state of belief and showing signs of their origin, are such animal stories as form the basis of the artistically worked-up tales of "Uncle Remus."

Thus in primitive myth, the divinities of natural forces are not personifications, for there was no figure of speech involved; the storm, the ocean, and the plague were to the mythmakers actually persons. The symbolical element in literary myths is a later development, possible only as man gradually arrived at the realization of his separateness in kind from the non-human objects of his senses. With this realization came the attempt to adapt the myths that had come down from more primitive times to his new way of thinking, and the long process of making the myths reasonable and credible set in.

But while the higher myths were being thus transformed into the religions of the civilized man, the ways of thinking that had *produced them in their original form survived to some extent in stories of less dignity, which made no pretensions to be either science or religion but which were told only because they entertained. Tales of this kind have come down from mouth to mouth in less sophisticated communities to our own day, and are now being killed out only by the printing-press and the diffusion of the art of reading. But happily many have been collected, and they are represented in the present volume by the "Märchen" or household tales preserved by Grimm.*

Far earlier written down, but less primitive in kind, are the Æsopic Fables. In these allegorical tales, the form of the old animistic story is used without any belief in the identity of the personalities of men and animals, but with a conscious double meaning and for the purpose of teaching a lesson. The fable is a product not of the folk but of the learned; and though at times it has been handed down by word of mouth, it is really a literary form.

Still more recent, both in kind and in date, are the Wonder stories of modern manufacture represented here by the tales of Hans Christian Andersen. This nineteenth-century Dane had a marvelous knack of entertaining children by repeating old folktales of the type collected by Grimm; and his success in this led him on to attempt inventing new ones. The new ones were successful, too; but though the incidents were often suggested by traditional stories, Hans Christian Andersen's finished products are to be regarded as a form of modern fiction worked out under the influence of more or less primitive folk-tales.

Æsop is little more than the shadow of a name. He was a slave from the island of Samos, who flourished, according to Herodotus, about the middle of the sixth century before Christ; and his name is associated with the special use of the fable for political purposes at a time when the reign of the tyrants in Greece made unveiled speech dangerous. About two hundred and fifty years after Æsop's time, Demetrius of Phaleron collected a large number of fables and called them by Æsop's name, and a version of these was turned into Latin verse by one Phædrus in the time of Augustus. This Phædrus is the main source of the modern "Æsop," but no one can point to any one fable existing to-day as certainly the invention of the Samian slave.

*In India as well as in Greece the fable was common from very
early times; and near the beginning of our era a Buddhist collection that had come west by Alexandria was combined with that
of Demetrius, and later turned into Greek verse by Valerius
Babrius. A Greek prose version of Babrius was accepted for
centuries as the original Æsop. The habit of summing up the
lesson of the fable in a "moral" at the end seems to have come in
with the Oriental contribution.*

*The history of collections of fables in Europe from Phædrus
and Babrius down is one of incredible complexity, on many of the
details of which scholars are yet far from agreement. Additions
to the common stock have come in from a vast variety of sources;
the stories have been retold scores of times, so that there is nothing approaching an authentic text; yet the name of Æsop has
clung till it has become merely a convenient name for this particular type of allegorical beast-tale.*

*In the present collection, the fables have been retold in simple
language by Mr. Joseph Jacobs. He has chosen those examples
that have become most universally popular, and at the same time
has given representatives from all the main sources. A glance
at the titles will be sufficient to show to what an extraordinary
extent these simple stories have become the common property of
all peoples.*

CONTENTS

ÆSOP'S FABLES—

CONTENTS

CONTENTS

FOLK-LORE AND FABLE

ÆSOP'S FABLES

THE COCK AND THE PEARL

A COCK was once strutting up and down the farmyard among the hens when suddenly he espied something shining amid the straw. "Ho! ho!" quoth he, "that's for me," and soon rooted it out from beneath the straw. What did it turn out to be but a Pearl that by some chance had been lost in the yard? "You may be a treasure," quoth Master Cock, "to men that prize you, but for me I would rather have a single barley-corn than a peck of pearls."

"PRECIOUS THINGS ARE FOR THOSE THAT CAN PRIZE THEM."

THE WOLF AND THE LAMB

ONCE upon a time a Wolf was lapping at a spring on a hillside, when, looking up, what should he see but a Lamb just beginning to drink a little lower down. "There's my supper," thought he, "if only I can find some excuse to seize it." Then he called out to the Lamb, "How dare you muddle the water from which I am drinking?"

"Nay, master, nay," said Lambikin; "if the water be muddy up there, I cannot be the cause of it, for it runs down from you to me."

"Well, then," said the Wolf, "why did you call me bad names this time last year?"

"That cannot be," said the Lamb; "I am only six months old."

"I don't care," snarled the Wolf; "if it was not you

it was your father;" and with that he rushed upon the poor little Lamb and—

WARRA WARRA WARRA WARRA WARRA—

ate her all up. But before she died she gasped out—

"ANY EXCUSE WILL SERVE A TYRANT."

THE DOG AND THE SHADOW

IT happened that a Dog had got a piece of meat and was carrying it home in his mouth to eat it in peace. Now on his way home he had to cross a plank lying across a running brook. As he crossed, he looked down and saw his own shadow reflected in the water beneath. Thinking it was another dog with another piece of meat, he made up his mind to have that also. So he made a snap at the shadow in the water, but as he opened his mouth the piece of meat fell out, dropped into the water and was never seen more.

"BEWARE LEST YOU LOSE THE SUBSTANCE BY GRASPING
AT THE SHADOW."

THE LION'S SHARE

THE Lion went once a-hunting along with the Fox, the Jackal, and the Wolf. They hunted and they hunted till at last they surprised a Stag, and soon took its life. Then came the question how the spoil should be divided. "Quarter me this Stag," roared the Lion; so the other animals skinned it and cut it into four parts. Then the Lion took his stand in front of the carcass and pronounced judgment: "The first quarter is for me in my capacity as King of Beasts; the second is mine as arbiter; another share comes to me for my part in the chase; and as for the fourth quarter, well, as for that, I should like to see which of you will dare to lay a paw upon it."

"Humph," grumbled the Fox as he walked away with his tail between his legs; but he spoke in a low growl—

"YOU MAY SHARE THE LABOURS OF THE GREAT, BUT YOU
WILL NOT SHARE THE SPOIL."

THE WOLF AND THE CRANE

A WOLF had been gorging on an animal he had killed, when suddenly a small bone in the meat stuck in his throat and he could not swallow it. He soon felt terrible pain in his throat, and ran up and down groaning and groaning and seeking for something to relieve the pain. He tried to induce every one he met to remove the bone. "I would give anything," said he, "if you would take it out." At last the Crane agreed to try, and told the Wolf to lie on his side and open his jaws as wide as he could. Then the Crane put its long neck down the Wolf's throat, and with its beak loosened the bone, till at last it got it out.

"Will you kindly give me the reward you promised?" said the Crane.

The Wolf grinned and showed his teeth and said: "Be content. You have put your head inside a Wolf's mouth and taken it out again in safety; that ought to be reward enough for you."

"GRATITUDE AND GREED GO NOT TOGETHER."

THE MAN AND THE SERPENT

A COUNTRYMAN'S son by accident trod upon a Serpent's tail, which turned and bit him so that he died. The father in a rage got his axe, and pursuing the Serpent, cut off part of its tail. So the Serpent in revenge began stinging several of the Farmer's cattle and caused him severe loss. Well, the Farmer thought it best to make it up with the Serpent, and brought food and honey to the mouth of its lair, and said to it: "Let's forget and forgive; perhaps you were right to punish my son, and take vengeance on my cattle, but surely I was right in trying to revenge him; now that we are both satisfied why should not we be friends again?"

"No, no," said the Serpent; "take away your gifts; you can never forget the death of your son, nor I the loss of my tail."

"INJURIES MAY BE FORGIVEN, BUT NOT FORGOTTEN."

THE TOWN MOUSE AND THE COUNTRY MOUSE

Now you must know that a Town Mouse once upon a time went on a visit to his cousin in the country. He was rough and ready, this cousin, but he loved his town friend and made him heartily welcome. Beans and bacon, cheese and bread, were all he had to offer, but he offered them freely. The Town Mouse rather turned up his long nose at this country fare, and said: "I cannot understand, Cousin, how you can put up with such poor food as this, but of course you cannot expect anything better in the country; come you with me and I will show you how to live. When you have been in town a week you will wonder how you could ever have stood a country life." No sooner said than done: the two mice set off for the town and arrived at the Town Mouse's residence late at night. "You will want some refreshment after our long journey," said the polite Town Mouse, and took his friend into the grand dining-room. There they found the remains of a fine feast, and soon the two mice were eating up jellies and cakes and all that was nice. Suddenly they heard growling and barking. "What is that?" said the Country Mouse. "It is only the dogs of the house," answered the other. "Only!" said the Country Mouse. "I do not like that music at my dinner." Just at that moment the door flew open, in came two huge mastiffs, and the two mice had to scamper down and run off. "Good-bye, Cousin," said the Country Mouse. "What! going so soon?" said the other. "Yes," he replied;

"BETTER BEANS AND BACON IN PEACE THAN CAKES
AND ALE IN FEAR."

THE FOX AND THE CROW

A FOX once saw a Crow fly off with a piece of cheese in its beak and settle on a branch of a tree. "That's for me, as I am a Fox," said Master Reynard, and he walked up to the foot of the tree. "Good-day, Mistress Crow," he cried. "How well you are looking to-day: how glossy your feathers; how bright your eye. I feel sure your voice must surpass that of other birds, just as your figure does; let me hear but one song from you that I may greet you as the Queen of Birds." The Crow lifted up her head and began to caw her best, but the moment she opened her mouth the piece of cheese fell to the ground, only to be snapped up by Master Fox. "That will do," said he. "That was all I wanted. In exchange for your cheese I will give you a piece of advice for the future—

"DO NOT TRUST FLATTERERS."

THE SICK LION

A LION had come to the end of his days and lay sick unto death at the mouth of his cave, gasping for breath. The animals, his subjects, came round him and drew nearer as he grew more and more helpless. When they saw him on the point of death they thought to themselves: "Now is the time to pay off old grudges." So the Boar came up and drove at him with his tusks; then a Bull gored him with his horns; still the Lion lay helpless before them: so the Ass, feeling quite safe from danger, came up, and turning his tail to the Lion kicked up his heels into his face. "This is a double death," growled the Lion.

"ONLY COWARDS INSULT DYING MAJESTY."

THE ASS AND THE LAPDOG

A FARMER one day came to the stables to see to his beasts of burden: among them was his favourite Ass, that was always well fed and often carried his master. With the Farmer came his Lapdog, who danced about and licked his hand and frisked about as happy as could be. The Farmer felt in his pocket, gave the Lapdog some dainty food, and sat down while he gave his orders to his servants. The Lapdog jumped into his master's lap, and lay there blinking while the Farmer stroked his ears. The Ass, seeing this, broke loose from his halter and commenced prancing about in imitation of the Lapdog. The Farmer could not hold his sides with laughter, so the Ass went up to him, and putting his feet upon the Farmer's shoulder attempted to climb into his lap. The Farmer's servants rushed up with sticks and pitchforks and soon taught the Ass that

"CLUMSY JESTING IS NO JOKE."

THE LION AND THE MOUSE

ONCE when a Lion was asleep a little Mouse began running up and down upon him; this soon wakened the Lion, who placed his huge paw upon him, and opened his big jaws to swallow him. "Pardon, O King," cried the little Mouse: "forgive me this time, I shall never forget it: who knows but what I may be able to do you a turn some of these days?" The Lion was so tickled at the idea of the Mouse being able to help him, that he lifted up his paw and let him go. Some time after the Lion was caught in a trap, and the hunters, who desired to carry him alive to the King, tied him to a tree while they went in search of a waggon to carry him on. Just then the little Mouse happened to pass by, and seeing the sad plight in which the Lion was, went up to him and soon gnawed away the ropes that bound the King of the Beasts. "Was I not right?" said the little Mouse.

"LITTLE FRIENDS MAY PROVE GREAT FRIENDS."

THE SWALLOW AND THE OTHER BIRDS

IT happened that a Countryman was sowing some hemp seeds in a field where a Swallow and some other birds were hopping about picking up their food. "Beware of that man," quoth the Swallow. "Why, what is he doing?" said the others. "That is hemp seed he is sowing; be careful to pick up every one of the seeds, or else you will repent it." The birds paid no heed to the Swallow's words, and by and by the hemp grew up and was made into cord, and of the cords nets were made, and many a bird that had despised the Swallow's advice was caught in nets made out of that very hemp. "What did I tell you?" said the Swallow.

"DESTROY THE SEED OF EVIL, OR IT WILL GROW
UP TO YOUR RUIN."

THE FROGS DESIRING A KING

THE Frogs were living as happy as could be in a marshy swamp that just suited them; they went splashing about caring for nobody and nobody troubling with them. But some of them thought that this was not right, that they should have a king and a proper constitution, so they determined to send up a petition to Jove to give them what they wanted. "Mighty Jove," they cried, "send unto us a king that will rule over us and keep us in order." Jove laughed at their croaking, and threw down into the swamp a huge Log, which came down—*kerplash*—into the swamp. The Frogs were frightened out of their lives by the commotion made in their midst, and all rushed to the bank to look at the horrible monster; but after a time, seeing that it did not move, one or two of the boldest of them ventured out towards the Log, and even dared to touch it; still it did not move. Then the greatest hero of the Frogs jumped upon the Log and commenced dancing up and down upon it, thereupon all the Frogs came and did the same; and for some time the Frogs went about their business every day without taking the slightest notice of their new King Log lying in their midst. But this did not suit them, so they sent another petition to Jove, and said to him, "We want a real king; one that will really rule over us." Now this made Jove angry, so he sent among them a big Stork that soon set to work gobbling them all up. Then the Frogs repented when too late.

"BETTER NO RULE THAN CRUEL RULE."

THE MOUNTAINS IN LABOUR

ONE day the Countrymen noticed that the Mountains were in labour; smoke came out of their summits, the earth was quaking at their feet, trees were crashing, and huge rocks were tumbling. They felt sure that something horrible was going to happen. They all gathered together in one place to see what terrible thing this would be. They waited and they waited, but nothing came. At last there was a still more violent earthquake, and a huge gap appeared in the side of the Mountains. They all fell down upon their knees and waited. At last, and at last, a teeny, tiny mouse poked its little head and bristles out of the gap and came running down towards them, and ever after they used to say:

"MUCH OUTCRY, LITTLE OUTCOME."

THE HARES AND THE FROGS

THE Hares were so persecuted by the other beasts, they did not know where to go. As soon as they saw a single animal approach them, off they used to run. One day they saw a troop of wild Horses stampeding about, and in quite a panic all the Hares scuttled off to a lake hard by, determined to drown themselves rather than live in such a continual state of fear. But just as they got near the bank of the lake, a troop of Frogs, frightened in their turn by the approach of the Hares, scuttled off, and jumped into the water. "Truly," said one of the Hares, "things are not so bad as they seem:

"THERE IS ALWAYS SOME ONE WORSE
OFF THAN YOURSELF."

THE WOLF AND THE KID

A KID was perched up on the top of a house, and looking down saw a Wolf passing under him. Immediately he be-

gan to revile and attack his enemy. "Murderer and thief,"
he cried, "what do you here near honest folks' houses?
How dare you make an appearance where your vile deeds
are known?"

"Curse away, my young friend," said the Wolf.

"IT IS EASY TO BE BRAVE FROM A SAFE DISTANCE."

THE WOODMAN AND THE SERPENT

ONE wintry day a Woodman was tramping home from
his work when he saw something black lying on the snow.
When he came closer, he saw it was a Serpent to all appearance dead. But he took it up and put it in his bosom
to warm while he hurried home. As soon as he got indoors
he put the Serpent down on the hearth before the fire. The
children watched it and saw it slowly come to life again.
Then one of them stooped down to stroke it, but the Serpent
raised its head and put out its fangs and was about to sting
the child to death. So the Woodman seized his axe, and
with one stroke cut the Serpent in two. "Ah," said he,

"NO GRATITUDE FROM THE WICKED."

THE BALD MAN AND THE FLY

THERE was once a Bald Man who sat down after work
on a hot summer's day. A Fly came up and kept buzzing
about his bald pate, and stinging him from time to time.
The Man aimed a blow at his little enemy, but—*whack*—
his palm came on his head instead; again the Fly tormented
him, but this time the Man was wiser and said:

"YOU WILL ONLY INJURE YOURSELF IF YOU TAKE
NOTICE OF DESPICABLE ENEMIES."

THE FOX AND THE STORK

AT one time the Fox and the Stork were on visiting terms
and seemed very good friends. So the Fox invited the Stork

to dinner, and for a joke put nothing before her but some soup in a very shallow dish. This the Fox could easily lap up, but the Stork could only wet the end of her long bill in it, and left the meal as hungry as when she began. "I am sorry," said the Fox, "the soup is not to your liking."

"Pray do not apologise," said the Stork. "I hope you will return this visit, and come and dine with me soon." So a day was appointed when the Fox should visit the Stork; but when they were seated at table all that was for their dinner was contained in a very long-necked jar with a narrow mouth, in which the Fox could not insert his snout, so all he could manage to do was to lick the outside of the jar.

"I will not apologise for the dinner," said the Stork:

"ONE BAD TURN DESERVES ANOTHER."

THE FOX AND THE MASK

A Fox had by some means got into the store-room of a theatre. Suddenly he observed a face glaring down on him, and began to be very frightened; but looking more closely he found it was only a Mask such as actors use to put over their face. "Ah," said the Fox, "you look very fine; it is a pity you have not got any brains."

"OUTSIDE SHOW IS A POOR SUBSTITUTE FOR INNER WORTH."

THE JAY AND THE PEACOCK

A Jay venturing into a yard where Peacocks used to walk, found there a number of feathers which had fallen from the Peacocks when they were moulting. He tied them all to his tail and strutted down towards the Peacocks. When he came near them they soon discovered the cheat, and striding up to him pecked at him and plucked away his borrowed plumes. So the Jay could do no better than go back to the other Jays, who had watched his behaviour from a distance; but they were equally annoyed with him, and told him

"IT IS NOT ONLY FINE FEATHERS THAT MAKE FINE BIRDS."

THE FROG AND THE OX

"Oh Father," said a little Frog to the big one sitting by the side of a pool, "I have seen such a terrible monster! It was as big as a mountain, with horns on its head, and a long tail, and it had hoofs divided in two."

"Tush, child, tush," said the old Frog, "that was only Farmer White's Ox. It isn't so big either; he may be a little bit taller than I, but I could easily make myself quite as broad; just you see." So he blew himself out, and blew himself out, and blew himself out. "Was he as big as that?" asked he.

"Oh, much bigger than that," said the young Frog.

Again the old one blew himself out, and asked the young one if the Ox was as big as that.

"Bigger, father, bigger," was the reply.

So the Frog took a deep breath, and blew and blew and blew, and swelled and swelled and swelled. And then he said: "I'm sure the Ox is not as big as—" But at this moment he burst.

"SELF-CONCEIT MAY LEAD TO SELF-DESTRUCTION."

ANDROCLES

A SLAVE named Androcles once escaped from his master and fled to the forest. As he was wandering about there he came upon a Lion lying down moaning and groaning. At first he turned to flee, but finding that the Lion did not pursue him, he turned back and went up to him. As he came near, the Lion put out his paw, which was all swollen and bleeding, and Androcles found that a huge thorn had got into it, and was causing all the pain. He pulled out the thorn and bound up the paw of the Lion, who was soon able to rise and lick the hand of Androcles like a dog. Then the Lion took Androcles to his cave, and every day used to bring him meat from which to live. But shortly afterwards both Androcles and the Lion were captured, and the slave was sentenced to be thrown to the Lion, after the latter had been kept without food for several days. The Emperor and all his Court came to see the spectacle, and Androcles was led out into the middle of the arena. Soon the Lion was let loose from his den, and rushed bounding and roaring towards his victim. But as soon as he came near to Androcles he recognised his friend, and fawned upon him, and licked his hands like a friendly dog. The Emperor, surprised at this, summoned Androcles to him, who told him the whole story. Whereupon the slave was pardoned and freed, and the Lion let loose to his native forest.

"GRATITUDE IS THE SIGN OF NOBLE SOULS."

THE BAT, THE BIRDS, AND THE BEASTS

A GREAT conflict was about to come off between the Birds and the Beasts. When the two armies were collected together the Bat hesitated which to join. The Birds that passed his perch said: "Come with us"; but he said: "I am a Beast." Later on, some Beasts who were passing underneath him looked up and said: "Come with us"; but he said: "I am a Bird." Luckily at the last moment peace was made, and no battle took place, so the Bat came to the Birds and wished to join in the rejoicings, but they all turned against him and he had to fly away. He then went to the Beasts, but soon had to beat a retreat, or else they would have torn him to pieces. "Ah," said the Bat, "I see now

"HE THAT IS NEITHER ONE THING NOR THE OTHER HAS NO FRIENDS."

THE HART AND THE HUNTER

THE Hart was once drinking from a pool and admiring the noble figure he made there. "Ah," said he, "where can you see such noble horns as these, with such antlers! I wish I had legs more worthy to bear such a noble crown; it is a pity they are so slim and slight." At that moment a Hunter approached and sent an arrow whistling after him. Away bounded the Hart, and soon, by the aid of his nimble legs, was nearly out of sight of the Hunter; but not noticing where he was going, he passed under some trees with branches growing low down in which his antlers were caught, so that the Hunter had time to come up. "Alas! alas!" cried the Hart:

"WE OFTEN DESPISE WHAT IS MOST USEFUL TO US."

THE SERPENT AND THE FILE

A SERPENT in the course of its wanderings came into an armourer's shop. As he glided over the floor he felt his skin pricked by a file lying there. In a rage he turned round upon it and tried to dart his fangs into it; but he could do no harm to heavy iron and had soon to give over his wrath.

"IT IS USELESS ATTACKING THE INSENSIBLE."

THE MAN AND THE WOOD

A MAN came into a Wood one day with an axe in his hand, and begged all the Trees to give him a small branch which he wanted for a particular purpose. The Trees were good-natured and gave him one of their branches. What did the Man do but fix it into the axe head, and soon set to work cutting down tree after tree. Then the Trees saw how foolish they had been in giving their enemy the means of destroying themselves.

THE DOG AND THE WOLF

A GAUNT Wolf was almost dead with hunger when he happened to meet a House-dog who was passing by. "Ah, Cousin," said the Dog, "I knew how it would be; your irregular life will soon be the ruin of you. Why do you not work steadily as I do, and get your food regularly given to you?"

"I would have no objection," said the Wolf, "if I could only get a place."

"I will easily arrange that for you," said the Dog; "come with me to my master and you shall share my work."

So the Wolf and the Dog went towards the town together. On the way there the Wolf noticed that the hair on a certain part of the Dog's neck was very much worn away, so he asked him how that had come about.

"Oh, it is nothing," said the Dog. "That is only the place where the collar is put on at night to keep me chained up; it chafes a bit, but one soon gets used to it."

"Is that all?" said the Wolf. "Then good-bye to you, Master Dog."

"BETTER STARVE FREE THAN BE A FAT SLAVE."

THE BELLY AND THE MEMBERS

ONE fine day it occurred to the Members of the Body that they were doing all the work and the Belly was having all the food. So they held a meeting, and after a long discussion, decided to strike work till the Belly consented to take its proper share of the work. So for a day or two, the Hands refused to take the food, the Mouth refused to receive it, and the Teeth had no work to do. But after a day or two the Members began to find that they themselves were not in a very active condition: the Hands could hardly move, and the Mouth was all parched and dry, while the Legs were unable to support the rest. So thus they found that even the Belly in its dull quiet way was doing necessary work for the Body, and that all must work together or the Body will go to pieces.

THE HART IN THE OX-STALL

A HART hotly pursued by the hounds fled for refuge into an ox-stall, and buried itself in a truss of hay, leaving nothing to be seen but the tips of his horns. Soon after the Hunters came up and asked if any one had seen the Hart.

The stable boys, who had been resting after their dinner, looked round, but could see nothing, and the Hunters went away. Shortly afterwards the master came in, and looking round, saw that something unusual had taken place. He pointed to the truss of hay and said: "What are those two curious things sticking out of the hay?" And when the stable boys came to look they discovered the Hart, and soon made an end of him. He thus learnt that

"NOTHING ESCAPES THE MASTER'S EYE."

THE FOX AND THE GRAPES

ONE hot summer's day a Fox was strolling through an orchard till he came to a bunch of Grapes just ripening on a vine which had been trained over a lofty branch. "Just the thing to quench my thirst," quoth he. Drawing back a few paces, he took a run and a jump, and just missed the bunch. Turning round again with a One, Two, Three, he jumped up, but with no greater success. Again and again he tried after the tempting morsel, but at last had to give it up, and walked away with his nose in the air, saying: I am sure they are sour."

"IT IS EASY TO DESPISE WHAT YOU CANNOT GET."

THE HORSE, HUNTER, AND STAG

A QUARREL had arisen between the Horse and the Stag, so the Horse came to a Hunter to ask his help to take revenge on the Stag. The Hunter agreed, but said: "If you desire to conquer the Stag, you must permit me to place this piece of iron between your jaws, so that I may guide you with these reins, and allow this saddle to be placed upon your back so that I may keep steady upon you as we follow after the enemy." The Horse agreed to the conditions, and the Hunter soon saddled and bridled him. Then with the aid of the Hunter the Horse soon overcame the Stag, and said to the Hunter: "Now, get off, and remove those things from my mouth and back."

"Not so fast, friend," said the Hunter. "I have now got you under bit and spur, and prefer to keep you as you are at present."

"IF YOU ALLOW MEN TO USE YOU FOR YOUR OWN PURPOSES, THEY WILL USE YOU FOR THEIRS."

THE PEACOCK AND JUNO

A PEACOCK once placed a petition before Juno desiring to have the voice of a nightingale in addition to his other attractions; but Juno refused his request. When he persisted, and pointed out that he was her favourite bird, she said:

"BE CONTENT WITH YOUR LOT; ONE CANNOT BE FIRST IN EVERYTHING."

THE FOX AND THE LION

WHEN first the Fox saw the Lion he was terribly frightened, and ran away and hid himself in the wood. Next time however he came near the King of Beasts he stopped at a safe distance and watched him pass by. The third time they came near one another the Fox went straight up to the Lion and passed the time of day with him, asking him how his family were, and when he should have the pleasure of seeing him again; then turning his tail, he parted from the Lion without much ceremony.

"FAMILIARITY BREEDS CONTEMPT."

THE LION AND THE STATUE

A MAN and a Lion were discussing the relative strength of men and lions in general. The Man contended that he and his fellows were stronger than lions by reason of their greater intelligence. "Come now with me," he cried, "and I will soon prove that I am right." So he took him into the public gardens and showed him a statue of Hercules overcoming the Lion and tearing his mouth in two.

"That is all very well," said the Lion, "but proves nothing, for it was a man who made the statue."

"WE CAN EASILY REPRESENT THINGS AS WE WISH THEM TO BE."

THE ANT AND THE GRASSHOPPER

IN a field one summer's day a Grasshopper was hopping about, chirping and singing to its heart's content. An Ant passed by, bearing along with great toil an ear of corn he was taking to the nest.

"Why not come and chat with me," said the Grasshopper, "instead of toiling and moiling in that way?"

"I am helping to lay up food for the winter," said the Ant, "and recommend you to do the same."

"Why bother about winter?" said the Grasshopper; "we have got plenty of food at present." But the Ant went on its way and continued its toil. When the winter came the Grasshopper had no food, and found itself dying of hunger, while it saw the ants distributing every day corn and grain from the stores they had collected in the summer. Then the Grasshopper knew

"IT IS BEST TO PRERARE FOR THE DAYS OF NECESSITY."

THE TREE AND THE REED

"WELL, little one," said a Tree to a Reed that was growing at its foot, "why do you not plant your feet deeply in the ground, and raise your head boldly in the air as I do?"

"I am contented with my lot," said the Reed. "I may not be so grand, but I think I am safer."

"Safe!" sneered the Tree. "Who shall pluck me up by the roots or bow my head to the ground?" But it soon had to repent of its boasting, for a hurricane arose which tore it up from its roots, and cast it a useless log on the ground, while the little Reed, bending to the force of the wind, soon stood upright again when the storm had passed over.

"OBSCURITY OFTEN BRINGS SAFETY."

THE FOX AND THE CAT

A Fox was boasting to a Cat of its clever devices for escaping its enemies. "I have a whole bag of tricks," he said, "which contains a hundred ways of escaping my enemies."

"I have only one," said the Cat; "but I can generally manage with that." Just at that moment they heard the cry of a pack of hounds coming towards them, and the Cat immediately scampered up a tree and hid herself in the boughs. "This is my plan," said the Cat. "What are you going to do?" The Fox thought first of one way, then of another, and while he was debating the hounds came nearer and nearer, and at last the Fox in his confusion was caught up by the hounds and soon killed by the huntsmen. Miss Puss, who had been looking on, said:

"BETTER ONE SAFE WAY THAN A HUNDRED ON WHICH YOU CANNOT RECKON."

THE WOLF IN SHEEP'S CLOTHING

A Wolf found great difficulty in getting at the sheep owing to the vigilance of the shepherd and his dogs. But one day it found the skin of a sheep that had been flayed and thrown aside, so it put it on over its own pelt and strolled down among the sheep. The Lamb that belonged to the sheep, whose skin the Wolf was wearing, began to follow the Wolf in the Sheep's clothing; so, leading the Lamb a little apart, he soon made a meal off her, and for some time he succeeded in deceiving the sheep, and enjoying hearty meals.

"APPEARANCES ARE DECEPTIVE."

THE DOG IN THE MANGER

A Dog looking out for its afternoon nap jumped into the Manger of an Ox and lay there cosily upon the straw. But soon the Ox, returning from its afternoon work, came up to the Manger and wanted to eat some of the straw. The Dog in a rage, being awakened from its slumber, stood up and barked at the Ox, and whenever it came near attempted to bite it. At last the Ox had to give up the hope of getting at the straw, and went away muttering:

"AH, PEOPLE OFTEN GRUDGE OTHERS WHAT THEY CANNOT ENJOY THEMSELVES."

THE MAN AND THE WOODEN GOD

IN the old days men used to worship stocks and stones and idols, and prayed to them to give them luck. It happened that a Man had often prayed to a wooden idol he had received from his father, but his luck never seemed to change. He prayed and he prayed, but still he remained as unlucky as ever. One day in the greatest rage he went to the Wooden God, and with one blow swept it down from its pedestal. The idol broke in two, and what did he see? An immense number of coins flying all over the place.

THE FISHER

A FISHER once took his bagpipes to the bank of a river, and played upon them with the hope of making the fish rise; but never a one put his nose out of the water. So he cast his net into the river and soon drew it forth filled with fish. Then he took his bagpipes again, and, as he played, the fish leapt up in the net. "Ah, you dance now when I play," said he.

"Yes," said an old Fish:

"WHEN YOU ARE IN A MAN'S POWER YOU MUST DO AS HE BIDS YOU."

THE SHEPHERD'S BOY

THERE was once a young Shepherd Boy who tended his sheep at the foot of a mountain near a dark forest. It was rather lonely for him all day, so he thought upon a plan by which he could get a little company and some excitement. He rushed down towards the village calling out " Wolf, Wolf," and the villagers came out to meet him, and some of them stopped with him for a considerable time. This pleased the boy so much that a few days afterwards he tried the same trick, and again the villagers came to his help. But shortly after this a Wolf actually did come out from the forest, and began to worry the sheep, and the boy of course cried out " Wolf, Wolf," still louder than before. But this time the villagers, who had been fooled twice before, thought the boy was again deceiving them, and nobody stirred to come to his help. So the Wolf made a good meal off the boy's flock, and when the boy complained, the wise man of the village said:

" A LIAR WILL NOT BE BELIEVED, EVEN WHEN HE
SPEAKS THE TRUTH."

THE YOUNG THIEF AND HIS MOTHER

A YOUNG Man had been caught in a daring act of theft and had been condemned to be executed for it. He expressed his desire to see his Mother, and to speak with her before he was led to execution, and of course this was granted. When his Mother came to him he said: " I want to whisper to you," and when she brought her ear near him, he nearly bit it off. All the bystanders were horrified, and asked him what he could mean by such brutal and inhuman conduct. " It is to punish her," he said. " When I was young I began with stealing little things, and brought them home to Mother. Instead of rebuking and punishing me, she laughed and said: ' It will not be noticed.' It is because of her that I am here to-day."

"He is right, woman," said the Priest; "the Lord hath said:

"TRAIN UP A CHILD IN THE WAY HE SHOULD GO; AND WHEN HE IS OLD HE WILL NOT DEPART THEREFROM."

THE MAN AND HIS TWO WIVES

IN the old days, when men were allowed to have many wives, a middle-aged Man had one wife that was old and one that was young; each loved him very much, and desired to see him like herself. Now the Man's hair was turning grey, which the young Wife did not like, as it made him look too old for her husband. So every night she used to comb his hair and pick out the white ones. But the elder Wife saw her husband growing grey with great pleasure, for she did not like to be mistaken for his mother. So every morning she used to arrange his hair and pick out as many of the black ones as she could. The consequence was the Man soon found himself entirely bald.

"YIELD TO ALL AND YOU WILL SOON HAVE NOTHING
TO YIELD."

THE NURSE AND THE WOLF

"BE quiet now," said an old Nurse to a child sitting on her lap. "If you make that noise again I will throw you to the Wolf."

Now it chanced that a Wolf was passing close under the window as this was said. So he crouched down by the side of the house and waited. "I am in good luck to-day," thought he. "It is sure to cry soon, and a daintier morsel I haven't had for many a long day." So he waited, and he waited, and he waited, till at last the child began to cry, and the Wolf came forward before the window, and looked up to the Nurse, wagging his tail. But all the Nurse did was to shut down the window and call for help, and the dogs of the house came rushing out. "Ah," said the Wolf **as** he galloped away,

"ENEMIES' PROMISES WERE MADE TO BE BROKEN."

THE TORTOISE AND THE BIRDS

A TORTOISE desired to change its place of residence, so he asked an Eagle to carry him to his new home, promising her a rich reward for her trouble. The Eagle agreed, and seizing the Tortoise by the shell with her talons, soared aloft. On their way they met a Crow, who said to the Eagle: "Tortoise is good eating." "The shell is too hard," said the Eagle in reply. "The rocks will soon crack the shell," was the Crow's answer; and the Eagle, taking the hint, let fall the Tortoise on a sharp rock, and the two birds made a hearty meal off the Tortoise.

"NEVER SOAR ALOFT ON AN ENEMY'S PINIONS."

THE TWO CRABS

ONE fine day two Crabs came out from their home to take a stroll on the sand. "Child," said the mother, "you are walking very ungracefully. You should accustom yourself to walking straight forward without twisting from side to side."

"Pray, mother," said the young one, "do but set the example yourself, and I will follow you."

"EXAMPLE IS THE BEST PRECEPT."

THE ASS IN THE LION'S SKIN

AN Ass once found a Lion's skin which the hunters had left out in the sun to dry. He put it on and went towards his native village. All fled at his approach, both men and animals, and he was a proud Ass that day. In his delight he lifted up his voice and brayed, but then every one knew him, and his owner came up and gave him a sound cudgelling for the fright he had caused. And shortly afterwards a Fox came up to him and said: "Ah, I knew you by your voice."

" FINE CLOTHES MAY DISGUISE, BUT SILLY WORDS
WILL DISCLOSE A FOOL."

THE TWO FELLOWS AND THE BEAR

Two Fellows were travelling together through a wood, when a Bear rushed out upon them. One of the travellers happened to be in front, and he seized hold of the branch of a tree, and hid himself among the leaves. The other, seeing no help for it, threw himself flat down upon the ground, with his face in the dust. The Bear, coming up to him, put his muzzle close to his ear, and sniffed and sniffed. But at last with a growl he shook his head and slouched off, for bears will not touch dead meat. Then the fellow in the tree came down to his comrade, and, laughing, said " What was it that Master Bruin whispered to you?"

"He told me," said the other,

" NEVER TRUST A FRIEND WHO DESERTS YOU AT A PINCH."

THE TWO POTS

Two Pots had been left on the bank of a river, one of brass, and one of earthenware. When the tide rose they both floated off down the stream. Now the earthenware pot tried its best to keep aloof from the brass one, which cried out: "Fear nothing, friend, I will not strike you."

"But I may come in contact with you," said the other, "if I come too close; and whether I hit you, or you hit me, I shall suffer for it."

" THE STRONG AND THE WEAK CANNOT KEEP COMPANY."

THE FOUR OXEN AND THE LION

A Lion used to prowl about a field in which Four Oxen used to dwell. Many a time he tried to attack them; but whenever he came near they turned their tails to one another, so that whichever way he approached them he was met by the horns of one of them. At last, however, they fell a-quarrelling among themselves, and each went off to pasture alone in a separate corner of the field. Then the Lion attacked them one by one and soon made an end of all four.

"UNITED WE STAND, DIVIDED WE FALL."

THE FISHER AND THE LITTLE FISH

It happened that a Fisher, after fishing all day, caught only a little fish. "Pray, let me go, master," said the Fish. "I am much too small for your eating just now. If you put me back into the river I shall soon grow, then you can make a fine meal off me."

"Nay, nay, my little Fish," said the Fisher, "I have you now. I may not catch you hereafter."

"A LITTLE THING IN HAND IS WORTH MORE THAN A GREAT THING IN PROSPECT."

AVARICIOUS AND ENVIOUS

Two neighbours came before Jupiter and prayed him to grant their hearts' desire. Now the one was full of avarice, and the other eaten up with envy. So to punish them both, Jupiter granted that each might have whatever he wished for himself, but only on condition that his neighbour had twice as much. The Avaricious man prayed to have a room full of gold. No sooner said than done; but all his joy was turned to grief when he found that his neighbour had two rooms full of the precious metal. Then came the turn of the Envious man, who could not bear to think that his neighbour had any joy at all. So he prayed that he might have one of his own eyes put out, by which means his companion would become totally blind.

"VICES ARE THEIR OWN PUNISHMENT."

THE CROW AND THE PITCHER

A CROW, half-dead with thirst, came upon a Pitcher which had once been full of water; but when the Crow put its beak into the mouth of the Pitcher he found that only very little water was left in it, and that he could not reach far enough down to get at it. He tried, and he tried, but at last had to give up in despair. Then a thought came to him, and he took a pebble and dropped it into the Pitcher. Then he took another pebble and dropped it into the Pitcher. Then he took another pebble and dropped that into the Pitcher. Then he took another pebble and dropped that into the Pitcher. Then he took another pebble and dropped that into the Pitcher. Then he took another pebble and dropped that into the Pitcher. At last, at last, he saw the water mount up near him, and after casting in a few more pebbles he was able to quench his thirst and save his life.

"LITTLE BY LITTLE DOES THE TRICK."

THE MAN AND THE SATYR

A MAN had lost his way in a wood one bitter winter's night. As he was roaming about, a Satyr came up to him, and finding that he had lost his way, promised to give him a lodging for the night, and guide him out of the forest in the morning. As he went along to the Satyr's cell, the Man raised both his hands to his mouth and kept on blowing at them. "What do you do that for?" said the Satyr.

"My hands are numb with the cold," said the Man, "and my breath warms them."

After this they arrived at the Satyr's home, and soon the Satyr put a smoking dish of porridge before him. But when the Man raised his spoon to his mouth he began blowing upon it. "And what do you do that for?" said the Satyr.

"The porridge is too hot, and my breath will cool it."

"Out you go," said the Satyr. "I will have nought to to do with a man who can blow hot and cold with the same breath."

THE GOOSE WITH THE GOLDEN EGGS

ONE day a countryman going to the nest of his Goose found there an egg all yellow and glittering. When he took it up it was as heavy as lead and he was going to throw it away, because he thought a trick had been played upon him. But he took it home on second thoughts, and soon found to his delight that it was an egg of pure gold. Every morning the same thing occurred, and he soon became rich by selling his eggs. As he grew rich he grew greedy; and thinking to get at once all the gold the Goose could give, he killed it and opened it only to find,—nothing.

"GREED OFT O'ERREACHES ITSELF."

THE LABOURER AND THE NIGHTINGALE

A LABOURER lay listening to a Nightingale's song throughout the summer night. So pleased was he with it that the next night he set a trap for it and captured it. "Now that I have caught thee," he cried, "thou shalt always sing to me."

"We Nightingales never sing in a cage," said the bird.

"Then I'll eat thee," said the Labourer. "I have always heard say that nightingale on toast is a dainty morsel."

"Nay, kill me not," said the Nightingale; "but let me free, and I'll tell thee three things far better worth than my poor body." The Labourer let him loose, and he flew up to a branch of a tree and said: "Never believe a captive's promise; that's one thing. Then again: Keep what you have. And third piece of advice is: Sorrow not over what is lost forever." Then the song-bird flew away.

THE FOX, THE COCK, AND THE DOG

ONE moonlight night a Fox was prowling about a farmer's hencoop, and saw a Cock roosting high up beyond his reach. "Good news, good news!" he cried.

"Why, what is that?" said the Cock.

"King Lion has declared a universal truce. No beast may hurt a bird henceforth, but all shall dwell together in brotherly friendship."

"Why, that is good news," said the Cock; "and there I see some one coming, with whom we can share the good tidings." And so saying he craned his neck forward and looked afar off.

"What is it you see?" said the Fox.

"It is only my master's Dog that is coming towards us. What, going so soon?" he continued, as the Fox began to turn away as soon as he had heard the news. "Will you not stop and congratulate the Dog on the reign of universal peace?"

"I would gladly do so," said the Fox, "but I fear he may not have heard of King Lion's decree."

"CUNNING OFTEN OUTWITS ITSELF."

THE WIND AND THE SUN

THE Wind and the Sun were disputing which was the stronger. Suddenly they saw a traveller coming down the road, and the Sun said: "I see a way to decide our dispute. Whichever of us can cause that traveller to take off his cloak shall be regarded as the stronger. You begin." So the Sun retired behind a cloud, and the Wind began to blow as hard as it could upon the traveller. But the harder he blew the more closely did the traveller wrap his cloak round him, till at last the Wind had to give up in despair. Then the Sun came out and shone in all his glory upon the traveller, who soon found it too hot to walk with his cloak on.

" KINDNESS EFFECTS MORE THAN SEVERITY."

HERCULES AND THE WAGGONER

A WAGGONER was once driving a heavy load along a very muddy way. At last he came to a part of the road where the wheels sank half-way into the mire, and the more the horses pulled, the deeper sank the wheels. So the Waggoner threw down his whip, and knelt down and prayed to Hercules the Strong. "O Hercules, help me in this my hour of distress," quoth he. But Hercules appeared to him, and said:

"Tut, man, don't sprawl there. Get up and put your shoulder to the wheel."

" THE GODS HELP THEM THAT HELP THEMSELVES."

THE MAN, THE BOY, AND THE DONKEY

A MAN and his son were once going with their Donkey to market. As they were walking along by its side a countryman passed them and said: "You fools, what is a Donkey for but to ride upon?"

So the Man put the Boy on the Donkey and they went on their way. But soon they passed a group of men, one of whom said: "See that lazy youngster, he lets his father walk while he rides."

So the Man ordered his Boy to get off, and got on himself. But they hadn't gone far when they passed two women, one of whom said to the other: "Shame on that lazy lout to let his poor little son trudge along."

Well, the Man didn't know what to do, but at last he took his Boy up before him on the Donkey. By this time they had come to the town, and the passers-by began to jeer and point at them. The Man stopped and asked what they were scoffing at. The men said: "Aren't you ashamed of yourself for overloading that poor Donkey of yours—you and your hulking son?"

The Man and Boy got off and tried to think what to do. They thought and they thought, till at last they cut down a pole, tied the Donkey's feet to it, and raised the pole and the Donkey to their shoulders. They went along amid the laughter of all who met them till they came to Market Bridge, when the Donkey, getting one of his feet loose, kicked out and caused the Boy to drop his end of the pole. In the struggle the Donkey fell over the bridge, and his fore-feet being tied together he was drowned.

"That will teach you," said an old man who had followed them:

"PLEASE ALL, AND YOU WILL PLEASE NONE."

THE MISER AND HIS GOLD

ONCE upon a time there was a Miser who used to hide his gold at the foot of a tree in his garden; but every week he used to go and dig it up and gloat over his gains. A robber, who had noticed this, went and dug up the gold and decamped with it. When the Miser next came to gloat over his treasures, he found nothing but the empty hole. He tore his hair, and raised such an outcry that all the neighbours came around him, and he told them how he used to come and visit his gold. "Did you ever take any of it out?" asked one of them.

"Nay," said he, "I only came to look at it."

"Then come again and look at the hole," said a neighbour; "it will do you just as much good."

"WEALTH UNUSED MIGHT AS WELL NOT EXIST."

THE FOX AND THE MOSQUITOES

A Fox after crossing a river got its tail entangled in a bush, and could not move. A number of Mosquitoes seeing its plight settled upon it and enjoyed a good meal undisturbed by its tail. A hedgehog strolling by took pity upon the Fox and went up to him: "You are in a bad way, neighbour," said the hedgehog; "shall I relieve you by driving off those Mosquitoes who are sucking your blood?"

" Thank you, Master Hedgehog," said the Fox, " but I would rather not."

" Why, how is that?" asked the hedgehog.

" Well, you see," was the answer, " these Mosquitoes have had their fill; if you drive these away, others will come with fresh appetite and bleed me to death."

THE FOX WITHOUT A TAIL

IT happened that a Fox caught its tail in a trap, and in struggling to release himself lost all of it but the stump. At first he was ashamed to show himself among his fellow foxes. But at last he determined to put a bolder face upon his misfortune, and summoned all the foxes to a general meeting to consider a proposal which he had to place before them. When they had assembled together the Fox proposed that they should all do away with their tails. He pointed out how inconvenient a tail was when they were pursued by their enemies, the dogs; how much it was in the way when they desired to sit down and hold a friendly conversation with one another. He failed to see any advantage in carrying about such a useless encumbrance. " That is all very well," said one of the older foxes; " but I do not think you would have recommended us to dispense with our chief ornament if you had not happened to lose it yourself."

" DISTRUST INTERESTED ADVICE."

THE ONE-EYED DOE

A DOE had had the misfortune to lose one of her eyes, and could not see any one approaching her on that side. So to avoid any danger she always used to feed on a high cliff near the sea, with her sound eye looking towards the land. By this means she could see whenever the hunters approached her on land, and often escaped by this means. But the hunters found out that she was blind of one eye, and hiring a boat rowed under the cliff where she used to feed and shot her from the sea. "Ah," cried she with her dying voice,

"YOU CANNOT ESCAPE YOUR FATE."

BELLING THE CAT

LONG ago, the mice had a general council to consider what measures they could take to outwit their common enemy, the Cat. Some said this, and some said that; but at last a young mouse got up and said he had a proposal to make, which he thought would meet the case. " You will all agree," said he, " that our chief danger consists in the sly and treacherous manner in which the enemy approaches us. Now, if we could receive some signal of her approach, we could easily escape from her. I venture, therefore, to propose that a small bell be procured, and attached by a ribbon round the neck of the Cat. By this means we should always know when she was about, and could easily retire while she was in the neighbourhood."

This proposal met with general applause, until an old mouse got up and said: " That is all very well, but who is to bell the Cat?" The mice looked at one another and nobody spoke. Then the old mouse said:

" IT IS EASY TO PROPOSE IMPOSSIBLE REMEDIES."

THE HARE AND THE TORTOISE

THE Hare was once boasting of his speed before the other animals. " I have never yet been beaten," said he, " when I put forth my full speed. I challenge any one here to race with me."

The Tortoise said quietly, " I accept your challenge."

" That is a good joke," said the Hare; " I could dance round you all the way."

" Keep your boasting till you've beaten," answered the Tortoise. " Shall we race?"

So a course was fixed and a start was made. The Hare darted almost out of sight at once, but soon stopped and, to

show his contempt for the Tortoise, lay down to have a nap.
The Tortoise plodded on and plodded on, and when the
Hare awoke from his nap, he saw the Tortoise just near
the winning-post and could not run up in time to save the
race. Then said the Tortoise:

"PLODDING WINS THE RACE."

THE OLD MAN AND DEATH

AN old labourer, bent double with age and toil, was gathering sticks in a forest. At last he grew so tired and hope-
less that he threw down the bundle of sticks, and cried out:
"I cannot bear this life any longer. Ah, I wish Death would
only come and take me!"

As he spoke, Death, a grisly skeleton, appeared and said
to him: "What wouldst thou, Mortal? I heard thee call me."

"Please, sir," replied the woodcutter, "would you kindly
help me to lift this faggot of sticks on to my shoulder?"

"WE WOULD OFTEN BE SORRY IF OUR WISHES
WERE GRATIFIED."

THE HARE WITH MANY FRIENDS

A HARE was very popular with the other beasts who all
claimed to be her friends. But one day she heard the hounds
approaching and hoped to escape them by the aid of her
many Friends. So she went to the horse, and asked him
to carry her away from the hounds on his back. But he
declined, stating that he had important work to do for his
master. "He felt sure," he said, "that all her other friends
would come to her assistance." She then applied to the bull,
and hoped that he would repel the hounds with his horns.
The bull replied: "I am very sorry, but I have an appointment with a lady; but I feel sure that our friend the goat
will do what you want." The goat, however, feared that
his back might do her some harm if he took her upon it.
The ram, he felt sure, was the proper friend to apply to.
So she went to the ram and told him the case. The ram re-

plied: "Another time, my dear friend. I do not like to interfere on the present occasion, as hounds have been known to eat sheep as well as hares." The Hare then applied, as a last hope, to the calf, who regretted that he was unable to help her, as he did not like to take the responsibility upon himself, as so many older persons than himself had declined the task. By this time the hounds were quite near, and the Hare took to her heels and luckily escaped.

"HE THAT HAS MANY FRIENDS, HAS NO FRIENDS."

THE LION IN LOVE

A Lion once fell in love with a beautiful maiden and proposed marriage to her parents. The old people did not know what to say. They did not like to give their daughter to the Lion, yet they did not wish to enrage the King of Beasts. At last the father said: "We feel highly honoured by your Majesty's proposal, but you see our daughter is a tender young thing, and we fear that in the vehemence of your affection you might possibly do her some injury. Might I venture to suggest that your Majesty should have your claws removed, and your teeth extracted, then we would gladly consider your proposal again." The Lion was so much in love that he had his claws trimmed and his big teeth taken out. But when he came again to the parents of the young girl they simply laughed in his face, and bade him do his worst.

"LOVE CAN TAME THE WILDEST."

THE BUNDLE OF STICKS

An old man on the point of death summoned his sons around him to give them some parting advice. He ordered his servants to bring in a faggot of sticks, and said to his eldest son: "Break it." The son strained and strained, but with all his efforts was unable to break the Bundle. The other sons also tried, but none of them was successful. "Untie the faggots," said the father, "and each of you take a stick." When they had done so, he called out to them: "Now, break," and each stick was easily broken. "You see my meaning," said their father.

"UNION GIVES STRENGTH."

THE LION, THE FOX, AND THE BEASTS

THE Lion once gave out that he was sick unto death and summoned the animals to come and hear his last Will and Testament. So the Goat came to the Lion's cave, and stopped there listening for a long time. Then a Sheep went in, and before she came out a Calf came up to receive the last wishes of the Lord of the Beasts. But soon the Lion seemed to recover, and came to the mouth of his cave, and saw the Fox, who had been waiting outside for some time. "Why do you not come to pay your respects to me?" said the Lion to the Fox.

"I beg your Majesty's pardon," said the Fox, "but I noticed the track of the animals that have already come to you; and while I see many hoof-marks going in, I see none coming out. Till the animals that have entered your cave come out again I prefer to remain in the open air."

"IT IS EASIER TO GET INTO THE ENEMY'S TOILS
THAN OUT AGAIN."

THE ASS'S BRAINS

THE Lion and the Fox went hunting together. The Lion, on the advice of the Fox, sent a message to the Ass, proposing to make an alliance between their two families. The Ass came to the place of meeting, overjoyed at the prospect of a royal alliance. But when he came there the Lion simply pounced on the Ass, and said to the Fox: "Here is our dinner for to-day. Watch you here while I go and have a nap. Woe betide you if you touch my prey." The Lion went away and the Fox waited; but finding that his master did not return, ventured to take out the brains of the Ass and ate them up. When the Lion came back he soon noticed the absence of the brains, and asked the

Fox in a terrible voice: "What have you done with the brains?"

"Brains, your Majesty! it had none, or it would never have fallen into your trap."

"WIT HAS ALWAYS AN ANSWER READY."

THE EAGLE AND THE ARROW

An Eagle was soaring through the air when suddenly it heard the whizz of an Arrow, and felt itself wounded to death. Slowly it fluttered down to the earth, with its life-blood pouring out of it. Looking down upon the Arrow with which it had been pierced, it found that the haft of the Arrow had been feathered with one of its own plumes. "Alas!" it cried, as it died,

"WE OFTEN GIVE OUR ENEMIES THE MEANS
FOR OUR OWN DESTRUCTION."

THE MILKMAID AND HER PAIL

Patty the Milkmaid was going to market carrying her milk in a Pail on her head. As she went along she began calculating what she would do with the money she would get for the milk. "I'll buy some fowls from Farmer Brown," said she, "and they will lay eggs each morning, which I will sell to the parson's wife. With the money that I get from the sale of these eggs I'll buy myself a new dimity frock and a chip hat; and when I go to market, won't all the young men come up and speak to me! Polly Shaw will be that jealous; but I don't care. I shall just look at her and toss my head like this." As she spoke she tossed her head back, the Pail fell off it and all the milk was spilt. So she had to go home and tell her mother what had occurred.

"Ah, my child," said the mother,

"DO NOT COUNT YOUR CHICKENS BEFORE
THEY ARE HATCHED."

THE CAT-MAIDEN

The gods were once disputing whether it was possible for a living being to change its nature. Jupiter said " Yes," but Venus said " No." So, to try the question, Jupiter turned a Cat into a Maiden, and gave her to a young man for a wife. The wedding was duly performed and the young couple sat down to the wedding-feast. " See," said Jupiter to Venus, " how becomingly she behaves. Who could tell that yesterday she was but a Cat? Surely her nature is changed?"

" Wait a minute," replied Venus, and let loose a mouse into the room. No sooner did the bride see this than she jumped up from her seat and tried to pounce upon the mouse. " Ah, you see," said Venus,

" NATURE WILL OUT."

THE HORSE AND THE ASS

A Horse and an Ass were travelling together, the Horse prancing along in its fine trappings, the Ass carrying with difficulty the heavy weight in its panniers. " I wish I were you," sighed the Ass; " nothing to do and well fed, and all that fine harness upon you." Next day, however, there was a great battle, and the Horse was wounded to death in the final charge of the day. His friend, the Ass, happened to pass by shortly afterwards and found him on the point of death. " I was wrong," said the Ass:

" BETTER HUMBLE SECURITY THAN GILDED DANGER."

THE TRUMPETER TAKEN PRISONER

A Trumpeter during a battle ventured too near the enemy and was captured by them. They were about to proceed to put him to death when he begged them to hear his plea for mercy. " I do not fight," said he, " and indeed carry no weapon; I only blow this trumpet, and surely that cannot harm you; then why should you kill me?"

"You may not fight yourself," said the others, "but you encourage and guide your men to the fight."

"WORDS MAY BE DEEDS."

THE BUFFOON AND THE COUNTRYMAN

AT a country fair there was a Buffoon who made all the people laugh by imitating the cries of various animals. He finished off by squeaking so like a pig that the spectators thought that he had a porker concealed about him. But a Countryman who stood by said: "Call that a pig's squeak! Nothing like it. You give me till to-morrow and I will show you what it's like." The audience laughed, but next day, sure enough, the Countryman appeared on the stage, and putting his head down squealed so hideously that the spectators hissed and threw stones at him to make him stop. "You fools!" he cried, "see what you have been hissing," and held up a little pig whose ear he had been pinching to make him utter the squeals.

"MEN OFTEN APPLAUD AN IMITATION AND
HISS THE REAL THING."

THE OLD WOMAN AND THE WINE-JAR

You must know that sometimes old women like a glass of wine. One of this sort once found a Wine-jar lying in the road, and eagerly went up to it hoping to find it full. But when she took it up she found that all the wine had been drunk out of it. Still she took a long sniff at the mouth of the Jar. "Ah," she cried,

"WHAT MEMORIES CLING 'ROUND THE INSTRUMENTS
OF OUR PLEASURE."

THE FOX AND THE GOAT

By an unlucky chance a Fox fell into a deep well from which he could not get out. A Goat passed by shortly afterwards, and asked the Fox what he was doing down there. "Oh, have you not heard?" said the Fox; "there is going to be a great drought, so I jumped down here in order to be sure to have water by me. Why don't you come down too?" The Goat thought well of this advice, and jumped down into the well. But the Fox immediately jumped on her back, and by putting his foot on her long horns managed to jump up to the edge of the well. "Good-bye, friend," said the Fox, "remember next time,

"NEVER TRUST THE ADVICE OF A MAN IN DIFFICULTIES."

And this is the end of Æsop's Fables. HURRAH!

GRIMM'S
HOUSEHOLD
TALES

INTRODUCTORY NOTE

THE "*Kinder-und Hausmärchen*" of the brothers Grimm was the first deliberate attempt to preserve in their pure form the traditional domestic tales of the German people. The stories published in their volumes of *1812* and *1815*, and revised and added to in successive editions, were collected by them chiefly from the mouths of the peasantry in their native county of Hanau in Prussia and in Hesse, but the other provinces of Germany, as well as German Austria and Switzerland, also contributed. It was the aim of the collectors, carried out with great fidelity and a remarkable instinct for the truly popular, to avoid all additions, logical or artistic; to retain as far as possible the actual language of the peasants, and to eliminate all foreign and sophisticated elements.

The result of their labors, extending through a long stretch of years, was twofold: they produced one of the most delightful story books in the world, and they preserved for the scientific student of mythology and folk-lore a mass of invaluable material which was even then beginning to disappear. Further, in the discussion and classification of variant forms of these tales, gathered in different parts of the world, they advanced notably the science of comparative mythology.

Wilhelm Grimm, the younger brother, who did the greater part of the work of collecting and revising, was born at Hanau on February 24, 1786. Together with Jakob, he acted as librarian at Cassel, and professor at Göttingen and at Berlin, where he died, December 16, 1859. Besides the works in which he collaborated with his brother, he produced an important book on the German Heroic Legend.

The elder brother, Jakob, was born in 1785, also at Hanau, and died in Berlin in 1863. He is chiefly distinguished for his work in Germanic philology, his German Grammar being practically the foundation work of this branch of learning. The brothers lived in the closest intimacy, occupying the same house and often working on the same subjects, and both the great German Dictionary known by their name and the collection of "*Märchen*" from which the following stories are taken were the result of this collaboration.

CONTENTS

GRIMM'S TALES—

CONTENTS

FOLK-LORE AND FABLE

GRIMM'S TALES

THE FROG-KING, OR IRON HENRY

IN old times when wishing still helped one, there lived a king whose daughters were all beautiful, but the youngest was so beautiful that the sun itself, which has seen so much, was astonished whenever it shone in her face. Close by the King's castle lay a great dark forest, and under an old lime-tree in the forest was a well, and when the day was very warm, the King's child went out into the forest and sat down by the side of the cool fountain, and when she was dull she took a golden ball, and threw it up on high and caught it, and this ball was her favourite plaything.

Now it so happened that on one occasion the princess's golden ball did not fall into the little hand which she was holding up for it, but on to the ground beyond, and rolled straight into the water. The King's daughter followed it with her eyes, but it vanished, and the well was deep, so deep that the bottom could not be seen. On this she began to cry, and cried louder and louder, and could not be comforted. And as she thus lamented, some one said to her, "What ails thee, King's daughter? Thou weepest so that even a stone would show pity." She looked round to the side from whence the voice came, and saw a frog stretching forth its thick, ugly head from the water. "Ah! old watersplasher, is it thou?" said she; "I am weeping for my golden ball, which has fallen into the well."

"Be quiet, and do not weep," answered the frog. "I can help thee, but what wilt thou give me if I bring thy plaything up again?" "Whatever thou wilt have, dear frog," said she—"my clothes, my pearls and jewels, and even the golden crown which I am wearing."

The frog answered, "I do not care for thy clothes, thy pearls and jewels, or thy golden crown, but if thou wilt love me and let me be thy companion and play-fellow, and sit by thee at thy little table, and eat off thy little golden plate, and drink out of thy little cup, and sleep in thy little bed—if thou wilt promise me this I will go down below, and bring thee thy golden ball up again."

"Oh, yes," said she, "I promise thee all thou wishest, if thou wilt but bring me my ball back again." She, however, thought, "How silly the frog does talk! He lives in the water with the other frogs and croaks, and can be no companion to any human being!"

But the frog when he had received this promise put his head into the water and sank down, and in a short time came swimming up again with the ball in his mouth, and threw it on the grass. The King's daughter was delighted to see her pretty plaything once more, and picked it up, and ran away with it. "Wait, wait," said the frog. "Take me with thee. I can't run as thou canst." But what did it avail him to scream his croak, croak, after her, as loudly as he could? She did not listen to it, but ran home and soon forgot the poor frog, who was forced to go back into his well again.

The next day when she had seated herself at table with the King and all the courtiers, and was eating from her little golden plate, something came creeping splish, splash, splish, splash, up the marble staircase, and when it had got to the top, it knocked at the door and cried, " Princess, youngest princess, open the door for me." She ran to see who was outside, but when she opened the door, there sat the frog in front of it. Then she slammed the door to, in great haste, sat down to dinner again, and was quite frightened. The King saw plainly that her heart was beating violently, and said, " My child, what art thou so afraid of? Is there perchance a giant outside who wants to carry thee away?" "Ah, no," replied she, "it is no giant, but a disgusting frog."

"What does the frog want with thee?" "Ah, dear father, yesterday when I was in the forest sitting by the well, playing, my golden ball fell into the water. And because

I cried so the frog brought it out again for me, and because
he insisted so on it, I promised him he should be my companion, but I never thought he would be able to come out
of his water! And now he is outside there, and wants to
come in to me."

In the meantime it knocked a second time, and cried,

> "Princess! youngest princess!
> Open the door for me!
> Dost thou not know what thou saidst to me
> Yesterday by the cool waters of the fountain?
> Princess, youngest princess!
> Open the door for me!"

Then said the King, "That which thou hast promised
must thou perform. Go and let him in." She went and
opened the door, and the frog hopped in and followed her,
step by step, to her chair. There he sat still and cried,
"Lift me up beside thee." She delayed, until at last the
King commanded her to do it. When the frog was once
on the chair he wanted to be on the table, and when he
was on the table he said, "Now, push thy little golden
plate nearer to me that we may eat together." She did
this, but it was easy to see that she did not do it willingly.
The frog enjoyed what he ate, but almost every mouthful
she took choked her. At length he said, " I have eaten
and am satisfied; now I am tired, carry me into thy little
room and make thy little silken bed ready, and we will
both lie down and go to sleep."

The King's daughter began to cry, for she was afraid of
the cold frog which she did not like to touch, and which
was now to sleep in her pretty, clean little bed. But the
King grew angry and said, "He who helped thee when thou
wert in trouble ought not afterwards to be despised by
thee." So she took hold of the frog with two fingers, carried him upstairs, and put him in a corner. But when she
was in bed he crept to her and said, "I am tired, I want
to sleep as well as thou, lift me up or I will tell thy father."
Then she was terribly angry, and took him up and threw
him with all her might against the wall. "Now, thou
wilt be quiet, odious frog," said she. But when he fell

down he was no frog but a king's son with beautiful, kind eyes. He by her father's will was now her dear companion and husband. Then he told her how he had been bewitched by a wicked witch, and how no one could have delivered him from the well but herself, and that to-morrow they would go together into his kingdom. Then they went to sleep, and next morning when the sun awoke them, a carriage came driving up with eight white horses, which had white ostrich feathers on their heads, and were harnessed with golden chains, and behind stood the young King's servant, faithful Henry. Faithful Henry had been so unhappy when his master was changed into a frog, that he had caused three iron bands to be laid round his heart, lest it should burst with grief and sadness. The carriage was to conduct the young King into his kingdom. Faithful Henry helped them both in, and placed himself behind again, and was full of joy because of this deliverance. And when they had driven a part of the way, the King's son heard a cracking behind him as if something had broken. So he turned round and cried, "Henry, the carriage is breaking."

"No, master, it is not the carriage. It is a band from my heart, which was put there in my great pain when you were a frog and imprisoned in the well." Again and once again while they were on their way something cracked, and each time the King's son thought the carriage was breaking; but it was only the bands which were springing from the heart of faithful Henry because his master was set free and was happy.

OUR LADY'S CHILD

HARD by a great forest dwelt a wood-cutter with his wife, who had an only child, a little girl of three years old. They were, however, so poor that they no longer had daily bread, and did not know how to get food for her. One morning the wood-cutter went out sorrowfully to his work in the forest, and while he was cutting wood, suddenly there stood before him a tall and beautiful woman with a crown of shining stars on her head, who said to him, "I am the Virgin

Mary, mother of the child Jesus. Thou art poor and needy, bring thy child to me, I will take her with me to be her mother, and care for her." The wood-cutter obeyed, brought his child, and gave her to the Virgin Mary, who took her up to heaven with her. There the child fared well, ate sugar-cakes, and drank sweet milk, and her clothes were of gold, and the little angels played with her. And when she was fourteen years of age, the Virgin Mary called her one day and said, "Dear child, I am about to make a long journey, so take into thy keeping the keys of the thirteen doors of heaven. Twelve of these thou mayest open, and behold the glory which is within them, but the thirteenth, to which this little key belongs, is forbidden to thee. Beware of opening it, or thou wilt bring misery on thyself." The girl promised to be obedient, and when the Virgin Mary was gone, she began to examine the dwellings of the kingdom of heaven. Each day she opened one of them, until she had made the round of the twelve. In each of them sat one of the Apostles in the midst of a great light, and she rejoiced in all the magnificence and splendour, and the little angels who always accompanied her rejoiced with her. Then the forbidden door alone remained, and she felt a great desire to know what could be hidden behind it, and said to the angels, " I will not quite open it, and I will not go inside it, but I will unlock it so that we can just see a little through the opening." " Oh, no," said the little angels, " that would be a sin. The Virgin Mary has forbidden it, and it might easily cause thy unhappiness." Then she was silent, but the desire in her heart was not stilled, but gnawed there and tormented her, and let her have no rest. And once when the angels had all gone out, she thought, " Now I am quite alone, and I could peep in. If I do it, no one will ever know." She sought out the key, and when she had got it in her hand, she put it in the lock, and when she had put it in, she turned it round as well. Then the door sprang open, and she saw there the Trinity sitting in fire and splendour. She stayed there awhile, and looked at everything in amazement; then she touched the light a little with her finger, and her finger became quite golden. Immediately a great fear fell on her. She shut the door violently, and ran away. Her terror too would not quit her, let her do what she might, and her heart beat continually, and would not be still; the gold too stayed on her finger, and would not go away, let her rub it and wash it ever so much.

It was not long before the Virgin Mary came back from her journey. She called the girl before her, and asked to have the keys of heaven back. When the maiden gave her the bunch, the Virgin looked into her eyes and said, "Hast thou not opened the thirteenth door also?" "No," she replied. Then she laid her hand on the girl's heart, and felt how it beat and beat, and saw right well that she had disobeyed her order and had opened the door. Then she said once again, "Art thou certain that thou hast not done it?" "Yes," said the girl, for the second time. Then she perceived the finger which had become golden from touching the fire of heaven, and saw well that the child had sinned, and said for the third time, "Hast thou not done it?" "No," said the girl for the third time. Then said the Virgin Mary, "Thou hast not obeyed me, and besides that thou hast lied, thou art no longer worthy to be in heaven."

Then the girl fell into a deep sleep, and when she awoke she lay on the earth below, and in the midst of a wilderness. She wanted to cry out, but she could bring forth no sound. She sprang up and wanted to run away, but whithersoever she turned herself, she was continually held back by thick hedges of thorns through which she could not break. In the desert, in which she was imprisoned, there stood an old hollow tree, and this had to be her dwelling place. Into this she crept when night came, and here she slept. Here, too, she found a shelter from storm and rain, but it was a miserable life, and bitterly did she weep when she remembered how happy she had been in heaven, and how the angels had played with her. Roots and wild berries were her only food, and for these she sought as far as she could go. In the autumn she picked up the fallen nuts and leaves, and carried them into the hole. The nuts were her food in winter, and when snow and ice came, she crept amongst the leaves like a poor little animal that she might not freeze. Before long her clothes were all torn, and one bit of them after another fell off her. As soon, however, as the sun shone warm again, she went out and sat in front of the tree, and her long hair covered her on all sides like a mantle. Thus she sat year after year, and felt the pain and misery of the world. One day, when the trees were once more clothed in fresh green, the King of the country was hunting in the forest, and followed a roe, and as it had fled into the thicket which shut in this bit of the forest, he got off his horse, tore the bushes asunder, and cut himself a path with his sword. When he had at last forced his way through, he saw a wonderfully beautiful maiden sitting under the tree; and she sat there and was entirely covered with her golden hair down to her very feet. He stood still and looked at her full of surprise, then he spoke to her and said, "Who art thou? Why art thou sitting here in the wilderness?" But she gave no answer, for she could not open her mouth. The King continued, "Wilt thou go with me to my castle?" Then she just nodded her head a little. The King took her in his arms, carried her to his horse, and rode home with her, and when he reached the royal castle he caused her to be dressed in beautiful garments, and gave her all things in abundance. Although she could not speak, she was still so beautiful and charming that he began to love her with all his heart, and it was not long before he married her.

After a year or so had passed, the Queen brought a son into the world. Thereupon the Virgin Mary appeared to her in the night when she lay in her bed alone, and said, "If thou wilt tell the truth and confess that thou didst unlock the forbidden door, I will open thy mouth and give thee back thy speech, but if thou perseverest in thy sin, and deniest obstinately, I will take thy new born child away with me." Then the Queen was permitted to answer, but she remained hard, and said, "No, I did not open the forbidden door"; and the Virgin Mary took the new-born child from her arms, and vanished with it. Next morning, when the child was not to be found, it was whispered among the people that the Queen was a man-eater, and had killed her own child. She heard all this and could say nothing to the contrary, but the King would not believe it, for he loved her so much.

When a year had gone by the Queen again bore a son, and in the night the Virgin Mary again came to her, and said, "If thou wilt confess that thou openedst the forbidden door, I will give thee thy child back and untie thy tongue; but if

thou continuest in sin and deniest it, I will take away with
me this new child also." Then the Queen again said, "No,
I did not open the forbidden door"; and the Virgin took the
child out of her arms, and away with her to heaven. Next
morning, when this child also had disappeared, the people declared quite loudly that the Queen had devoured it, and the
King's councillors demanded that she should be brought to
justice. The King, however, loved her so dearly that he
would not believe it, and commanded the councillors under
pain of death not to say any more about it.

The following year the Queen gave birth to a beautiful
little daughter, and for the third time the Virgin Mary appeared to her in the night and said, "Follow me." She took
the Queen by the hand and led her to heaven, and showed
her there her two eldest children, who smiled at her, and
were playing with the ball of the world. When the Queen
rejoiced thereat, the Virgin Mary said, "Is thy heart not yet
softened? If thou wilt own that thou openedst the forbidden
door, I will give thee back thy two little sons." But for the
third time the Queen answered, " No, I did not open the forbidden door." Then the Virgin let her sink down to earth
once more, and took from her likewise her third child.

Next morning, when the loss was reported abroad, all the
people cried loudly, " The Queen is a man-eater! She must
be judged," and the King was no longer able to restrain his
councillors. Thereupon a trial was held, and as she could
not answer, and defend herself, she was condemned to be
burnt alive. The wood was got together, and when she was
fast bound to the stake, and the fire began to burn round
about her, the hard ice of pride melted, her heart was moved
by repentance, and she thought, "If I could but confess before my death that I opened the door." Then her voice came
back to her, and she cried out loudly, " Yes, Mary, I did it ";
and straightway rain fell from the sky and extinguished the
flames of fire, and a light broke forth above her, and the
Virgin Mary descended with the two little sons by her side,
and the new-born daughter in her arms. She spoke kindly
to her, and said, " He who repents his sin and acknowledges
it, is forgiven." Then she gave her the three children, untied
her tongue, and granted her happiness for her whole life.

THE WOLF AND THE SEVEN LITTLE KIDS

THERE was once on a time an old goat who had seven little kids, and loved them with all the love of a mother for her children. One day she wanted to go into the forest and fetch some food. So she called all seven to her and said, "Dear children, I have to go into the forest, be on your guard against the wolf; if he come in, he will devour you all—skin, hair, and all. The wretch often disguises himself, but you will know him at once by his rough voice and his black feet." The kids said, "Dear mother, we will take good care of ourselves; you may go away without any anxiety." Then the old one bleated, and went on her way with an easy mind.

It was not long before some one knocked at the house-door and cried, "Open the door, dear children; your mother is here, and has brought something back with her for each of you." But the little kids knew that it was the wolf, by the rough voice; "We will not open the door," cried they, "thou art not our mother. She has a soft, pleasant voice, but thy voice is rough; thou art the wolf!" Then the wolf went away to a shopkeeper and bought himself a great lump of chalk, ate this and made his voice soft with it. Then he came back, knocked at the door of the house, and cried, "Open the door, dear children, your mother is here and has brought something back with her for each of you." But the wolf had laid his black paws against the window, and the children saw them and cried, "We will not open the door, our mother has not black feet like thee: thou art the wolf!" Then the wolf ran to a baker and said, "I have hurt my feet, rub some dough over them for me." And when the baker had rubbed his feet over, he ran to the miller and said, "Strew some white meal over my feet for me." The miller thought to himself, "The wolf wants to deceive some one," and refused; but the wolf said, "If thou wilt not do it, I will devour thee." Then the miller was afraid, and made his paws white for him. Truly men are like that.

So now the wretch went for the third time to the house-door, knocked at it and said, "Open the door for me, children, your dear little mother has come home, and has brought every one of you something back from the forest with her." The little kids cried, " First show us thy paws that we may know if thou art our dear little mother." Then he put his paws in through the window, and when the kids saw that they were white, they believed that all he said was true, and opened the door. But who should come in but the wolf! They were terrified and wanted to hide themselves. One sprang under the table, the second into the bed, the third into the stove, the fourth into the kitchen, the fifth into the cupboard, the sixth under the washing-bowl, and the seventh into the clock-case. But the wolf found them all, and used no great ceremony; one after the other he swallowed them down his throat. The youngest in the clock-case was the only one he did not find. When the wolf had satisfied his appetite he took himself off, laid himself down under a tree in the green meadow outside, and began to sleep. Soon afterwards the old goat came home again from the forest! Ah! what a sight she saw there! The house-door stood wide open. The table, chairs, and benches were thrown down, the washing-bowl lay broken to pieces, and the quilts and pillows were pulled off the bed. She sought her children, but they were nowhere to be found. She called them one after another by name, but no one answered. At last, when she came to the youngest, a soft voice cried, " Dear mother, I am in the clock-case." She took the kid out, and it told her that the wolf had come and had eaten all the others. Then you may imagine how she wept over her poor children.

At length in her grief she went out, and the youngest kid ran with her. When they came to the meadow, there lay the wolf by the tree and snored so loud that the branches shook. She looked at him on every side and saw that something was moving and struggling in his gorged body. " Ah, heavens," said she, " is it possible that my poor children whom he has swallowed down for his supper, can be still alive?" Then the kid had to run home and fetch scissors, and a needle and thread, and the goat cut open the monster's stomach, and hardly had she made one cut, than one little kid thrust its head out, and when she had cut farther, all six sprang out one after another, and were all still alive, and had suffered no injury whatever, for in his greediness the monster had swallowed them down whole. What rejoicing there was! Then they embraced their dear mother, and jumped like a tailor at his wedding. The mother, however, said, "Now go and look for some big stones, and we will fill the wicked beast's stomach with them while he is still asleep." Then the seven kids dragged the stones thither with all speed, and put as many of them into his stomach as they could get in; and the mother sewed him up again in the greatest haste, so that he was not aware of anything and never once stirred.

When the wolf at length had had his sleep out, he got on his legs, and as the stones in his stomach made him very thirsty, he wanted to go to a well to drink. But when he began to walk and to move about, the stones in his stomach knocked against each other and rattled. Then cried he,

> "What rumbles and tumbles
> Against my poor bones?
> I thought 'twas six kids,
> But it's naught but big stones."

And when he got to the well and stooped over the water and was just about to drink, the heavy stones made him fall in and there was no help, but he had to drown miserably. When the seven kids saw that, they came running to the spot and cried aloud, "The wolf is dead! The wolf is dead!" and danced for joy round about the well with their mother.

FAITHFUL JOHN

THERE was once on a time an old king who was ill, and thought to himself, "I am lying on what must be my death-bed." Then said he, "Tell Faithful John to come to me." Faithful John was his favourite servant, and was so called, because he had for his whole life long been so true to him. When therefore he came beside the bed, the King said to him, "Most faithful John, I feel my end approaching, and have no anxiety except about my son. He is still of tender age, and cannot always know how to guide himself. If thou dost not promise me to teach him everything that he ought to know, and to be his foster-father, I cannot close my eyes in peace." Then answered Faithful John, " I will not forsake him, and will serve him with fidelity, even if it should cost me my life." On this, the old King said, " Now I die in comfort and peace." Then he added, " After my death, thou shalt show him the whole castle: all the chambers, halls, and vaults, and all the treasures which lie therein, but the last chamber in the long gallery, in which is the picture of the princess of the Golden Dwelling, shalt thou not show. If he sees that picture, he will fall violently in love with her, and will drop down in a swoon, and go through great danger for her sake, therefore thou must preserve him from that." And when Faithful John had once more given his promise to the old King about this, the King said no more, but laid his head on his pillow, and died.

When the old King had been carried to his grave, Faithful John told the young King all that he had promised his father on his deathbed, and said, " This will I assuredly perform, and will be faithful to thee as I have been faithful to him, even if it should cost me my life." When the mourning was over, Faithful John said to him: "It is now time that thou shouldst see thine inheritance. I will show thee thy father's palace." Then he took him about everywhere, up and down, and let him see all the riches, and the magnificent apartments, only there was one room which he did not open, that in which hung the dangerous picture. The picture was, however, so placed that when the door was opened you looked straight on it, and it was so admirably painted that it seemed to breathe and live, and there was nothing more charming or more beautiful in the whole world. The young King, however, plainly remarked that Faithful John always walked past this one door, and said, " Why dost thou never open this one for me?" "There is something within it," he replied, "which would terrify thee." But the King answered, "I have seen all the palace, and I will know what is in this room also," and he went and tried to break open the door by force. Then Faithful John held him back and said, "I promised thy father before his death that thou shouldst not see that which is in this chamber, it might bring the greatest misfortune on thee and on me." " Ah, no," replied the young King, "if I do not go in, it will be my certain destruction. I should have no rest day or night until I had seen it with my own eyes. I shall not leave the place now until thou hast unlocked the door."

Then Faithful John saw that there was no help for it now, and with a heavy heart and many sighs, sought out the key from the great bunch. When he had opened the door, he went in first, and thought by standing before him he could hide the portrait so that the King should not see it in front of him, but what availed that? The King stood on tip-toe and saw it over his shoulder. And when he saw the portrait of the maiden, which was so magnificent and shone with gold and precious stones, he fell fainting on the ground. Faithful John took him up, carried him to his bed, and sorrowfully thought, " The misfortune has befallen us, Lord God, what will be the end of it?" Then he strengthened him with wine, until he came to himself again. The first words the King said, were, "Ah, the beautiful portrait! whose is it?" " That is the princess of the Golden Dwelling," answered Faithful John. Then the King continued, " My love for her is so great, that if all the leaves on all the trees were tongues, they could not declare it. I will give my life to win her. Thou art my most Faithful John, thou must help me."

The faithful servant considered within himself for a long time how to set about the matter, for it was difficult even to obtain a sight of the King's daughter. At length he thought of a way, and said to the King, " Everything which she has about her is of gold—tables, chairs, dishes, glasses, bowls, and household furniture. Among thy treasures are five tons of gold; let one of the goldsmiths of the kingdom work these up into all manner of vessels and utensils, into all kinds of birds, wild beasts and strange animals, such as may please her, and we will go there with them and try our luck."

The King ordered all the goldsmiths to be brought to him, and they had to work night and day until at last the most splendid things were prepared. When everything was stowed on board a ship, Faithful John put on the dress of a merchant, and the King was forced to do the same in order to make himself quite unrecognizable. Then they sailed across the sea, and sailed on until they came to the town wherein dwelt the princess of the Golden Dwelling.

Faithful John bade the King stay behind on the ship, and wait for him. "Perhaps I shall bring the princess with me," said he, "therefore see that everything is in order; have the golden vessels set out and the whole ship decorated." Then he gathered together in his apron all kinds of gold things, went on shore and walked straight to the royal palace. When he entered the courtyard of the palace, a beautiful girl was standing there by the well with two golden buckets in her hand, drawing water with them. And when she was just turning round to carry away the sparkling water she saw the stranger, and asked who he was. So he answered, "I am a merchant," and opened his apron, and let her look in. Then she cried, "Oh, what beautiful gold things!" and put her pails down and looked at the golden wares one after the other. Then said the girl, "The princess must see these, she has such great pleasure in golden things, that she will buy all you have." She took him by the hand and led him upstairs, for she was the waiting-maid. When the King's daughter saw the wares, she was quite delighted and said, "They are so beautifully worked, that I will buy them all of thee." But Faithful John said, "I am only the servant of a rich merchant. The things I have here are not to be compared with those my master has in his ship. They are the most beautiful and valuable things that have ever been made in gold." She wanted to have everything brought to her there, but he said, "There are so many of them that it would take a great many days to do that, and so many rooms would be required to exhibit them, that your house is not big enough." Then her curiosity and longing were still more excited, until at last she said, "Conduct me to the ship, I will go there myself, and behold the treasures of thy master."

On this Faithful John was quite delighted, and led her to the ship, and when the King saw her, he perceived that her beauty was even greater than the picture had represented it to be, and thought no other than that his heart would burst in twain. Then she got into the ship, and the King led her within. Faithful John, however, remained behind with the pilot, and ordered the ship to be pushed off, saying, "Set all sail, till it fly like a bird in air." Within, however, the King showed her the golden vessels, every one of them, also the wild beasts and strange animals. Many hours went by whilst she was seeing everything, and in her delight she did not observe that the ship was sailing away. After she had looked at the last, she thanked the merchant and wanted to go home, but when she came to the side of the ship, she saw that it was on the deep sea far from land, and hurrying onwards with all sail set. "Ah," cried she in her alarm, "I am betrayed! I am carried away and have fallen into the power of a merchant—I would die rather!" The King, however, seized her hand, and said, "I am not a merchant. I am a king, and of no meaner origin than thou art, and if I have carried thee away with subtlety, that has come to pass because of my exceeding great love for thee. The first time that I looked on thy portrait, I fell fainting to the ground." When the princess of the Golden Dwelling heard that, she was comforted, and her heart was inclined unto him, so that she willingly consented to be his wife.

It happened, however, while they were sailing onwards over the deep sea, that Faithful John, who was sitting on the fore part of the vessel, making music, saw three ravens in the air, which came flying towards them. On this he stopped playing and listened to what they were saying to each other, for that he well understood. One cried, "Oh, there he is carrying home the princess of the Golden Dwelling." "Yes," replied the second, "but he has not got her yet." Said the third, "But he has got her, she is sitting beside him in the ship." Then the first began again, and cried, "What good will that do him? When they reach land a chestnut horse will leap forward to meet him, and the prince will want to mount it, but if he does that, it will run away with him, and rise up into the air with him, and he will never see his maiden more." Spake the second, "But is there no escape?"

"Oh, yes, if any one else gets on it swiftly, and takes out the pistol which must be in its holster, and shoots the horse dead with it, the young King is saved. But who knows that? And whosoever does know it, and tells it to him, will be turned to stone from the toe to the knee." Then said the second, "I know more than that; even if the horse be killed, the young King will still not keep his bride. When they go into the castle together, a wrought bridal garment will be lying there in a dish, and looking as if it were woven of gold and silver; it is, however, nothing but sulphur and pitch, and if he put it on, it will burn him to the very bone and marrow." Said the third, "Is there no escape at all?"

"Oh, yes," replied the second, "if any one with gloves on seizes the garment and throws it into the fire and burns it, the young King will be saved. But what avails that? Whosoever knows it and tells it to him, half his body will become stone from the knee to the heart."

Then said the third, "I know still more; even if the bridal garment be burnt, the young King will still not have his bride. After the wedding, when the dancing begins and the young Queen is dancing, she will suddenly turn pale and fall down as if dead, and if some one does not lift her up and draw three drops of blood from her right breast and spit them out again, she will die. But if any one who knows that were to declare it, he would become stone from the crown of his head to the sole of his foot." When the ravens had spoken of this together they flew onwards, and Faithful John had well understood everything, but from that time forth he became quiet and sad, for if he concealed what he had heard from his master, the latter would be unfortunate, and if he discovered it to him, he himself must sacrifice his life. At length, however, he said to himself, "I will save my master, even if it bring destruction on myself."

When therefore they came to shore, all happened as had been foretold by the ravens, and a magnificent chestnut horse sprang forward. "Good," said the King, "he shall carry me to my palace," and was about to mount it when Faithful John got before him, jumped quickly on it, drew the pistol out of the holster, and shot the horse. Then the other at-tendants of the King, who after all were not very fond of Faithful John, cried, "How shameful to kill the beautiful animal, that was to have carried the King to his palace!" But the King said, "Hold your peace and leave him alone, he is my most faithful John, who knows what may be the good of that!" They went into the palace, and in the hall there stood a dish, and therein lay the bridal garment looking no otherwise than as if it were made of gold and silver. The young King went towards it and was about to take hold of it, but Faithful John pushed him away, seized it with gloves on, carried it quickly to the fire and burnt it. The other attendants again began to murmur, and said, "Behold, now he is even burning the King's bridal garment!" But the young King said, "Who knows what good he may have done, leave him alone, he is my most faithful John."

And now the wedding was solemnized: the dance began, and the bride also took part in it; then Faithful John was watchful and looked into her face, and suddenly she turned pale and fell to the ground as if she were dead. On this he ran hastily to her, lifted her up and bore her into a chamber—then he laid her down, and knelt and sucked the three drops of blood from her right breast, and spat them out. Immediately she breathed again and recovered herself, but the young King had seen this, and being ignorant why Faithful John had done it, was angry and cried, "Throw him into a dungeon." Next morning Faithful John was condemned, and led to the gallows, and when he stood on high, and was about to be executed, he said, "Every one who has to die is permitted before his end to make one last speech; may I too claim the right?" "Yes," answered the King, "it shall be granted unto thee." Then said Faithful John, "I am unjustly condemned, and have always been true to thee," and related how he had hearkened to the conversation of the ravens when on the sea, and how he had been obliged to do all these things in order to save his master. Then cried the King, "Oh, my most faithful John. Pardon, pardon—bring him down." But as Faithful John spoke the last word he had fallen down lifeless and become a stone.

Thereupon the King and the Queen suffered great anguish and the King said, "Ah, how ill I have requited great fidelity!" and ordered the stone figure to be taken up and placed in his bedroom beside his bed. And as often as he looked on it he wept and said, "Ah, if I could bring thee to life again, my most faithful John." Some time passed and the Queen bore twins, two sons who grew fast and were her delight. Once when the Queen was at church and the two children were sitting playing beside their father, the latter full of grief again looked at the stone figure, sighed and said, "Ah, if I could but bring thee to life again, my most faithful John." Then the stone began to speak and said, "Thou canst bring me to life again if thou wilt use for that purpose what is dearest to thee." Then cried the King, "I will give everything I have in the world for thee." The stone continued, "If thou wilt cut off the heads of thy two children with thine own hand, and sprinkle me with their blood, I shall be restored to life."

The King was terrified when he heard that he himself must kill his dearest children, but he thought of Faithful John's great fidelity, and how he had died for him, drew his sword, and with his own hand cut off the children's heads. And when he had smeared the stone with their blood, life returned to it, and Faithful John stood once more safe and healthy before him. He said to the King, "Thy truth shall not go unrewarded," and took the heads of the children, put them on again, and rubbed the wounds with their blood, on which they became whole again immediately, and jumped about, and went on playing as if nothing had happened. Then the King was full of joy, and when he saw the Queen coming he hid Faithful John and the two children in a great cupboard. When she entered, he said to her, "Hast thou been praying in the church?" "Yes," answered she, "but I have constantly been thinking of Faithful John and what misfortune has befallen him through us." Then said he, "Dear wife, we can give him his life again, but it will cost us our two little sons, whom we must sacrifice." The Queen turned pale, and her heart was full of terror, but she said, "We owe it to him, for his great fidelity." Then the King was rejoiced that she thought as he had thought, and went and opened the cupboard, and brought forth Faithful John and the children, and said, "God be praised, he is delivered, and we have our little sons again also," and told her how everything had occurred. Then they dwelt together in much happiness until their death.

THE PACK OF RAGAMUFFINS

THE cock once said to the hen, " It is now the time when
the nuts are ripe, so let us go to the hill together and for
once eat our fill before the squirrel takes them all away."
" Yes," replied the hen, " come, we will have some pleasure together." Then they went away to the hill, and as
it was a bright day they stayed till evening. Now I do not
know whether it was that they had eaten till they were too
fat, or whether they had become proud, but they would
not go home on foot, and the cock had to build a little carriage of nut-shells. When it was ready, the little hen
seated herself in it and said to the cock, " Thou canst just
harness thyself to it." " I like that! " said the cock, " I
would rather go home on foot than let myself be harnessed
to it; no, that is not our bargain. I do not mind being
coachman and sitting on the box, but drag it myself I
will not."

As they were thus disputing, a duck quacked to them,
" You thieving folks, who bade you go to my nut-hill?
Wait, you shall suffer for it! " and ran with open beak at
the cock. But the cock also was not idle, and fell boldly
on the duck, and at last wounded her so with his spurs
that she begged for mercy, and willingly let herself be
harnessed to the carriage as a punishment. The little cock
now seated himself on the box and was coachman, and
thereupon they went off in a gallop, with " Duck, go as
fast as thou canst." When they had driven a part of the
way they met two foot-passengers, a pin and a needle.
They cried " Stop! stop! " and said that it would soon be
as dark as pitch, and then they could not go a step further,
and that it was so dirty on the road, and asked if they
could not get into the carriage for a while. They had
been at the tailor's public-house by the gate, and had
stayed too long over the beer. As they were thin
people, who did not take up much room, the cock let them
both get in, but they had to promise him and his little hen
not to step on their feet. Late in the evening they came
to an inn, and as they did not like to go further by night,

and as the duck also was not strong on her feet, and fell from one side to the other, they went in. The host at first made many objections, his house was already full, besides he thought they could not be very distinguished persons; but at last, as they made pleasant speeches, and told him that he should have the egg which the little hen had laid on the way, and should likewise keep the duck, which laid one every day, he at length said that they might stay the night. And now they had themselves well served and feasted and rioted. Early in the morning, when day was breaking, and every one was asleep, the cock awoke the hen, brought the egg, pecked it open, and they ate it together, but they threw the shell on the hearth. Then they went to the needle which was still asleep, took it by the head and stuck it into the cushion of the landlord's chair, and put the pin in his towel, and at last without more ado they flew away over the heath. The duck who liked to sleep in the open air and had stayed in the yard, heard them going away, made herself merry and found a stream down which she swam, which was a much quicker way of travelling than being harnessed to a carriage. The host did not get out of bed for two hours after this; he washed himself and wanted to dry himself, then the pin went over his face and made a red streak from one ear to the other. After this he went into the kitchen and wanted to light a pipe, but when he came to the hearth the egg-shell darted into his eyes. "This morning everything attacks my head," said he, and angrily sat down on his grandfather's chair, but he quickly started up again and cried, "Woe is me," for the needle had pricked him still worse than the pin, and not in the head. Now he was thoroughly angry, and suspected the guests who had come so late the night before, and when he went and looked about for them, they were gone. Then he made a vow to take no more ragamuffins into his house, for they consume much, pay for nothing, and play mischievous tricks into the bargain by way of gratitude.

RAPUNZEL[1]

THERE was once a man and a woman who had long in vain wished for a child. At length the woman hoped that God was about to grant her desire. These people had a little window at the back of their house from which a splendid garden could be seen, which was full of the most beautiful flowers and herbs. It was, however, surrounded by a high wall, and no one dared to go into it because it belonged to an enchantress, who had great power and was dreaded by all the world. One day the woman was standing by this window and looking down into the garden, when she saw a bed which was planted with the most beautiful rampion (rapunzel), and it looked so fresh and green that she longed for it, and had the greatest desire to eat some. This desire increased every day, and as she knew that she could not get any of it, she quite pined away, and looked pale and miserable. Then her husband was alarmed, and asked, "What aileth thee, dear wife?" "Ah," she replied, "if I can't get some of the rampion, which is in the garden behind our house, to eat, I shall die." The man, who loved her, thought, "Sooner than let thy wife die, bring her some of the rampion thyself, let it cost thee what it will." In the twilight of evening, he clambered down over the wall into the garden of the enchantress, hastily clutched a handful of rampion, and took it to his wife. She at once made herself a salad of it, and ate it with much relish. She, however, liked it so much—so very much—that the next day she longed for it three times as much as before. If he was to have any rest, her husband must once more descend into the garden. In the gloom of evening, therefore, he let himself down again; but when he had clambered down the wall he was terribly afraid, for he saw the enchantress standing before him. "How canst thou dare," said she with angry look, "to descend into my garden and steal my rampion like a thief? Thou shalt suffer for it!" "Ah,"

[1] Rapunzel, *Campanula rapunculus* (rampion), a congener of the common harebell. It has a long white spindle-shaped root which is eaten raw like a radish, and has a pleasant sweet flavour. Its leaves and young shoots are also used in salads—and so are the roots, sliced.—TR.

answered he, "let mercy take the place of justice, I only made up my mind to do it out of necessity. My wife saw your rampion from the window, and felt such a longing for it that she would have died if she had not got some to eat." Then the enchantress allowed her anger to be softened, and said to him, "If the case be as thou sayest, I will allow thee to take away with thee as much rampion as thou wilt, only I make one condition, thou must give me the child which thy wife will bring into the world; it shall be well treated, and I will care for it like a mother." The man in his terror consented to everything, and when the woman was brought to bed, the enchantress appeared at once, gave the child the name of Rapunzel, and took it away with her.

Rapunzel grew into the most beautiful child beneath the sun. When she was twelve years old, the enchantress shut her into a tower, which lay in a forest, and had neither stairs nor door, but quite at the top was a little window. When the enchantress wanted to go in, she placed herself beneath this and cried,

> "Rapunzel, Rapunzel,
> Let down thy hair to me."

Rapunzel had magnificent long hair, fine as spun gold, and when she heard the voice of the enchantress she unfastened her braided tresses, wound them round one of the hooks of the window above, and then the hair fell twenty ells down, and the enchantress climbed up by it.

After a year or two, it came to pass that the King's son rode through the forest and went by the tower. Then he heard a song, which was so charming that he stood still and listened. This was Rapunzel, who in her solitude passed her time in letting her sweet voice resound. The King's son wanted to climb up to her, and looked for the door of the tower, but none was to be found. He rode home, but the singing had so deeply touched his heart, that every day he went out into the forest and listened to it. Once when he was thus standing behind a tree, he saw that an enchantress came there, and he heard how she cried,

> "Rapunzel, Rapunzel,
> Let down thy hair."

Then Rapunzel let down the braids of her hair, and the enchantress climbed up to her. "If that is the ladder by which one mounts, I will for once try my fortune," said he, and the next day when it began to grow dark, he went to the tower and cried,

> "Rapunzel, Rapunzel,
> Let down thy hair."

Immediately the hair fell down and the King's son climbed up.

At first Rapunzel was terribly frightened when a man such as her eyes had never yet beheld, came to her; but the King's son began to talk to her quite like a friend, and told her that his heart had been so stirred that it had let him have no rest, and he had been forced to see her. Then Rapunzel lost her fear, and when he asked her if she would take him for her husband, and she saw that he was young and handsome, she thought, "He will love me more than old Dame Gothel does;" and she said yes, and laid her hand in his. She said, "I will willingly go away with thee, but I do not know how to get down. Bring with thee a skein of silk every time that thou comest, and I will weave a ladder with it, and when that is ready I will descend, and thou wilt take me on thy horse." They agreed that until that time he should come to her every evening, for the old woman came by day. The enchantress remarked nothing of this, until once Rapunzel said to her, "Tell me, Dame Gothel, how it happens that you are so much heavier for me to draw up than the young King's son—he is with me in a moment." "Ah! thou wicked child," cried the enchantress, "What do I hear thee say! I thought I had separated thee from all the world, and yet thou hast deceived me!" In her anger she clutched Rapunzel's beautiful tresses, wrapped them twice round her left hand, seized a pair of scissors with the right, and snip, snap, they were cut off, and the lovely braids lay on the ground. And she was so pitiless that she took poor Rapunzel into a desert where she had to live in great grief and misery.

On the same day, however, that she cast out Rapunzel, the enchantress in the evening fastened the braids of hair which she had cut off to the hook of the window, and when the King's son came and cried,

> "Rapunzel, Rapunzel,
> Let down thy hair,"

she let the hair down. The King's son ascended, but he did not find his dearest Rapunzel above, but the enchantress, who gazed at him with wicked and venomous looks. "Aha!" she cried mockingly, "Thou wouldst fetch thy dearest, but the beautiful bird sits no longer singing in the nest; the cat has got it, and will scratch out thy eyes as well. Rapunzel is lost to thee; thou wilt never see her more." The King's son was beside himself with pain, and in his despair he leapt down from the tower. He escaped with his life, but the thorns into which he fell pierced his eyes. Then he wandered quite blind about the forest, ate nothing but roots and berries, and did nothing but lament and weep over the loss of his dearest wife. Thus he roamed about in misery for some years, and at length came to the desert where Rapunzel, with the twins to which she had given birth, a boy and a girl, lived in wretchedness. He heard a voice, and it seemed so familiar to him that he went towards it, and when he approached, Rapunzel knew him and fell on his neck and wept. Two of her tears wetted his eyes and they grew clear again, and he could see with them as before. He led her to his kingdom where he was joyfully received, and they lived for a long time afterwards, happy and contented.

THE THREE LITTLE MEN IN THE WOOD

THERE was once a man whose wife died, and a woman whose husband died, and the man had a daughter, and the woman also had a daughter. The girls were acquainted with each other, and went out walking together, and afterwards came to the woman in her house. Then said she to the man's daughter, "Listen, tell thy father that I would like to marry him, and then thou shalt wash thyself in milk every morning, and drink wine, but my own daughter shall wash herself in water and drink water." The girl went home, and told her father what the woman had said. The man said, "What shall I do? Marriage is a joy and also a torment." At length as he could come to no decision, he pulled off his boot, and said, "Take this boot, it has a hole in the sole of it. Go with it up to the loft, hang it on the big nail, and then pour water into it. If it hold the water, then I will again take a wife, but if it run through, I will not." The girl did as she was ordered, but the water drew the hole together and the boot became full to the top. She informed her father how it had turned out. Then he himself went up, and when he saw that she was right, he went to the widow and wooed her, and the wedding was celebrated.

The next morning, when the two girls got up, there stood before the man's daughter milk for her to wash in and wine for her to drink, but before the woman's daughter stood water to wash herself with and water for drinking. On the second morning, stood water for washing and water for drinking before the man's daughter as well as before the woman's daughter. And on the third morning stood water for washing and water for drinking before the man's daughter, and milk for washing and wine for drinking, before the woman's daughter, and so it continued. The woman became bitterly unkind to her step-daughter, and day by day did her best to treat her still worse. She was envious too because her step-daughter was beautiful and lovable, and her own daughter ugly and repulsive.

Once, in winter, when everything was frozen as hard as a stone, and hill and vale lay covered with snow, the woman made a frock of paper, called her step-daughter, and said, "Here, put on this dress and go out into the wood, and fetch me a little basketful of strawberries,—I have a fancy for some." "Good heavens!" said the girl, "no strawberries grow in winter! The ground is frozen, and besides the snow has covered everything. And why am I to go in this paper frock? It is so cold outside that one's very breath freezes! The wind will blow through the frock, and the thorns will tear it off my body." "Wilt thou contradict me again?" said the step-mother. "See that thou goest, and do not show thy face again until thou hast the basketful of strawberries!" Then she gave her a little piece of hard bread, and said, "This will last thee the day," and thought, "Thou wilt die of cold and hunger outside, and wilt never be seen again by me."

Then the maiden was obedient, and put on the paper frock, and went out with the basket. Far and wide there was nothing but snow, and not a green blade to be seen. When she got into the wood she saw a small house out of which peeped three little dwarfs.[1] She wished them good day, and knocked modestly at the door. They cried, "Come in," and she entered the room and seated herself on the bench by the stove, where she began to warm herself and eat her breakfast. The elves said, "Give us, too, some of it." "Willingly," said she, and divided her bit of bread in two, and gave them the half. They asked, "What dost thou here in the forest in the winter time, in thy thin dress?" "Ah," she answered, "I am to look for a basketful of strawberries, and am not to go home until I can take them with me." When she had eaten her bread, they gave her a broom and said, "Sweep away the snow at the back door with it." But when she was outside, the three little men said to each other, "What shall we give her as she is so good, and has shared her bread with us?" Then said the first, "My gift is, that she shall every day grow more beautiful." The second said, "My gift is, that gold pieces shall fall out of her mouth every time she speaks." The third said, "My gift is that a king shall come and take her to wife."

The girl, however, did as the little men had bidden her, swept away the snow behind the little house with the broom, and what did she find but real ripe strawberries, which came up quite dark-red out of the snow! In her joy she hastily gathered her basket full, thanked the little men, shook hands with each of them, and ran home to take her step-mother what she had longed for so much. When

[1] In the original Haulemännerchen—i. e., Höhlen-Waldmännlein. They are so called because they live in caves in the forests. They are little dwarfs with large heads, and are supposed to steal unbaptized children.—TR.

she went in and said good-evening, a piece of gold at once
fell out of her mouth. Thereupon she related what had
happened to her in the wood, but with every word she spoke,
gold pieces fell from her mouth, until very soon the whole
room was covered with them. "Now look at her arrogance," cried the step-sister, "to throw about gold in that
way!" but she was secretly envious of it, and wanted to
go into the forest also to seek strawberries. The mother
said, "No, my dear little daughter, it is too cold, thou
mightest die of cold." However, as her daughter let her
have no peace, the mother at last yielded, made her a magnificent dress of fur, which she was obliged to put on, and
gave her bread-and-butter and cake with her.

The girl went into the forest and straight up to the little
house. The three little elves peeped out again, but she did
not greet them, and without looking round at them and
without speaking to them, she went awkwardly into the
room, seated herself by the stove, and began to eat her
bread-and-butter and cake. "Give us some of it," cried the
little men; but she replied, "There is not enough for myself,
so how can I give it away to other people?" When she
had done eating, they said, "There is a broom for thee,
sweep all clean for us outside by the back-door." "Humph!
Sweep for yourselves," she answered, "I am not your
servant." When she saw that they were not going to
give her anything she went out by the door. Then the little
men said to each other, "What shall we give her as she
is so naughty, and has a wicked envious heart, that will
never let her do a good turn to any one?" The first said,
"I grant that she may grow uglier every day." The second
said, "I grant that at every word she says, a toad shall
spring out of her mouth." The third said, "I grant that she
may die a miserable death." The maiden looked for strawberries outside, but as she found none, she went angrily
home. And when she opened her mouth, and was about to
tell her mother what had happened to her in the wood, with
every word she said, a toad sprang out of her mouth, so that
every one was seized with horror of her.

Then the step-mother was still more enraged, and thought
of nothing but how to do every possible injury to the man's

daughter, whose beauty, however, grew daily greater. At length she took a cauldron, set it on the fire, and boiled yarn in it. When it was boiled, she flung it on the poor girl's shoulder, and gave her an axe in order that she might go on the frozen river, cut a hole in the ice, and rinse the yarn. She was obedient, went thither and cut a hole in the ice; and while she was in the midst of her cutting, a splendid carriage came driving up, in which sat the King. The carriage stopped, and the King asked, "My child, who art thou, and what art thou doing here?" "I am a poor girl, and I am rinsing yarn." Then the King felt compassion, and when he saw that she was so very beautiful, he said to her, "Wilt thou go away with me?" "Ah, yes, with all my heart," she answered, for she was glad to get away from the mother and sister.

So she got into the carriage and drove away with the King, and when they arrived at his palace, the wedding was celebrated with great pomp, as the little men had granted to the maiden. When a year was over, the young Queen bore a son, and as the step-mother had heard of her great good-fortune, she came with her daughter to the palace and pretended that she wanted to pay her a visit. Once, however, when the King had gone out, and no one else was present, the wicked woman seized the Queen by the head, and her daughter seized her by the feet, and they lifted her out of the bed, and threw her out of the window into the stream which flowed by. Then the ugly daughter laid herself in the bed, and the old woman covered her up over her head. When the King came home again and wanted to speak to his wife, the old woman cried, "Hush, hush, that can't be now, she is lying in a violent perspiration; you must let her rest to-day." The King suspected no evil, and did not come back again till next morning; and as he talked with his wife and she answered him, with every word a toad leaped out, whereas formerly a piece of gold had fallen out. Then he asked what that could be, but the old woman said that she had got that from the violent perspiration, and would soon lose it again. During the night, however, the scullion saw a duck come swimming up the gutter, and it said,

"King, what art thou doing now?
Sleepest thou, or wakest thou?"

And as he returned no answer it said,

"And my guests, What may they do?"

The scullion said,

"They are sleeping soundly, too."

Then it asked again,

"What does little baby mine?"

He answered,

"Sleepeth in her cradle fine."

Then she went upstairs in the form of the Queen, nursed the baby, shook up its little bed, covered it over, and then swam away again down the gutter in the shape of a duck. She came thus for two nights; on the third, she said to the scullion, "Go and tell the King to take his sword and swing it three times over me on the threshold." Then the scullion ran and told this to the King, who came with his sword and swung it thrice over the spirit, and at the third time, his wife stood before him strong, living, and healthy as she had been before. Thereupon the King was full of great joy, but he kept the Queen hidden in a chamber until the Sunday when the baby was to be christened. And when it was christened he said, "What does a person deserve who drags another out of bed and throws him in the water?" "The wretch deserves nothing better," answered the old woman, "than to be taken and put in a barrel stuck full of nails, and rolled down hill into the water." "Then," said the King, "thou hast pronounced thine own sentence;" and he ordered such a barrel to be brought, and the old woman to be put into it with her daughter, and then the top was hammered on, and the barrel rolled down hill until it went into the river.

THE THREE SPINNERS

THERE was once a girl who was idle and would not spin, and let her mother say what she would, she could not bring her to it. At last the mother was once so overcome with anger and impatience, that she beat her, on which the girl began to weep loudly. Now at this very moment the Queen drove by, and when she heard the weeping she stopped her carriage, went into the house and asked the mother why she was beating her daughter so that the cries could be heard out on the road? Then the woman was ashamed to reveal the laziness of her daughter and said, " I cannot get her to leave off spinning. She insists on spinning for ever and ever, and I am poor, and cannot procure the flax." Then answered the Queen, " There is nothing that I like better to hear than spinning, and I am never happier than when the wheels are humming. Let me have your daughter with me in the palace, I have flax enough, and there she shall spin as much as she likes." The mother was heartily satisfied with this, and the Queen took the girl with her. When they had arrived at the palace, she led her up into three rooms which were filled from the bottom to the top with the finest flax. " Now spin me this flax," said she, " and when thou hast done it, thou shalt have my eldest son for a husband, even if thou art poor. I care not for that, thy indefatigable industry is dowry enough." The girl was secretly terrified, for she could not have spun the flax, no, not if she had lived till she was three hundred years old, and had sat at it every day from morning till night. When therefore she was alone, she began to weep, and sat thus for three days without moving a finger. On the third day came the Queen, and when she saw that nothing had been spun yet, she was surprised; but the girl excused herself by saying that she had not been able to begin because of her great distress at leaving her mother's house. The Queen was satisfied with this, but said when she was going away, " To-morrow thou must begin to work."

When the girl was alone again, she did not know what

to do, and in her distress went to the window. Then she saw three women coming towards her, the first of whom had a broad flat foot, the second had such a great underlip that it hung down over her chin, and the third had a broad thumb. They remained standing before the window, looked up, and asked the girl what was amiss with her? She complained of her trouble, and then they offered her their help and said, " If thou wilt invite us to the wedding, not be ashamed of us, and wilt call us thine aunts, and likewise wilt place us at thy table, we will spin up the flax for thee, and that in a very short time." " With all my heart," she replied, " do but come in and begin the work at once." Then she let in the three strange women, and cleared a place in the first room, where they seated themselves and began their spinning. The one drew the thread and trod the wheel, the other wetted the thread, the third twisted it, and struck the table with her finger, and as often as she struck it, a skein of thread fell to the ground that was spun in the finest manner possible. The girl concealed the three spinners from the Queen, and showed her whenever she came the great quantity of spun thread, until the latter could not praise her enough. When the first room was empty she went to the second, and at last to the third, and that too was quickly cleared. Then the three women took leave and said to the girl, "Do not forget what thou hast promised us, —it will make thy fortune."

When the maiden showed the Queen the empty rooms, and the great heap of yarn, she gave orders for the wedding, and the bridegroom[1] rejoiced that he was to have such a clever and industrious wife, and praised her mightily. " I have three aunts," said the girl, " and as they have been very kind to me, I should not like to forget them in my good fortune; allow me to invite them to the wedding, and let them sit with us at table." The Queen and the bridegroom said, " Why should we not allow that?" Therefore when the feast began, the three women entered in strange apparel, and the bride said, " Welcome, dear aunts." "Ah," said the bridegroom, " how comest thou by these odious

[1] Braütigam, betrothed. The old English brŷdguma had the same signification, and was only applied to a betrothed man, just as brŷd, bride, was only applied to a betrothed woman.—TR.

friends?" Thereupon he went to the one with the broad
flat foot and said, "How do you come by such a broad
foot?" "By treading," she answered, "by treading." Then
the bridegroom went to the second, and said, "How do you
come by your falling lip?" "By licking," she answered, "by
licking." Then he asked the third, "How do you come by
your broad thumb?" "By twisting the thread," she answered, "by twisting the thread." On this the King's son
was alarmed and said, "Neither now nor ever shall my beautiful bride touch a spinning-wheel." And thus she got rid
of the hateful flax-spinning.

HÄNSEL AND GRETHEL

HARD by a great forest dwelt a poor wood-cutter with his
wife and his two children. The boy was called Hänsel and
the girl Grethel. He had little to bite and to break, and once
when great scarcity fell on the land, he could no longer procure daily bread. Now when he thought over this by night
in his bed, and tossed about in his anxiety, he groaned and
said to his wife, "What is to become of us? How are we
to feed our poor children, when we no longer have anything
even for ourselves?" "I'll tell you what, husband," answered
the woman, "early to-morrow morning we will take the
children out into the forest to where it is the thickest, there
we will light a fire for them, and give each of them one piece
of bread more, and then we will go to our work and leave
them alone. They will not find the way home again, and we
shall be rid of them." "No, wife," said the man, "I will
not do that; how can I bear to leave my children alone in the
forest?—the wild animals would soon come and tear them
to pieces." "O, thou fool!" said she, "then we must all
four die of hunger, thou mayest as well plane the planks for
our coffins," and she left him no peace until he consented.
"But I feel very sorry for the poor children, all the same,"
said the man.

The two children had also not been able to sleep for
hunger, and had heard what their step-mother had said to
their father. Grethel wept bitter tears, and said to Hänsel,

"Now all is over with us." "Be quiet, Grethel," said Hänsel, "do not distress thyself, I will soon find a way to help us." And when the old folks had fallen asleep, he got up, put on his little coat, opened the door below, and crept outside. The moon shone brightly, and the white pebbles which lay in front of the house glittered like real silver pennies. Hänsel stooped and put as many of them in the little pocket of his coat as he could possibly get in. Then he went back and said to Grethel, "Be comforted, dear little sister, and sleep in peace, God will not forsake us," and he lay down again in his bed. When day dawned, but before the sun had risen, the woman came and awoke the two children, saying, "Get up, you sluggards! we are going into the forest to fetch wood." She gave each a little piece of bread, and said, "There is something for your dinner, but do not eat it up before then, for you will get nothing else." Grethel took the bread under her apron, as Hänsel had the stones in his pocket. Then they all set out together on the way to the forest. When they had walked a short time, Hänsel stood still and peeped back at the house, and did so again and again. His father said, "Hänsel, what art thou looking at there and staying behind for? Mind what thou art about, and do not forget how to use thy legs." "Ah, father," said Hänsel, "I am looking at my little white cat, which is sitting up on the roof, and wants to say good-bye to me." The wife said, "Fool, that is not thy little cat, that is the morning sun which is shining on the chimneys." Hänsel, however, had not been looking back at the cat, but had been constantly throwing one of the white pebble-stones out of his pocket on the road.

When they had reached the middle of the forest, the father said, "Now, children, pile up some wood, and I will light a fire that you may not be cold." Hänsel and Grethel gathered brushwood together, as high as a little hill. The brushwood was lighted, and when the flames were burning very high the woman said, "Now, children, lay yourselves down by the fire and rest, we will go into the forest and cut some wood. When we have done, we will come back and fetch you away."

Hänsel and Grethel sat by the fire, and when noon came, each ate a little piece of bread, and as they heard the strokes

of the wood-axe they believed that their father was near.
It was, however, not the axe, it was a branch which he had
fastened to a withered tree which the wind was blowing
backwards and forwards. And as they had been sitting such
a long time, their eyes shut with fatigue, and they fell fast
asleep. When at last they awoke, it was already dark night.
Grethel began to cry and said, " How are we to get out of
the forest now?" But Hänsel comforted her and said, " Just
wait a little, until the moon has risen, and then we will soon
find the way." And when the full moon had risen, Hänsel
took his little sister by the hand, and followed the pebbles
which shone like newly-coined silver pieces, and showed
them the way.

They walked the whole night long, and by break of day
came once more to their father's house. They knocked at
the door, and when the woman opened it and saw that it was
Hänsel and Grethel, she said, " You naughty children, why
have you slept so long in the forest?—we thought you were
never coming back at all!" The father, however, rejoiced,
for it had cut him to the heart to leave them behind alone.

Not long afterwards, there was once more great scarcity
in all parts, and the children heard their mother saying at
night to their father, " Everything is eaten again, we have
one half loaf left, and after that there is an end. The children must go, we will take them farther into the wood, so
that they will not find their way out again; there is no other
means of saving ourselves!" The man's heart was heavy,
and he thought " it would be better for thee to share the last
mouthful with thy children." The woman, however, would
listen to nothing that he had to say, but scolded and re-
proached him. He who says A must say B, likewise, and as
he had yielded the first time, he had to do so a second time
also.

The children were, however, still awake and had heard the
conversation. When the old folks were asleep, Hänsel again
got up, and wanted to go out and pick up pebbles, but the
woman had locked the door, and Hänsel could not get out.
Nevertheless he comforted his little sister, and said, " Do not
cry, Grethel, go to sleep quietly, the good God will help us."
Early in the morning came the woman, and took the chil-

dren out of their beds. Their bit of bread was given to them,
but it was still smaller than the time before. On the way
into the forest Hänsel crumbled his in his pocket, and often
stood still and threw a morsel on the ground. "Hänsel, why
dost thou stop and look around?" said the father, "go on."
"I am looking back at my little pigeon which is sitting on
the roof, and wants to say good-bye to me," answered Hänsel.
"Simpleton!" said the woman, "that is not thy little pigeon,
that is the morning sun that is shining on the chimney."
Hänsel, however, little by little, threw all the crumbs on the
path.

The woman led the children still deeper into the forest,
where they had never in their lives been before. Then a
great fire was again made, and the mother said, "Just sit
there, you children, and when you are tired you may sleep a
little; we are going into the forest to cut wood, and in the
evening when we are done, we will come and fetch you
away." When it was noon, Grethel shared her piece of bread
with Hänsel, who had scattered his by the way. Then they
fell asleep and evening came and went, but no one came to
the poor children. They did not awake until it was dark
night, and Hänsel comforted his little sister and said, "Just
wait, Grethel, until the moon rises, and then we shall see the
crumbs of bread which I have strewn about, they will show
us our way home again." When the moon came they set out,
but they found no crumbs, for the many thousands of birds
which fly about in the woods and fields had picked them all
up. Hänsel said to Grethel, "We shall soon find the way,"
but they did not find it. They walked the whole night and all
the next day too from morning till evening, but they did not
get out of the forest, and were very hungry, for they had
nothing to eat but two or three berries, which grew on the
ground. And as they were so weary that their legs would
carry them no longer, they lay down beneath a tree and fell
asleep.

It was now three mornings since they had left their father's
house. They began to walk again, but they always got deeper
into the forest, and if help did not come soon, they must die
of hunger and weariness. When it was mid-day, they saw a
beautiful snow-white bird sitting on a bough, which sang so

delightfully that they stood still and listened to it. And when it had finished its song, it spread its wings and flew away before them, and they followed it until they reached a little house, on the roof of which it alighted; and when they came quite up to the little house they saw that it was built of bread and covered with cakes, but that the windows were of clear sugar. " We will set to work on that," said Hänsel, " and have a good meal. I will eat a bit of the roof, and thou, Grethel, canst eat some of the window, it will taste sweet." Hänsel reached up above, and broke off a little of the roof to try how it tasted, and Grethel leant against the window and nibbled at the panes. Then a soft voice cried from the room,

> "Nibble, nibble, gnaw,
> Who is nibbling at my little house?"

The children answered,

> "The wind, the wind,
> The heaven-born wind,"

and went on eating without disturbing themselves. Hänsel who thought the roof tasted very nice, tore down a great piece of it, and Grethel pushed out the whole of one round window-pane, sat down, and enjoyed herself with it. Suddenly the door opened, and a very, very old woman, who supported herself on crutches, came creeping out. Hänsel and Grethel were so terribly frightened that they let fall what they had in their hands. The old woman, however, nodded her head, and said, " Oh, you dear children, who has brought you here? Do come in, and stay with me. No harm shall happen to you." She took them both by the hand, and led them into her little house. Then good food was set before them, milk and pancakes, with sugar, apples, and nuts. Afterwards two pretty little beds were covered with clean white linen, and Hänsel and Grethel lay down in them, and thought they were in heaven.

The old woman had only pretended to be so kind; she was in reality a wicked witch, who lay in wait for children, and had only built the little bread house in order to entice them there. When a child fell into her power, she killed it, cooked and ate it, and that was a feast day with her. Witches have red eyes, and cannot see far, but they have a keen scent like the beasts, and are aware when human beings draw near. When Hänsel and Grethel came into her neighbourhood, she laughed maliciously, and said mockingly, " I have them, they shall not escape me again !" Early in the morning before the children were awake, she was already up, and when she saw both of them sleeping and looking so pretty, with their plump red cheeks, she muttered to herself, "That will be a dainty mouthful !" Then she seized Hänsel with her shrivelled hand, carried him into a little stable, and shut him in with a grated door. He might scream as he liked, that was of no use. Then she went to Grethel, shook her till she awoke, and cried, " Get up, lazy thing, fetch some water, and cook something good for thy brother, he is in the stable outside, and is to be made fat. When he is fat, I will eat him." Grethel began to weep bitterly, but it was all in vain, she was forced to do what the wicked witch ordered her.

And now the best food was cooked for poor Hänsel, but Grethel got nothing but crab-shells. Every morning the woman crept to the little stable, and cried, " Hänsel, stretch out thy finger that I may feel if thou wilt soon be fat." Hänsel, however, stretched out a little bone to her, and the old woman, who had dim eyes, could not see it, and thought it was Hänsel's finger, and was astonished that there was no way of fattening him. When four weeks had gone by, and Hänsel still continued thin, she was seized with impatience and would not wait any longer, " Hola, Grethel," she cried to the girl, " be active, and bring some water. Let Hänsel be fat or lean, to-morrow I will kill him, and cook him." Ah, how the poor little sister did lament when she had to fetch the water, and how her tears did flow down over her cheeks ! " Dear God, do help us," she cried. " If the wild beasts in the forest had but devoured us, we should at any rate have died together." " Just keep thy noise to thyself," said the old woman, " all that won't help thee at all."

Early in the morning, Grethel had to go out and hang up the cauldron with the water, and light the fire. " We will bake first," said the old woman, " I have already heated the oven, and kneaded the dough." She pushed poor Grethel out to the oven, from which flames of fire were already darting.

"Creep in," said the witch, "and see if it is properly heated, so that we can shut the bread in." And when once Grethel was inside, she intended to shut the oven and let her bake in it, and then she would eat her, too. But Grethel saw what she had in her mind, and said, "I do not know how I am to do it; how do you get in?" "Silly goose," said the old woman. "The door is big enough; just look, I can get in myself!" and she crept up and thrust her head into the oven. Then Grethel gave her a push that drove her far into it, and shut the iron door, and fastened the bolt. Oh! then she began to howl quite horribly, but Grethel ran away, and the godless witch was miserably burnt to death.

Grethel, however, ran as quick as lightning to Hänsel, opened his little stable, and cried, "Hänsel, we are saved! The old witch is dead!" Then Hänsel sprang out like a bird from its cage when the door is opened for it. How they did rejoice and embrace each other, and dance about and kiss each other! And as they had no longer any need to fear her, they went into the witch's house, and in every corner there stood chests full of pearls and jewels. "These are far better than pebbles!" said Hänsel, and thrust into his pockets whatever could be got in, and Grethel said, "I, too, will take something home with me," and filled her pinafore full. "But now we will go away," said Hänsel, "that we may get out of the witch's forest."

When they had walked for two hours, they came to a great piece of water. "We cannot get over," said Hänsel, "I see no foot-plank, and no bridge." "And no boat crosses either," answered Grethel, "but a white duck is swimming there; if I ask her, she will help us over." Then she cried,

> "Little duck, little duck, dost thou see,
> Hänsel and Grethel are waiting for thee?
> There's never a plank, or bridge in sight,
> Take us across on thy back so white."

The duck came to them, and Hänsel seated himself on its back, and told his sister to sit by him. "No," replied Grethel, "that will be too heavy for the little duck; she shall take us across, one after the other." The good little duck did so, and when they were once safely across and had walked for a short time, the forest seemed to be more and more familiar to them, and at length they saw from afar their father's house. Then they began to run, rushed into the parlour, and threw themselves into their father's arms. The man had not known one happy hour since he had left the children in the forest; the woman, however, was dead. Grethel emptied her pinafore until pearls and precious stones ran about the room, and Hänsel threw one handful after another out of his pocket to add to them. Then all anxiety was at an end, and they lived together in perfect happiness. My tale is done, there runs a mouse, whosoever catches it, may make himself a big fur cap out of it.

THE FISHERMAN AND HIS WIFE[1]

THERE was once on a time a Fisherman who lived with his wife in a miserable hovel close by the sea, and every day he went out fishing. And once as he was sitting with his rod, looking at the clear water, his line suddenly went down, far down below, and when he drew it up again, he brought out a large Flounder. Then the Flounder said to him, "Hark, you Fisherman, I pray you, let me live, I am no Flounder really, but an enchanted prince. What good will it do you to kill me? I should not be good to eat, put me in the water again, and let me go." "Come," said the Fisherman, "there is no need for so many words about it—a fish that can talk I should certainly let go, anyhow," with that he put him back again into the clear water, and the Flounder went to the bottom, leaving a long streak of blood behind him. Then the Fisherman got up and went home to his wife in the hovel.

"Husband," said the woman, "have you caught nothing to-day?" "No," said the man, "I did catch a Flounder, who said he was an enchanted prince, so I let him go again." "Did you not wish for anything first?" said the woman. "No," said the man; "what should I wish for?" "Ah," said the woman, "it is surely hard to have to live always in this dirty hovel; you might have wished for a small cottage

[1] According to the late William Howitt, this story was communicated to the Brothers Grimm by Mr. Henry Crabbe Robinson, who had it from an old woman. See "Diary of H. C. Robinson."—TR.

for us. Go back and call him. Tell him we want to have a small cottage, he will certainly give us that." "Ah," said the man, "why should I go there again?" "Why," said the woman, "you did catch him, and you let him go again; he is sure to do it. Go at once." The man still did not quite like to go, but did not like to oppose his wife, and went to the sea.

When he got there the sea was all green and yellow, and no longer so smooth; so he stood and said,

> "Flounder, flounder in the sea,
> Come, I pray thee, here to me;
> For my wife, good Ilsabil,[2]
> Wills not as I'd have her will."

Then the Flounder came swimming to him and said, "Well, what does she want, then?" "Ah," said the man, "I did catch you, and my wife says I really ought to have wished for something. She does not like to live in a wretched hovel any longer; she would like to have a cottage." "Go, then," said the Flounder, "she has it already."

When the man went home, his wife was no longer in the hovel, but instead of it there stood a small cottage, and she was sitting on a bench before the door. Then she took him by the hand and said to him, "Just come inside, look, now isn't this a great deal better?" So they went in, and there was a small porch, and a pretty little parlour and bed-room, and a kitchen and pantry, with the best of furniture, and fitted up with the most beautiful things made of tin and brass, whatsoever was wanted. And behind the cottage there was a small yard, with hens and ducks, and a little garden with flowers and fruit. "Look," said the wife, "is not that nice!" "Yes," said the husband, "and so we must always think it,— now we will live quite contented." "We will think about that," said the wife. With that they ate something and went to bed.

Everything went well for a week or a fortnight, and then the woman said, "Hark you, husband, this cottage is far too small for us, and the garden and yard are little; the Flounder might just as well have given us a larger house. I should like to live in a great stone castle; go to the Flounder, and

[2] Isabel.—Tr.

tell him to give us a castle." "Ah, wife," said the man, "the cottage is quite good enough; why should we live in a castle?" "What!" said the woman; "just go there, the Flounder can always do that." "No, wife," said the man, "the Flounder has just given us the cottage, I do not like to go back so soon, it might make him angry." "Go," said the woman, "he can do it quite easily, and will be glad to do it; just you go to him."

The man's heart grew heavy, and he would not go. He said to himself, "It is not right," and yet he went. And when he came to the sea the water was quite purple and dark-blue, and grey and thick, and no longer so green and yellow, but it was still quiet. And he stood there and said—

> "Flounder, flounder in the sea,
> Come, I pray thee, here to me;
> For my wife, good Ilsabil,
> Wills not as I'd have her will."

"Well, what does she want, then?" said the Flounder. "Alas," said the man, half scared, "she wants to live in a great stone castle." "Go to it, then, she is standing before the door," said the Flounder.

Then the man went away, intending to go home, but when he got there, he found a great stone palace, and his wife was just standing on the steps going in, and she took him by the hand and said, "Come in." So he went in with her, and in the castle was a great hall paved with marble, and many servants, who flung wide the doors; and the walls were all bright with beautiful hangings, and in the rooms were chairs and tables of pure gold, and crystal chandeliers hung from the ceilings, and all the rooms and bed-rooms had carpets, and food and wine of the very best were standing on all the tables so that they nearly broke down beneath it. Behind the house, too, there was a great court-yard, with stables for horses and cows, and the very best of carriages; there was a magnificent large garden, too, with the most beautiful flowers and fruit-trees, and a park quite half a mile long, in which were stags, deer, and hares, and everything that could be desired. "Come," said the woman, "isn't that beautiful?" "Yes, indeed," said the man, "now let it be; and we will live in this beautiful castle and be content." "We will consider about that," said the woman, "and sleep upon it"; thereupon they went to bed.

Next morning the wife awoke first, and it was just daybreak, and from her bed she saw the beautiful country lying before her. Her husband was still stretching himself, so she poked him in the side with her elbow, and said, " Get up, husband, and just peep out of the window. Look you, couldn't we be the King over all that land? Go to the Flounder, we will be the King." "Ah, wife," said the man, "why should we be King? I do not want to be King." "Well," said the wife, " if you won't be King, I will; go to the Flounder, for I will be King." "Ah, wife," said the man, " why do you want to be King? I do not like to say that to him." "Why not?" said the woman; "go to him this instant; I must be King!" So the man went, and was quite unhappy because his wife wished to be King. "It is not right; it is not right," thought he. He did not wish to go, but yet he went.

And when he came to the sea, it was quite dark-grey, and the water heaved up from below, and smelt putrid. Then he went and stood by it, and said,

> "Flounder, flounder in the sea,
>   Come, I pray thee, here to me;
> For my wife, good Ilsabil,
>   Wills not as I'd have her will."

"Well, what does she want, then?" said the Flounder. "Alas!" said the man, " she wants to be King." " Go to her; she is King already."

So the man went, and when he came to the palace, the castle had become much larger, and had a great tower and magnificent ornaments, and the sentinel was standing before the door, and there were numbers of soldiers with kettle-drums and trumpets. And when he went inside the house, everything was of real marble and gold, with velvet covers and great golden tassels. Then the doors of the hall were opened, and there was the court in all its splendour, and his wife was sitting on a high throne of gold and diamonds, with a great crown of gold on her head, and a sceptre of pure gold and jewels in her hand, and on both sides of her stood her maids-in-waiting in a row, each of them always one head shorter than the last.

Then he went and stood before her, and said, " Ah, wife, and now you are King." "Yes," said the woman, "now I am King." So he stood and looked at her, and when he had looked at her thus for some time, he said, " And now that you are King, let all else be, now we will wish for nothing more." "Nay, husband," said the woman, quite anxiously, "I find time pass very heavily, I can bear it no longer; go to the Flounder—I am King, but I must be Emperor, too." "Alas, wife, why do you wish to be Emperor?" "Husband," said she, "go to the Flounder. I will be Emperor." " Alas, wife," said the man, " he cannot make you Emperor; I may not say that to the fish. There is only one Emperor in the land. An Emperor the Flounder cannot make you! I assure you he cannot."

"What!" said the woman, "I am the King, and you are nothing but my husband; will you go this moment? go at once! If he can make a king he can make an emperor. I will be Emperor; go instantly." So he was forced to go. As the man went, however, he was troubled in mind, and thought to himself, "It will not end well; it will not end well! Emperor is too shameless! The Flounder will at last be tired out."

With that he reached the sea, and the sea was quite black and thick, and began to boil up from below, so that it threw up bubbles, and such a sharp wind blew over it that it curled, and the man was afraid. Then he went and stood by it, and said,

> "Flounder, flounder in the sea,
> Come, I pray thee, here to me;
> For my wife, good Ilsabil,
> Wills not as I'd have her will."

"Well, what does she want, then?" said the Flounder. "Alas, Flounder," said he, "my wife wants to be Emperor." "Go to her," said the Flounder; "she is Emperor already."

So the man went, and when he got there the whole palace was made of polished marble with alabaster figures and golden ornaments, and soldiers were marching before the door blowing trumpets, and beating cymbals and drums; and in the house, barons, and counts, and dukes were going about as servants. Then they opened the doors to him, which were of pure gold. And when he entered, there sat his wife on a throne, which was made of one piece of gold, and was quite two miles high; and she wore a great golden crown that was three yards high, and set with diamonds and carbuncles, and in one hand she had the sceptre, and in the other the imperial orb; and on both sides of her stood the yeomen of the guard in two rows, each being smaller than the one before him, from the biggest giant, who was two miles high, to the very smallest dwarf, just as big as my little finger. And before it stood a number of princes and dukes.

Then the man went and stood among them, and said, "Wife, are you Emperor now?" "Yes, said she, "now I am Emperor." Then he stood and looked at her well, and when he had looked at her thus for some time, he said, "Ah, wife, be content, now that you are Emperor." "Husband," said she, "why are you standing there? Now, I am Emperor, but I will be Pope too; go to the Flounder." "Alas, wife," said the man, "what will you not wish for? You cannot be Pope; there is but one in Christendom; he cannot make you Pope." "Husband," said she, "I will be Pope; go immediately, I must be Pope this very day." "No, wife," said the man, "I do not like to say that to him; that would not do, it is too much; the Flounder can't make you Pope." "Husband," said she, "what nonsense! if he can make an emperor he can make a pope. Go to him directly. I am Emperor, and you are nothing but my husband; will you go at once?"

Then he was afraid and went; but he was quite faint, and shivered and shook, and his knees and legs trembled. And a high wind blew over the land, and the clouds flew, and towards evening all grew dark, and the leaves fell from the trees, and the water rose and roared as if it were boiling, and splashed upon the shore; and in the distance he saw ships which were firing guns in their sore need, pitching and tossing on the waves. And yet in the midst of the sky there was still a small bit of blue, though on every side it was as red as in a heavy storm. So, full of despair, he went and stood in much fear and said,

> "Flounder, flounder in the sea,
>   Come, I pray thee, here to me;
> For my wife, good Ilsabil,
>   Wills not as I'd have her will."

"Well, what does she want, then?" said the Flounder. "Alas," said the man, "she wants to be Pope." "Go to her then," said the Flounder; "she is Pope already."

So he went, and when he got there, he saw what seemed to be a large church surrounded by palaces. He pushed his way through the crowd. Inside, however, everything was lighted up with thousands and thousands of candles, and his wife was clad in gold, and she was sitting on a much higher throne, and had three great golden crowns on, and round about her there was much ecclesiastical splendour; and on both sides of her was a row of candles the largest of which was as tall as the very tallest tower, down to the very smallest kitchen candle, and all the emperors and kings were on their knees before her, kissing her shoe. "Wife," said the man, and looked attentively at her, "are you now Pope?" "Yes," said she, "I am Pope." So he stood and looked at her, and it was just as if he was looking at the bright sun. When he had stood looking at her thus for a short time, he said, "Ah, wife, if you are Pope, do let well alone!" But she looked as stiff as a post, and did not move or show any signs of life. Then said he, "Wife, now that you are Pope, be satisfied, you cannot become anything greater now." "I will consider about that," said the woman. Thereupon they both went to bed, but she was not satisfied, and greediness let her have no sleep, for she was continually thinking what there was left for her to be.

The man slept well and soundly, for he had run about a great deal during the day; but the woman could not fall asleep at all, and flung herself from one side to the other the whole night through, thinking always what more was left for her to be, but unable to call to mind anything else. At length the sun began to rise, and when the woman saw the red of dawn, she sat up in bed and looked at it. And when, through the window, she saw the sun thus rising, she said, "Cannot I, too, order the sun and moon to rise?" "Husband," said she, poking him in the ribs with her elbows, "wake up! go to the Flounder, for I wish to be even as God is." The man was still half asleep, but he was so horrified that he fell out of bed. He thought he must have heard amiss, and rubbed his eyes, and said, "Alas, wife, what are you saying?" "Husband," said she, "if I can't order the sun and moon to rise, and have to look on and see the sun and moon rising, I can't bear it. I shall not know what it is to have another happy hour, unless I can make them rise myself." Then she looked at him so terribly that a shudder ran over him, and said, "Go at once; I wish to be like unto God." "Alas, wife," said the man, falling on his knees before her, "the Flounder cannot do that; he can make an emperor and a pope; I beseech you, go on as you are, and be Pope." Then she fell into a rage, and her hair flew wildly about her head, and she cried, "I will not endure this, I'll not bear it any longer; wilt thou go?" Then he put on his trousers and ran away like a madman. But outside a great storm was raging, and blowing so hard that he could scarcely keep his feet; houses and trees toppled over, the mountains trembled, rocks rolled into the sea, the sky was pitch black, and it thundered and lightened, and the sea came in with black waves as high as church-towers and mountains, and all with crests of white foam at the top. Then he cried, but could not hear his own words,

> "Flounder, flounder in the sea,
> Come, I pray thee, here to me;
> For my wife, good Ilsabil,
> Wills not as I'd have her will."

"Well, what does she want, then?" said the Flounder. "Alas," said he, "she wants to be like unto God." "Go to her, and you will find her back again in the dirty hovel." And there they are living still at this very time.

THE VALIANT LITTLE TAILOR

ONE summer's morning a little tailor was sitting on his table by the window; he was in good spirits, and sewed with all his might. Then came a peasant woman down the street crying, " Good jams, cheap! Good jams, cheap! " This rang pleasantly in the tailor's ears; he stretched his delicate head out of the window, and called, " Come up here, dear woman; here you will get rid of your goods." The woman came up the three steps to the tailor with her heavy basket, and he made her unpack the whole of the pots for him. He inspected all of them, lifted them up, put his nose to them, and at length said, " The jam seems to me to be good, so weigh me out four ounces, dear woman, and if it is a quarter of a pound that is of no consequence." The woman who had hoped to find a good sale, gave him what he desired, but went away quite angry and grumbling. " Now, God bless the jam to my use," cried the little tailor, " and give me health and strength;" so he brought the bread out of the cupboard, cut himself a piece right across the loaf and spread the jam over it. " This won't taste bitter," said he, " but I will just finish the jacket before I take a bite." He laid the bread near him, sewed on, and in his joy, made bigger and bigger stitches. In the meantime the smell of the sweet jam ascended so to the wall, where the flies were sitting in great numbers, that they were attracted and descended on it in hosts. " Hola! who invited you? " said the little tailor, and drove the unbidden guests away. The flies, however, who understood no German, would not be turned away, but came back again in ever-increasing companies. Then the little tailor at last lost all patience, and got a bit of cloth from the hole under his work-table, and saying, " Wait, and I will give it to you," struck it mercilessly on them. When he drew it away and counted, there lay before him no fewer than seven, dead and with legs stretched out. " Art thou a fellow of that sort? " said he, and could not help admiring his own bravery. " The whole town shall know of this! " And the little tailor hastened to cut himself a girdle, stitched it, and em-

broidered on it in large letters, "Seven at one stroke!"
"What, the town!" he continued, "the whole world shall
hear of it!" and his heart wagged with joy like a lamb's
tail. The tailor put on the girdle, and resolved to go forth
into the world, because he thought his workshop was too
small for his valour. Before he went away, he sought about
in the house to see if there was anything which he could take
with him; however, he found nothing but an old cheese, and
that he put in his pocket. In front of the door he observed a
bird which had caught itself in the thicket. It had to go
into his pocket with the cheese. Now he took to the road
boldly, and as he was light and nimble, he felt no fatigue.
The road led him up a mountain, and when he had reached
the highest point of it, there sat a powerful giant looking
about him quite comfortably. The little tailor went bravely
up, spoke to him, and said, "Good day, comrade, so thou
art sitting there, overlooking the wide-spread world! I
am just on my way thither, and want to try my luck. Hast
thou any inclination to go with me?" The giant looked
contemptuously at the tailor, and said, "Thou ragamuffin!
Thou miserable creature!"

"Oh, indeed?" answered the little tailor, and unbuttoned
his coat, and showed the giant the girdle. "There mayst thou
read what kind of a man I am!" The giant read, "Seven
at one stroke," and thought that they had been men whom
the tailor had killed, and began to feel a little respect for
the tiny fellow. Nevertheless, he wished to try him first,
and took a stone in his hand and squeezed it together so that
water dropped out of it. "Do that likewise," said the giant,
"if thou hast strength?" "Is that all?" said the tailor,
"that is child's play with us!" and put his hand into his
pocket, brought out the soft cheese, and pressed it until
the liquid ran out of it. "Faith," said he, "that was a little
better, wasn't it?" The giant did not know what to say,
and could not believe it of the little man. Then the giant
picked up a stone and threw it so high that the eye could
scarcely follow it. "Now, little mite of a man, do that
likewise." "Well thrown," said the tailor, "but after all
the stone came down to earth again; I will throw you one
which shall never come back at all," and he put his hand into

his pocket, took out the bird, and threw it into the air. The bird, delighted with its liberty, rose, flew away and did not come back. "How does that shot please you, comrade?" asked the tailor. "Thou canst certainly throw," said the giant, "but now we will see if thou art able to carry anything properly." He took the tailor to a mighty oak tree which lay there felled on the ground, and said, "If thou art strong enough, help me to carry the tree out of the forest." "Readily," answered the little man; "take thou the trunk on thy shoulders, and I will raise up the branches and twigs; after all, they are the heaviest." The giant took the trunk on his shoulder, but the tailor seated himself on a branch, and the giant who could not look round, had to carry away the whole tree and the little tailor into the bargain: he behind, was quite merry and happy, and whistled the song, "Three tailors rode forth from the gate," as if carrying the tree were child's play. The giant, after he had dragged the heavy burden part of the way, could go no further, and cried, "Hark you, I shall have to let the tree fall!" The tailor sprang nimbly down, seized the tree with both arms as if he had been carrying it, and said to the giant, "Thou art such a great fellow, and yet canst not even carry the tree!"

They went on together, and as they passed a cherry-tree, the giant laid hold of the top of the tree where the ripest fruit was hanging, bent it down, gave it into the tailor's hand, and bade him eat. But the little tailor was much too weak to hold the tree, and when the giant let it go, it sprang back again, and the tailor was hurried into the air with it. When he had fallen down again without injury, the giant said, "What is this? Hast thou not strength enough to hold the weak twig?" "There is no lack of strength," answered the little tailor. "Dost thou think that could be anything to a man who has struck down seven at one blow? I leapt over the tree because the huntsmen are shooting down there in the thicket. Jump as I did, if thou canst do it." The giant made the attempt, but could not get over the tree, and remained hanging in the branches, so that in this also the tailor kept the upper hand.

The giant said, "If thou art such a valiant fellow, come

with the into our cavern and spend the night with us." The
little fellow was willing, and followed him. When they
went into the cave, other giants were sitting there by the
fire, and each of them had a roasted sheep in his hand and
was eating it. The little tailor looked round and thought,
"It is much more spacious here than in my workshop." The
giant showed him a bed, and said he was to lie down in it
and sleep. The bed was, however, too big for the little
tailor; he did not lie down in it, but crept into a corner.
When it was midnight, and the giant thought that the little
tailor was lying in a sound sleep, he got up, took a great
iron bar, cut through the bed with one blow, and thought
he had given the grasshopper his finishing stroke. With
the earliest dawn the giants went into the forest, and had
quite forgotten the little tailor, when all at once he walked up
to them quite merrily and boldly. The giants were terrified,
they were afraid that he would strike them all dead, and
ran away in a great hurry.

The little tailor went onwards, always following his own
pointed nose. After he had walked for a long time, he came
to the court-yard of a royal palace, and as he felt weary, he
lay down on the grass and fell asleep. Whilst he lay there,
the people came and inspected him on all sides, and read
on his girdle, "Seven at one stroke." "Ah!" said they,
"what does the great warrior here in the midst of peace?
He must be a mighty lord." They went and announced him
to the King, and gave it as their opinion that if war should
break out, this would be a weighty and useful man who
ought on no account to be allowed to depart. The counsel
pleased the King, and he sent one of his courtiers to the little
tailor to offer him military service when he awoke. The
ambassador remained standing by the sleeper, waited until
he stretched his limbs and opened his eyes, and then con-
veyed to him this proposal. "For this very reason have
I come here," the tailor replied, "I am ready to enter the
King's service." He was therefore honourably received, and
a separate dwelling was assigned him.

The soldiers, however, were set against the little tailor,
and wished him a thousand miles away. "What is to be
the end of this?" they said amongst themselves. "If we

quarrel with him, and he strikes about him, seven of us will fall at every blow; not one of us can stand against him." They came therefore to a decision, betook themselves in a body to the King, and begged for their dismissal. "We are not prepared," said they, "to stay with a man who kills seven at one stroke." The King was sorry that for the sake of one he should lose all his faithful servants, wished that he had never set eyes on the tailor, and would willingly have been rid of him again. But he did not venture to give him his dismissal, for he dreaded lest he should strike him and all his people dead, and place himself on the royal throne. He thought about it for a long time, and at last found good counsel. He sent to the little tailor and caused him to be informed that as he was such a great warrior, he had one request to make to him. In a forest of his country lived two giants, who caused great mischief with their robbing, murdering, ravaging, and burning, and no one could approach them without putting himself in danger of death. If the tailor conquered and killed these two giants, he would give him his only daughter to wife, and half of his kingdom as a dowry, likewise one hundred horsemen should go with him to assist him. "That would indeed be a fine thing for a man like me!" thought the little tailor. "One is not offered a beautiful princess and half a kingdom every day of one's life!" "Oh, yes," he replied, "I will soon subdue the giants, and do not require the help of the hundred horsemen to do it; he who can hit seven at one blow, has no need to be afraid of two."

The little tailor went forth, and the hundred horsemen followed him. When he came to the outskirts of the forest, he said to his followers, "Just stay waiting here, I alone will soon finish off the giants." Then he bounded into the forest and looked about right and left. After a while he perceived both giants. They lay sleeping under a tree, and snored so that the branches waved up and down. The little tailor, not idle, gathered two pocketsful of stones, and with these climbed up the tree. When he was half-way up, he slipped down by a branch, until he sat just above the sleepers, and then let one stone after another fall on the breast of one of the giants. For a long time the giant felt nothing, but at last he awoke, pushed his comrade, and said, "Why art thou knocking me?" "Thou must be dreaming," said the other, "I am not knocking thee." They laid themselves down to sleep again, and then the tailor threw a stone down on the second. "What is the meaning of this?" cried the other. "Why art thou pelting me?" "I am not pelting thee," answered the first, growling. They disputed about it for a time, but as they were weary they let the matter rest, and their eyes closed once more. The little tailor began his game again, picked out the biggest stone, and threw it with all his might on the breast of the first giant. "That is too bad!" cried he, and sprang up like a madman, and pushed his companion against the tree until it shook. The other paid him back in the same coin, and they got into such a rage that they tore up trees and belaboured each other so long, that at last they both fell down dead on the ground at the same time. Then the little tailor leapt down. "It is a lucky thing," said he, "that they did not tear up the tree on which I was sitting, or I should have had to spring on to another like a squirrel; but we tailors are nimble." He drew out his sword and gave each of them a couple of thrusts in the breast, and then went out to the horsemen and said, "The work is done; I have given both of them their finishing stroke, but it was hard work! They tore up trees in their sore need, and defended themselves with them, but all that is to no purpose when a man like myself comes, who can kill seven at one blow." "But are you not wounded?" asked the horsemen. "You need not concern yourself about that," answered the tailor, "they have not bent one hair of mine." The horsemen would not believe him, and rode into the forest; there they found the giants swimming in their blood, and all round about, lay the torn-up trees.

The little tailor demanded of the King the promised reward; he however, repented of his promise, and again bethought himself how he could get rid of the hero. "Before thou receivest my daughter, and half of my kingdom," said he to him, "thou must perform one more heroic deed. In the forest roams a unicorn which does great harm, and thou must catch it first." "I fear one unicorn still less than two giants. Seven at one blow, is my kind of affair." He took a rope and an axe with him, went forth into the forest, and bade those who were sent with him to wait outside. He had not to seek long. The unicorn soon came towards him, and rushed directly on the tailor, as if it would spit him on its horn without more ceremony. " Softly, softly; it can't be done as quickly as that," said he, and stood still and waited until the animal was quite close, and then sprang nimbly behind the tree. The unicorn ran against the tree with all its strength, and struck its horn so fast in the trunk that it had not strength enough to draw it out again, and thus it was caught. " Now, I have got the bird," said the tailor, and came out from behind the tree and put the rope round its neck, and then with his axe he hewed the horn out of the tree, and when all was ready he led the beast away and took it to the King.

The King still would not give him the promised reward, and made a third demand. Before the wedding the tailor was to catch him a wild boar that made great havoc in the forest, and the huntsmen should give him their help. " Willingly," said the tailor, " that is child's play ! " He did not take the huntsmen with him into the forest, and they were pleased that he did not, for the wild boar had several times received them in such a manner that they had no inclination to lie in wait for him. When the boar perceived the tailor, it ran on him with foaming mouth and whetted tusks, and was about to throw him to the ground, but the active hero sprang into a chapel which was near, and up to the window at once, and in one bound out again. The boar ran in after him, but the tailor ran round outside and shut the door behind it, and then the raging beast, which was much too heavy and awkward to leap out of the window, was caught. The little tailor called the huntsmen thither that they might see the prisoner with their own eyes. The hero, however, went to the King, who was now, whether he liked it or not, obliged to keep his promise, and gave him his daughter and the half of his kingdom. Had he known that it was no warlike hero, but a little tailor who was standing before him, it would have gone to his heart still more than it did. The wedding was held with great magnificence and small joy, and out of a tailor a king was made.

After some time the young Queen heard her husband say

in his dreams at night, "Boy, make me the doublet, and patch the pantaloons, or else I will rap the yard-measure over thine ears." Then she discovered in what state of life the young lord had been born, and next morning complained of her wrongs to her father, and begged him to help her to get rid of her husband, who was nothing else but a tailor. The King comforted her and said, "Leave thy bed-room door open this night, and my servants shall stand outside, and when he has fallen asleep shall go in, bind him, and take him on board a ship which shall carry him into the wide world." The woman was satisfied with this; but the King's armour-bearer, who had heard all, was friendly with the young lord, and informed him of the whole plot. "I'll put a screw into that business," said the little tailor. At night he went to bed with his wife at the usual time, and when she thought that he had fallen asleep, she got up, opened the door, and then lay down again. The little tailor, who was only pretending to be asleep, began to cry out in a clear voice, "Boy, make me the doublet and patch me the pantaloons, or I will rap the yard-measure over thine ears. I smote seven at one blow. I killed two giants, I brought away one unicorn, and caught a wild boar, and am I to fear those who are standing outside the room?" When these men heard the tailor speaking thus, they were overcome by a great dread, and ran as if the wild huntsman were behind them, and none of them would venture anything further against him. So the little tailor was a king, and remained one to the end of his life.

CINDERELLA

THE wife of a rich man fell sick, and as she felt that her end was drawing near, she called her only daughter to her bedside and said, "Dear child, be good and pious, and then the good God will always protect thee, and I will look down on thee from heaven and be near thee." Thereupon she closed her eyes and departed. Every day the maiden went out to her mother's grave and wept, and she remained pious and good. When winter came the snow spread a white sheet over the grave, and when the spring sun had drawn it off again, the man had taken another wife.

The woman had brought two daughters into the house with her, who were beautiful and fair of face, but vile and black of heart. Now began a bad time for the poor step-child. "Is the stupid goose to sit in the parlour with us?" said they. "He who wants to eat bread must earn it; out with the kitchen-wench." They took her pretty clothes away from her, put an old grey bedgown on her, and gave her wooden shoes. "Just look at the proud princess, how decked out she is!" they cried, and laughed, and led her into the kitchen. There she had to do hard work from morning till night, get up before daybreak, carry water, light fires, cook and wash. Besides this, the sisters did her every imaginable injury—they mocked her and emptied her peas and lentils into the ashes, so that she was forced to sit and pick them out again. In the evening when she had worked till she was weary she had no bed to go to, but had to sleep by the fireside in the ashes. And as on that account she always looked dusty and dirty, they called her Cinderella. It happened that the father was once going to the fair, and he asked his two step-daughters what he should bring back for them. "Beautiful dresses," said one, "Pearls and jewels," said the second. "And thou, Cinderella," said he, "what wilt thou have?" "Father, break off for me the first branch which knocks against your hat on your way home." So he brought beautiful dresses, pearls and jewels for his two step-daughters, and on his way home, as he was riding through a green thicket, a hazel twig brushed against him and knocked off his hat. Then he broke off the branch and took it with him. When he reached home he gave his step-daughters the things which they wished for, and to Cinderella he gave the branch from the hazel-bush. Cinderella thanked him, went to her mother's grave and planted the branch on it, and wept so much that the tears fell down on it and watered it. It grew, however, and became a handsome tree. Thrice a day Cinderella went and sat beneath it, and wept and prayed, and a little white bird always came on the tree, and if Cinderella expressed a wish, the bird threw down to her what she had wished for.

It happened, however, that the King appointed a festival which was to last three days, and to which all the beautiful young girls in the country were invited, in order that his son might choose a bride. When the two step-daughters heard that they too were to appear among the number, they were delighted, called Cinderella and said, "Comb our hair for us, brush our shoes and fasten our buckles, for we are going to the festival at the King's palace." Cinderella obeyed, but wept, because she too would have liked to go with them to the dance, and begged her step-mother to allow her to do so. "Thou go, Cinderella!" said she. "Thou art dusty and dirty, and wouldst go to the festival? Thou hast no clothes and shoes, and yet wouldst dance!" As, however, Cinderella went on asking, the step-mother at last said, "I have emptied a dish of lentils into the ashes for thee, if thou hast picked them out again in two hours, thou shalt go with us." The maiden went through the back-door into the garden, and called, "You tame pigeons, you turtle-doves, and all you birds beneath the sky, come and help me to pick

"The good into the pot,
The bad into the crop."

Then two white pigeons came in by the kitchen-window, and afterwards the turtle-doves, and at last all the birds beneath the sky, came whirring and crowding in, and alighted amongst the ashes. And the pigeons nodded with their heads and began pick, pick, pick, pick, and the rest began also pick, pick, pick, pick, and gathered all the good grains into the dish. Hardly had one hour passed before they had finished, and all flew out again. Then the girl took the dish to her step-mother, and was glad, and believed that now she would be allowed to go with them to the festival. But the step-mother said, "No, Cinderella, thou hast no clothes and thou canst not dance; thou wouldst only be laughed at." And as Cinderella wept at this, the step-mother said, "If thou canst pick two dishes of lentils out of the ashes for me in one hour, thou shalt go with us." And she thought to herself "That she most certainly cannot do." When the step-mother had emptied the two dishes of lentils amongst the ashes, the maiden went through the back-door into the garden and cried, "You tame pigeons, you turtle-doves, and all you birds under heaven, come and help me to pick

> "The good into the pot,
> The bad into the crop."

Then two white pigeons came in by the kitchen-window, and afterwards the turtle-doves, and at length all the birds beneath the sky, came whirring and crowding in, and alighted amongst the ashes. And the doves nodded with their heads and began pick, pick, pick, pick, and others began also pick, pick, pick, pick, and gathered all the good seeds into the dishes, and before half an hour was over they had already finished, and all flew out again. Then the maiden carried the dishes to the step-mother and was delighted, and believed that she might now go with them to the festival. But the step-mother said, "All this will not help thee; thou goest not with us, for thou hast no clothes and canst not dance; we should be ashamed of thee!" On this she turned her back on Cinderella, and hurried away with her two proud daughters.

As no one was now at home, Cinderella went to her mother's grave beneath the hazel-tree, and cried,

> "Shiver and quiver, little tree,
> Silver and gold throw down over me."

Then the bird threw a gold and silver dress down to her, and slippers embroidered with silk and silver. She put on the dress with all speed, and went to the festival. Her step-mother, however, did not know her, and thought she must be a foreign princess, for she looked so beautiful in the golden dress. They never once thought of Cinderella, and believed that she was sitting at home in the dirt, picking lentils out of the ashes. The prince went to meet her, took her by the hand, and danced with her. He would dance with no other maiden, and never left loose of her hand, and if any one else came to invite her, he said, "This is my partner."

She danced till it was evening, and then she wanted to go home. But the King's son said, "I will go with thee and bear thee company," for he wished to see to whom the

beautiful maiden belonged. She escaped from him, however, and sprang into the pigeon-house. The King's son
waited until her father came, and then he told him that the
stranger maiden had leapt into the pigeon-house. The
old man thought, "Can it be Cinderella?" and they had
to bring him an axe and a pickaxe that he might hew the
pigeon-house to pieces, but no one was inside it. And when
they got home Cinderella lay in her dirty clothes among
the ashes, and a dim little oil-lamp was burning on the
mantel-piece, for Cinderella had jumped quickly down from
the back of the pigeon-house and had run to the little hazel-
tree, and there she had taken off her beautiful clothes and
laid them on the grave, and the bird had taken them away
again, and then she had placed herself in the kitchen amongst
the ashes in her grey gown.

Next day when the festival began afresh, and her parents
and the step-sisters had gone once more, Cinderella went
to the hazel-tree and said—

> "Shiver and quiver, my little tree,
> Silver and gold throw down over me."

Then the bird threw down a much more beautiful dress
than on the preceding day. And when Cinderella appeared
at the festival in this dress, every one was astonished at her
beauty. The King's son had waited until she came, and
instantly took her by the hand and danced with no one but
her. When others came and invited her, he said, "She is my
partner." When evening came she wished to leave, and the
King's son followed her and wanted to see into which house
she went. But she sprang away from him, and into the
garden behind the house. Therein stood a beautiful tall
tree on which hung the most magnificent pears. She
clambered so nimbly between the branches like a squirrel,
that the King's son did not know where she was gone.
He waited until her father came, and said to him, "The
stranger maiden has escaped from me, and I believe she has
climbed up the pear-tree." The father thought, "Can it be
Cinderella?" and had an axe brought and cut the tree down,
but no one was in it. And when they got into the kitchen,
Cinderella lay there amongst the ashes, as usual, for she

had jumped down on the other side of the tree, had taken the beautiful dress to the bird on the little hazel-tree, and put on her grey gown.

On the third day, when the parents and sisters had gone away, Cinderella once more went to her mother's grave and said to the little tree—

> "Shiver and quiver, my little tree,
> Silver and gold throw down over me."

And now the bird threw down to her a dress which was more splendid and magnificent than any she had yet had, and the slippers were golden. And when she went to the festival in the dress, no one knew how to speak for astonishment. The King's son danced with her only, and if any one invited her to dance, he said, "She is my partner."

When evening came, Cinderella wished to leave, and the King's son was anxious to go with her, but she escaped from him so quickly that he could not follow her. The King's son had, however, used a stratagem, and had caused the whole staircase to be smeared with pitch, and there, when she ran down, had the maiden's left slipper remained sticking. The King's son picked it up, and it was small and dainty, and all golden. Next morning, he went with it to the father, and said to him, "No one shall be my wife but she whose foot this golden slipper fits." Then were the two sisters glad, for they had pretty feet. The eldest went with the shoe into her room and wanted to try it on, and her mother stood by. But she could not get her big toe into it, and the shoe was too small for her. Then her mother gave her a knife and said, "Cut the toe off; when thou art Queen thou wilt have no more need to go on foot." The maiden cut the toe off, forced the foot into the shoe, swallowed the pain, and went out to the King's son. Then he took her on his horse as his bride and rode away with her. They were, however, obliged to pass the grave, and there, on the hazel-tree, sat the two pigeons and cried,

> "Turn and peep, turn and peep,
> There's blood within the shoe,
> The shoe it is too small for her,
> The true bride waits for you."

Then he looked at her foot and saw how the blood was
streaming from it. He turned his horse round and took the
false bride home again, and said she was not the true one,
and that the other sister was to put the shoe on. Then this
one went into her chamber and got her toes safely into the
shoe, but her heel was too large. So her mother gave her
a knife and said, "Cut a bit off thy heel; when thou art
Queen thou wilt have no more need to go on foot." The
maiden cut a bit off her heel, forced her foot into the shoe,
swallowed the pain, and went out to the King's son. He
took her on his horse as his bride, and rode away with her,
but when they passed by the hazel-tree, two little pigeons
sat on it and cried,

> "Turn and peep, turn and peep,
> There's blood within the shoe,
> The shoe it is too small for her,
> The true bride waits for you."

He looked down at her foot and saw how the blood was
running out of her shoe, and how it had stained her white
stocking. Then he turned his horse and took the false bride
home again. "This also is not the right one," said he, "have
you no other daughter?" "No," said the man, "There is
still a little stunted kitchen-wench which my late wife left
behind her, but she cannot possibly be the bride." The
King's son said he was to send her up to him; but the mother
answered, "Oh no, she is much too dirty, she cannot show
herself!" He absolutely insisted on it, and Cinderella had to
be called. She first washed her hands and face clean, and
then went and bowed down before the King's son, who gave
her the golden shoe. Then she seated herself on a stool,
drew her foot out of the heavy wooden shoe, and put it
into the slipper, which fitted like a glove. And when she
rose up and the King's son looked at her face he recognized
the beautiful maiden who had danced with him and cried,
"That is the true bride!" The step-mother and the
two sisters were terrified and became pale with rage; he,
however, took Cinderella on his horse and rode away with
her. As they passed by the hazel-tree, the two white doves
cried,

"Turn and peep, turn and peep,
No blood is in the shoe,
The shoe is not too small for her,
The true bride rides with you."

and when they had cried that, the two came flying down and placed themselves on Cinderella's shoulders, one on the right, the other on the left, and remained sitting there.

When the wedding with the King's son had to be celebrated, the two false sisters came and wanted to get into favour with Cinderella and share her good fortune. When the betrothed couple went to church, the elder was at the right side and the younger at the left, and the pigeons pecked out one eye of each of them. Afterwards as they came back, the elder was at the left, and the younger at the right, and then the pigeons pecked out the other eye of each. And thus, for their wickedness and falsehood, they were punished with blindness as long as they lived.

MOTHER HOLLE

THERE was once a widow who had two daughters—one of whom was pretty and industrious, whilst the other was ugly and idle. But she was much fonder of the ugly and idle one, because she was her own daughter; and the other, who was a step-daughter, was obliged to do all the work, and be the Cinderella of the house. Every day the poor girl had to sit by a well, in the highway, and spin and spin till her fingers bled.

Now it happened that one day the shuttle was marked with her blood, so she dipped it in the well, to wash the mark off; but it dropped out of her hand and fell to the bottom. She began to weep, and ran to her step-mother and told her of the mishap. But she scolded her sharply, and was so merciless as to say, "Since you have let the shuttle fall in, you must fetch it out again."

So the girl went back to the well, and did not know what to do: and in the sorrow of her heart she jumped into the well to get the shuttle. She lost her senses; and when she awoke and came to herself again, she was in a lovely meadow where the sun was shining and many thousands of flowers were growing. Along this meadow she went, and at last came to a baker's oven full of bread, and the bread cried out, "Oh, take me out! take me out! or I shall burn; I have been baked a long time!" So she went up to it, and took out all the loaves one after another with the bread-shovel. After that she went on till she came to a tree covered with apples, which called out to her, "Oh, shake me! shake me! we apples are all ripe!" So she shook the tree till the apples fell like rain, and went on shaking till they were all down, and when she had gathered them into a heap, she went on her way.

At last she came to a little house, out of which an old woman peeped; but she had such large teeth that the girl was frightened, and was about to run away.

But the old woman called out to her, "What are you afraid of, dear child? Stay with me; if you will do all the work in the house properly, you shall be the better for it. Only you must take care to make my bed well, and to shake it thoroughly till the feathers fly—for then there is snow on the earth. I am Mother Holle."[1]

As the old woman spoke so kindly to her, the girl took courage and agreed to enter her service. She attended to everything to the satisfaction of her mistress, and always shook her bed so vigorously that the feathers flew about like snow-flakes. So she had a pleasant life with her; never an angry word; and boiled or roast meat every day.

She stayed some time with Mother Holle, and then she became sad. At first she did not know what was the matter with her, but found at length that it was homesickness; although she was many thousand times better off here than at home, still she had a longing to be there. At last she said to the old woman, "I have a longing for home; and however well off I am down here, I cannot stay any longer; I must go up again to my own people." Mother Holle said, "I am pleased that you long for your home again, and as you have served me truly, I myself will take you up again." Thereupon she took her by the hand, and led her to a large

---

[1] Thus in Hesse, when it snows, they say, "Mother Holle is making her bed."

door. The door was opened, and just as the maiden was standing beneath the doorway, a heavy shower of golden rain fell, and all the gold remained sticking to her, so that she was completely covered with it.

"You shall have that because you are so industrious," said Mother Holle; and at the same time she gave her back the shuttle which she had let fall into the well. Thereupon the door closed, and the maiden found herself up above upon the earth, not far from her mother's house.

And as she went into the yard the cock was standing by the well-side, and cried—

"Cock-a-doodle-doo!
Your golden girl's come back to you!"

So she went in to her mother, and as she arrived thus covered with gold, she was well received, both by her and her sister.

The girl told all that had happened to her; and as soon as the mother heard how she had come by so much wealth, she was very anxious to obtain the same good luck for the ugly and lazy daughter. She had to seat herself by the well and spin; and in order that her shuttle might be stained with blood, she stuck her hand into a thorn bush and pricked her finger. Then she threw her shuttle into the well, and jumped in after it.

She came, like the other, to the beautiful meadow and walked along the very same path. When she got to the oven the bread again cried, "Oh, take me out! take me out! or I shall burn; I have been baked a long time!"

But the lazy thing answered, "As if I had any wish to make myself dirty?" and on she went. Soon she came to the apple-tree, which cried, "Oh, shake me! shake me! we apples are all ripe!" But she answered, "I like that! one of you might fall on my head," and so went on.

When she came to Mother Holle's house she was not afraid, for she had already heard of her big teeth, and she hired herself to her immediately.

The first day she forced herself to work diligently, and obeyed Mother Holle when she told her to do anything, for she was thinking of all the gold that she would give her.

But on the second day she began to be lazy, and on the third day still more so, and then she would not get up in the morning at all. Neither did she make Mother Holle's bed as she ought, and did not shake it so as to make the feathers fly up. Mother Holle was soon tired of this, and gave her notice to leave. The lazy girl was willing enough to go, and thought that now the golden rain would come. Mother Holle led her too to the great door; but while she was standing beneath it, instead of the gold a big kettle of pitch was emptied over her. " That is the reward of your service," said Mother Holle, and shut the door.

So the lazy girl went home; but she was quite covered with pitch and the cock by the well-side, as soon as he saw her, cried out—

> "Cock-a-doodle-doo !
> Your pitchy girl's come back to you !"

But the pitch stuck fast to her, and could not be got off as long as she lived.

THE SEVEN RAVENS

THERE was once a man who had seven sons, and still he had no daughter, however much he wished for one. At length his wife again gave him hope of a child, and when it came into the world it was a girl. The joy was great, but the child was sickly and small, and had to be privately baptized on account of its weakness. The father sent one of the boys in haste to the spring to fetch water for the baptism. The other six went with him, and as each of them wanted to be first to fill it, the jug fell into the well. There they stood and did not know what to do, and none of them dared to go home. As they still did not return, the father grew impatient, and said, " They have certainly for-gotten it for some game, the wicked boys! " He became afraid that the girl would have to die without being baptized, and in his anger cried, " I wish the boys were all turned into ravens." Hardly was the word spoken before he heard a whirring of wings over his head in the air, looked up and

saw seven coal-black ravens flying away. The parents could
not recall the curse, and however sad they were at the loss
of their seven sons, they still to some extent comforted
themselves with their dear little daughter, who soon grew
strong and every day became more beautiful. For a long
time she did not know that she had had brothers, for her
parents were careful not to mention them before her, but
one day she accidentally heard some people saying of herself, "that the girl was certainly beautiful, but that in
reality she was to blame for the misfortune which had befallen her seven brothers." Then she was much troubled,
and went to her father and mother and asked if it was
true that she had had brothers, and what had become of
them? The parents now dared to keep the secret no longer,
but said that what had befallen her brothers was the will
of Heaven, and that her birth had only been the innocent
cause. But the maiden laid it to heart daily, and thought
she must deliver her brothers. She had no rest or peace
until she set out secretly, and went forth into the wide world
to trace out her brothers and set them free, let it cost what
it might. She took nothing with her but a little ring belonging to her parents as a keepsake, a loaf of bread against
hunger, a little pitcher of water against thirst, and a little
chair as a provision against weariness.

And now she went continually onwards, far, far, to the
very end of the world. Then she came to the sun, but it
was too hot and terrible, and devoured little children. Hastily she ran away, and ran to the moon, but it was far too
cold, and also awful and malicious, and when it saw the
child, it said, "I smell, I smell the flesh of men." On this
she ran swiftly away, and came to the stars, which were
kind and good to her and each of them sat on its own
particular little chair. But the morning star arose, and gave
her the drumstick of a chicken, and said, "If thou hast not
that drumstick thou canst not open the Glass mountain,
and in the Glass mountain are thy brothers."

The maiden took the drumstick, wrapped it carefully in a
cloth, and went onwards again until she came to the Glass
mountain. The door was shut, and she thought she would
take out the drumstick; but when she undid the cloth, it

was empty, and she had lost the good star's present. What was she now to do? She wished to rescue her brothers, and had no key to the Glass mountain. The good sister took a knife, cut off one of her little fingers, put it in the door, and succeeded in opening it. When she had gone inside, a little dwarf came to meet her, who said, "My child, what are you looking for?" "I am looking for my brothers, the seven ravens," she replied. The dwarf said, "The lord ravens are not at home, but if you will wait here until they come, step in." Thereupon the little dwarf carried the ravens' dinner in, on seven little plates, and in seven little glasses, and the little sister ate a morsel from each plate, and from each little glass she took a sip, but in the last little glass she dropped the ring which she had brought away with her.

Suddenly she heard a whirring of wings and a rushing through the air, and then the little dwarf said, "Now the lord ravens are flying home." Then they came, and wanted to eat and drink, and looked for their little plates and glasses. Then said one after the other, "Who has eaten something from my plate? Who has drunk out of my little glass? It was a human mouth." And when the seventh came to the bottom of the glass, the ring rolled against his mouth. Then he looked at it, and saw that it was a ring belonging to his father and mother, and said, "God grant that our sister may be here, and then we shall be free." When the maiden, who was standing behind the door watching, heard that wish, she came forth, and on this all the ravens were restored to their human form again. And they embraced and kissed each other, and went joyfully home.

LITTLE RED-CAP[1]

ONCE upon a time there was a dear little girl who was loved by every one who looked at her, but most of all by her grandmother, and there was nothing that she would

[1] The English version of this story, the well-known Little Red-Riding-Hood, is probably derived more immediately from the French, "Le Petit Chaperon Rouge," as given by Perrault, where it ends with the death of the girl.

not have given to the child. Once she gave her a little cap of red velvet, which suited her so well that she would never wear anything else; so she was always called "Little Red-Cap."

One day her mother said to her, "Come, Little Red-Cap, here is a piece of cake and a bottle of wine; take them to your grandmother, she is ill and weak, and they will do her good. Set out before it gets hot, and when you are going walk nicely and quietly and do not run off the path, or you may fall and break the bottle, and then your grandmother will get nothing; and when you go into her room, don't forget to say, 'Good-morning,' and don't peep into every corner before you do it."

"I will take great care," said Little Red-Cap to her mother, and gave her hand on it.

The grandmother lived out in the wood, half a league from the village, and just as Little Red-Cap entered the wood, a wolf met her. Red-Cap did not know what a wicked creature he was, and was not at all afraid of him.

"Good-day, Little Red-Cap," said he.

"Thank you kindly, wolf."

"Whither away so early, Little Red-Cap?"

"To my grandmother's."

"What have you got in your apron?"

"Cake and wine; yesterday was baking-day, so poor sick grandmother is to have something good, to make her stronger."

"Where does your grandmother live, Little Red-Cap?"

"A good quarter of a league farther on in the wood; her house stands under the the three large oak-trees, the nut-trees are just below; you surely must know it," replied Little Red-Cap.

The wolf thought to himself, "What a tender young creature! what a nice plump mouthful—she will be better to eat than the old woman. I must act craftily, so as to catch both." So he walked for a short time by the side of Little Red-Cap, and then he said, "See, Little Red-Cap, how pretty the flowers are about here—why do you not look round? I believe, too, that you do not hear how sweetly the little birds are singing; you walk gravely along as if you were going to school, while everything else out here in the wood is merry."

Little Red-Cap raised her eyes, and when she saw the sunbeams dancing here and there through the trees, and pretty flowers growing everywhere, she thought, " Suppose I take grandmother a fresh nosegay; that would please her too. It is so early in the day that I shall still get there in good time; " and so she ran from the path into the wood to look for flowers. And whenever she had picked one, she fancied that she saw a still prettier one farther on, and ran after it, and so got deeper and deeper into the wood.

Meanwhile the wolf ran straight to the grandmother's house and knocked at the door.

" Who is there? "

" Little Red-Cap," replied the wolf. " She is bringing cake and wine; open the door."

" Lift the latch," called out the grandmother, " I am too weak, and cannot get up."

The wolf lifted the latch, the door flew open, and without saying a word he went straight to the grandmother's bed, and devoured her. Then he put on her clothes, dressed himself in her cap, laid himself in bed and drew the curtains.

Little Red-Cap, however had been running about picking flowers, and when she had gathered so many that she could carry no more, she remembered her grandmother, and set out on the way to her.

She was surprised to find the cottage-door standing open, and when she went into the room, she had such a strange feeling that she said to herself, " Oh dear! how uneasy I feel to-day, and at other times I like being with grandmother so much." She called out, " Good morning," but received no answer; so she went to the bed and drew back the curtains. There lay her grandmother with her cap pulled far over her face and looking very strange.

" Oh! grandmother," she said, " what big ears you have! "

" The better to hear you with, my child," was the reply.

" But, grandmother, what big eyes you have! " she said.

" The better to see you with," my dear."

" But grandmother, what large hands you have! "

" The better to hug you with."

"Oh! but, grandmother, what a terrible big mouth you have!"

"The better to eat you with!"

And scarcely had the wolf said this, than with one bound he was out of bed and swallowed up Red-Cap.

When the wolf had appeased his appetite, he lay down again in the bed, fell asleep and began to snore very loud. The huntsman was just passing the house, and thought to himself, "How the old woman is snoring! I must just see if she wants anything." So he went into the room, and when he came to the bed, he saw that the wolf was lying in it. "Do I find thee here, thou old sinner!" said he. "I have long sought thee!" Then just as he was going to fire at him, it occurred to him that the wolf might have devoured the grandmother, and that she might still be saved, so he did not fire, but took a pair of scissors, and began to cut open the stomach of the sleeping wolf. When he had made two snips, he saw the little Red-Cap shining, and then he made two snips more, and the little girl sprang out, crying, "Ah, how frightened I have been! How dark it was inside the wolf;" and after that the aged grandmother came out alive also, but scarcely able to breathe. Red-Cap, however, quickly fetched great stones with which they filled the wolf's body, and when he awoke, he wanted to run away, but the stones were so heavy that he fell down at once, and fell dead.

Then all three were delighted. The huntsman drew off the wolf's skin and went home with it; the grandmother ate the cake and drank the wine which Red-Cap had brought, and revived, but Red-Cap thought to herself, "As long as I live, I will never by myself leave the path, to run into the wood, when my mother has forbidden me to do so."

It is also related that once when Red-Cap was again taking cakes to the old grandmother, another wolf spoke to her, and tried to entice her from the path. Red-Cap was, however, on her guard, and went straight forward on her way, and told her grandmother that she had met the wolf, and that he had said "good-morning" to her, but with such a wicked look in his eyes, that if they had not been on the public road she was certain he would have eaten her up. "Well," said the grandmother, "we will shut the door, that he may not come in." Soon afterwards the wolf knocked, and cried, "Open the door, grandmother, I am little Red-Cap, and am fetching you some cakes." But they did not speak, or open the door, so the grey-beard stole twice or thrice round the house, and at last jumped on the roof, intending to wait until Red-Cap went home in the evening, and then to steal after and devour her in the darkness. But the grandmother saw what was in his thoughts. In front of the house was a great stone trough, so she said to the child, "Take the pail, Red-Cap; I made some sausages yesterday, so carry the water in which I boiled them to the trough." Red-Cap carried until the great trough was quite full. Then the smell of the sausages reached the wolf, and he sniffed and peeped down, and at last stretched out his neck so far that he could no longer keep his footing and began to slip, and slipped down from the roof into the great trough, and was drowned. But Red-Cap went joyously home, and never did anything to harm any one.

THE BREMEN TOWN-MUSICIANS

A CERTAIN man had a donkey, which had carried the corn-sacks to the mill indefatigably for many a long year; but his strength was going, and he was growing more and more unfit for work. Then his master began to consider how he might best save his keep; but the donkey, seeing that no good wind was blowing, ran away and set out on the road to Bremen. "There," he thought, "I can surely be town-musician." When he had walked some distance, he found a hound lying on the road, gasping like one who had run till he was tired. "What are you gasping so for, you big fellow?" asked the donkey.

"Ah," replied the hound, "as I am old, and daily grow weaker, and no longer can hunt, my master wanted to kill me, so I took to flight; but now how am I to earn my bread?"

"I tell you what," said the donkey, "I am going to Bremen, and shall be town-musician there; go with me and engage yourself also as a musician. I will play the lute, and you shall beat the kettledrum."

The hound agreed, and on they went.

Before long they came to a cat, sitting on the path, with a face like three rainy days! "Now then, old shaver, what has gone askew with you?" asked the donkey.

"Who can be merry when his neck is in danger?" answered the cat. "Because I am now getting old, and my teeth are worn to stumps, and I prefer to sit by the fire and spin, rather than hunt about after mice, my mistress wanted to drown me, so I ran away. But now good advice is scarce. Where am I to go?"

"Go with us to Bremen. You understand night-music, so you can be a town-musician."

The cat thought well of it, and went with them. After this the three fugitives came to a farm-yard, where the cock was sitting upon the gate, crowing with all his might. "Your crow goes through and through one," said the donkey. "What is the matter?"

"I have been foretelling fine weather, because it is the day on which Our Lady washes the Christ-child's little shirts, and wants to dry them," said the cock; "but guests are coming for Sunday, so the housewife has no pity, and has told the cook that she intends to eat me in the soup to-morrow, and this evening I am to have my head cut off. Now I am crowing at full pitch while I can."

"Ah, but red-comb," said the donkey, "you had better come away with us. We are going to Bremen; you can find something better than death everywhere: you have a good voice, and if we make music together it must have some quality!"

The cock agreed to this plan, and all four went on together. They could not, however, reach the city of Bremen in one day, and in the evening they came to a forest where they meant to pass the night. The donkey and the hound laid themselves down under a large tree, the cat and the cock settled themselves in the branches; but the cock flew right to the top, where he was most safe. Before he went to sleep he looked round on all the four sides, and thought he saw in the distance a little spark burning; so he called out to his companions that there must be a house not far off, for he saw a light. The donkey said, "If so, we had better get up and go on, for the shelter here is bad." The hound thought that a few bones with some meat on would do him good too!

So they made their way to the place where the light was, and soon saw it shine brighter and grow larger, until they came to a well-lighted robber's house. The donkey, as the biggest, went to the window and looked in.

"What do you see, my grey-horse?" asked the cock. "What do I see?" answered the donkey; "a table covered with good things to eat and drink, and robbers sitting at it enjoying themselves." "That would be the sort of thing for us," said the cock. "Yes, yes; ah, how I wish we were there!" said the donkey.

Then the animals took counsel together how they should manage to drive away the robbers, and at last they thought of a plan. The donkey was to place himself with his fore-feet upon the window-ledge, the hound was to jump on the donkey's back, the cat was to climb upon the dog, and lastly the cock was to fly up and perch upon the head of the cat.

When this was done, at a given signal, they began to perform their music together: the donkey brayed, the hound barked, the cat mewed, and the cock crowed; then they burst through the window into the room, so that the glass clattered! At this horrible din, the robbers sprang up, thinking no otherwise than that a ghost had come in, and fled in a great fright out into the forest. The four companions now sat down at the table, well content with what was left, and ate as if they were going to fast for a month.

As soon as the four minstrels had done, they put out the light, and each sought for himself a sleeping-place according to his nature and to what suited him. The donkey laid him-self down upon some straw in the yard, the hound behind the door, the cat upon the hearth near the warm ashes, and the cock perched himself upon a beam of the roof; and being tired with their long walk, they soon went to sleep.

When it was past midnight, and the robbers saw from afar that the light was no longer burning in their house, and all appeared quiet, the captain said, "We ought not to have let ourselves be frightened out of our wits;" and ordered one of them to go and examine the house.

The messenger finding all still, went into the kitchen to light a candle, and, taking the glistening fiery eyes of the cat for live coals, he held a lucifer-match to them to light it. But the cat did not understand the joke, and flew in his face, spitting and scratching. He was dreadfully frightened, and ran to the back-door, but the dog, who lay there, sprang up and bit his leg; as he ran across the yard by the straw-heap, the donkey gave him a smart kick with its hind foot. The cock, too, who had been awakened by the noise, and had become lively, cried down from the beam, "Cock-a-doodle-doo!"

Then the robber ran back as fast as he could to his captain, and said, "Ah, there is a horrible witch sitting in the house, who spat on me and scratched my face with her long claws; and by the door stands a man with a knife, who stabbed me in the leg; and in the yard there lies a black monster, who beat me with a wooden club; and above, upon the roof, sits the judge, who called out, 'Bring the rogue here to me!' so I got away as well as I could."

After this the robbers did not trust themselves in the house again; but it suited the four musicians of Bremen so well that they did not care to leave it any more. And the mouth of him who last told this story is still warm.

THE GIRL WITHOUT HANDS

A CERTAIN miller had little by little fallen into poverty, and had nothing left but his mill and a large apple-tree behind it. Once when he had gone into the forest to fetch wood, an old man stepped up to him whom he had never seen before, and said, " Why dost thou plague thyself with cutting wood, I will make thee rich, if thou wilt promise me what is standing behind the mill?" " What can that be but my apple-tree?" thought the miller, and said, " Yes," and gave a written promise to the stranger. He, however, laughed mockingly and said, " When three years have passed, I will come and carry away what belongs to me," and then he went.

When the miller got home, his wife came to meet him and said, " Tell me, miller, from whence comes this sudden wealth into our house? All at once every box and chest was filled; no one brought it in, and I know not how it happened." He answered, " It comes from a stranger who met me in the forest, and promised me great treasure. I, in return, have promised him what stands behind the mill; we can very well give him the big apple-tree for it." " Ah, husband," said the terrified wife, " that must have been the devil! He did not mean the apple-tree, but our daughter, who was standing behind the mill sweeping the yard."

The miller's daughter was a beautiful, pious girl, and lived through the three years in the fear of God and without sin. When therefore the time was over, and the day came when the Evil-one was to fetch her, she washed herself clean, and made a circle round herself with chalk. The devil appeared quite early, but he could not come near to her. Angrily, he said to the miller, " Take all water away from her, that she may no longer be able to wash herself, for otherwise I have no power over her." The miller was afraid, and did so. The next morning the devil came again, but she had wept on her hands, and they were quite clean. Again he could not get near her, and furiously said to the miller, " Cut her hands off, or else I cannot get the better of her." The miller was shocked and answered, " How could I cut off my own child's hands?" Then the Evil-one threatened him and said, " If thou dost not do it thou art mine, and I will take thee thyself." The father became alarmed, and promised to obey him. So he went to the girl and said, " My child, if I do not cut off both thine hands, the devil will carry me away, and in my terror I have promised to do it. Help me in my need, and forgive me the harm I do thee." She replied, " Dear father, do with me what you will, I am your child." Thereupon she laid down both her hands, and let them be cut off. The devil came for the third time, but she had wept so long and so much on the stumps, that after all they were quite clean. Then he had to give in, and had lost all right over her.

The miller said to her, " I have by means of thee received such great wealth that I will keep thee most delicately as long as thou livest." But she replied, " Here I cannot stay, I will go forth, compassionate people will give me as much as I require." Thereupon she caused her maimed arms to be bound to her back, and by sunrise she set out on her way, and walked the whole day until night fell. Then she came to a royal garden, and by the shimmering of the moon she saw that trees covered with beautiful fruits grew in it, but she could not enter, for there was much water round about it. And as she had walked the whole day and not eaten one mouthful, and hunger tormented her, she thought, " Ah, if I were but inside, that I might eat of the fruit, else must I die of hunger ! " Then she knelt down, called on God the Lord, and prayed. And suddenly an angel came towards her, who made a dam in the water, so that the moat became dry and she could walk through it. And now she went into the garden and the angel went with her. She saw a tree covered with beautiful pears, but they were all counted. Then she went to them, and to still her hunger, ate one with her mouth from the tree, but no more. The gardener was watching; but as the angel was standing by, he was afraid and thought the maiden was a spirit and was silent, neither did he dare to cry out, or to speak to the spirit. When she had eaten the pear, she was satisfied, and went and concealed herself among the bushes. The King to whom the garden belonged, came down to it the next morning, and counted, and saw that one of the pears was missing, and asked the gardener what had become of it, as it was not lying beneath the tree, but was gone. Then answered the gardener, " Last night, a spirit came in, who had no hands, and ate off one of the pears with its mouth." The King said, "How did the spirit get over the water, and where did it go after it had eaten the pear ? " The gardener answered, " Some one came in a snow-white garment from heaven who made a dam, and kept back the water, that the spirit might walk through the moat. And as it must have been an angel, I was afraid, and asked no questions, and did not cry out. When the spirit had eaten the pear, it went back again." The King said, " If it be as thou sayest, I will watch with thee to-night."

When it grew dark the King came into the garden and brought a priest with him, who was to speak to the spirit.

All three seated themselves beneath the tree and watched.
At midnight the maiden came creeping out of the thicket,
went to the tree, and again ate one pear off it with her mouth,
and beside her stood the angel in white garments. Then the
priest went out to them and said, " Comest thou from heaven
or from earth? Art thou a spirit, or a human being?" She
replied, "I am no spirit, but an unhappy mortal deserted by
all but God." The King said, "If thou art forsaken by all
the world, yet will I not forsake thee." He took her with
him into his royal palace, and as she was so beautiful and
good, he loved her with all his heart, had silver hands made
for her, and took her to wife.

After a year the King had to take the field, so he commended his young Queen to the care of his mother and said,
"If she is brought to bed take care of her, nurse her well,
and tell me of it at once in a letter." Then she gave birth to
a fine boy. So the old mother made haste to write and an-
nounce the joyful news to him. But the messenger rested
by a brook on the way, and as he was fatigued by the great
distance, he fell asleep. Then came the Devil, who was
always seeking to injure the good Queen, and exchanged the
letter for another, in which was written that the Queen had
brought a monster into the world. When the King read the
letter he was shocked and much troubled, but he wrote in
answer that they were to take great care of the Queen and
nurse her well until his arrival. The messenger went back
with the letter, but rested at the same place and again fell
asleep. Then came the Devil once more, and put a different
letter in his pocket, in which it was written that they were
to put the Queen and her child to death. The old mother
was terribly shocked when she received the letter, and could
not believe it. She wrote back again to the King, but received no other answer, because each time the Devil substi-
tuted a false letter, and in the last letter it was also written
that she was to preserve the Queen's tongue and eyes as a
token that she had obeyed.

But the old mother wept to think such innocent blood was
to be shed, and had a hind brought by night and cut out her
tongue and eyes, and kept them. Then said she to the Queen,
"I cannot have thee killed as the King commands, but here

thou mayst stay no longer. Go forth into the wide world
with thy child, and never come here again." The poor woman
tied her child on her back, and went away with eyes full of
tears. She came into a great wild forest, and then she fell
on her knees and prayed to God, and the angel of the Lord
appeared to her and led her to a little house on which was a
sign with the words, "Here all dwell free." A snow-white
maiden came out of the little house and said, "Welcome, Lady
Queen," and conducted her inside. Then they unbound the
little boy from her back, and held him to her breast that he
might feed, and then laid him in a beautifully-made little
bed. Then said the poor woman, "From whence knowest
thou that I was a queen?" The white maiden answered, "I
am an angel sent by God, to watch over thee, and thy child."
The Queen stayed seven years in the little house, and was
well cared for, and by God's grace, because of her piety, her
hands which had been cut off, grew once more.

At last the King came home again from the war, and his
first wish was to see his wife and the child. Then his aged
mother began to weep, and said, "Thou wicked man, why
didst thou write to me that I was to take those two innocent
lives?" and she showed him the two letters which the Evil-
one had forged, and then continued, "I did as thou badest
me," and she showed the tokens, the tongue and eyes. Then
the King began to weep for his poor wife and his little son so
much more bitterly than she was doing, that the aged mother
had compassion on him and said, "Be at peace, she still lives; I
secretly caused a hind to be killed, and took these tokens from
it; but I bound the child to thy wife's back and bade her go
forth into the wide world, and made her promise never to
come back here again, because thou wert so angry with her."
Then spake the King, "I will go as far as the sky is blue, and
will neither eat nor drink until I have found again my dear
wife and my child, if in the meantime they have not been
killed, nor died of hunger."

Thereupon the King travelled about for seven long years,
and sought her in every cleft of the rocks and in every cave,
but he found her not, and thought she had died of want.
During the whole of this time he neither ate nor drank, but
God supported him. At length he came to a great forest,

and found therein the little house whose sign was, "Here all dwell free." Then forth came the white maiden, took him by the hand, led him in, and said, "Welcome, Lord King," and asked him from whence he came. He answered, "Soon shall I have travelled about for the space of seven years, and I seek my wife and her child, but cannot find them." The angel offered him meat and drink, but he did not take anything, and only wished to rest a little. Then he lay down to sleep, and put a handkerchief over his face.

Thereupon the angel went into the chamber where the Queen sat with her son, whom she usually called "Sorrowful," and said to her, "Go out with thy child, thy husband hath come." So she went to the place where he lay, and the handkerchief fell from his face. Then said she, "Sorrowful, pick up thy father's handkerchief, and cover his face again." The child picked it up, and put it over his face again. The King in his sleep heard what passed, and had pleasure in letting the handkerchief fall once more. But the child grew impatient, and said, "Dear mother, how can I cover my father's face when I have no father in this world? I have learnt to say the prayer, 'Our Father, which art in Heaven,' thou hast told me that my father was in Heaven, and was the good God, and how can I know a wild man like this? He is not my father." When the King heard that, he got up, and asked who they were. Then said she, "I am thy wife, and that is thy son, Sorrowful." And he saw her living hands, and said, "My wife had silver hands." She answered, "The good God has caused my natural hands to grow again;" and the angel went into the inner room, and brought the silver hands, and showed them to him. Hereupon he knew for a certainty that it was his dear wife and his dear child, and he kissed them, and was glad, and said, "A heavy stone has fallen from off my heart." Then the angel of God gave them one meal with her, and after that they went home to the King's aged mother. There were great rejoicings everywhere, and the King and Queen were married again, and lived contentedly to their happy end.

CLEVER ELSIE

THERE was once a man who had a daughter who was called Clever Elsie. And when she had grown up her father said, "We will get her married." "Yes," said the mother, "if only any one would come who would have her." At length a man came from a distance and wooed her, who was called Hans; but he stipulated that Clever Elsie should be really wise. "Oh," said the father, "she's sharp enough;" and the mother said, "Oh, she can see the wind coming up the street, and hear the flies coughing." "Well," said Hans, "if she is not really wise, I won't have her." When they were sitting at dinner and had eaten, the mother said, "Elsie, go into the cellar and fetch some beer." Then Clever Elsie took the pitcher from the wall, went into the cellar, and tapped the lid briskly as she went that the time might not appear long. When she was below she fetched herself a chair, and set it before the barrel so that she had no need to stoop, and did not hurt her back or do herself any unexpected injury. Then she placed the can before her, and turned the tap, and while the beer was running she would not let her eyes be idle, but looked up at the wall, and after much peering here and there, saw a pick-axe exactly above her, which the masons had accidentally left there.

Then Clever Elsie began to weep and said, "If I get Hans, and we have a child, and he grows big, and we send him into the cellar here to draw beer, then the pick-axe will fall on his head and kill him." Then she sat and wept and screamed with all the strength of her body, over the misfortune which lay before her. Those upstairs waited for the drink, but Clever Elsie still did not come. Then the woman said to the servant, "Just go down into the cellar and see where Elsie is." The maid went and found her sitting in front of the barrel, screaming loudly. "Elsie, why weepest thou?" asked the maid. "Ah," she answered, "have I not reason to weep? If I get Hans, and we have a child, and he grows big, and has to draw beer here, the pick-axe will perhaps fall on his head, and kill him." Then

HC XVII—E

said the maid, "What a clever Elsie we have!" and sat down beside her and began loudly to weep over the misfortune. After a while, as the maid did not come back, and those upstairs were thirsty for the beer, the man said to the boy, "Just go down into the cellar and see where Elsie and the girl are." The boy went down, and there sat Clever Elsie and the girl both weeping together. Then he asked, "Why are ye weeping?" "Ah," said Elsie, "have I not reason to weep? If I get Hans, and we have a child, and he grows big, and has to draw beer here, the pick-axe will fall on his head and kill him." Then said the boy, "What a clever Elsie we have!" and sat down by her, and likewise began to howl loudly. Upstairs they waited for the boy, but as he still did not return, the man said to the woman, "Just go down into the cellar and see where Elsie is!" The woman went down, and found all three in the midst of their lamentations, and inquired what was the cause; then Elsie told her also that her future child was to be killed by the pick-axe, when it grew big and had to draw beer, and the pick-axe fell down. Then said the mother likewise, "What a clever Elsie we have!" and sat down and wept with them. The man upstairs waited a short time, but as his wife did not come back and his thirst grew ever greater, he said, "I must go into the cellar myself and see where Elsie is." But when he got into the cellar, and they were all sitting together crying, and he heard the reason, and that Elsie's child was the cause, and that Elsie might perhaps bring one into the world some day, and that it might be killed by the pick-axe, if it should happen to be sitting beneath it, drawing beer just at the very time when it fell down, he cried, "Oh, what a clever Elsie!" and sat down, and likewise wept with them. The bridegroom stayed upstairs alone for a long time; then as no one would come back he thought, "They must be waiting for me below; I too must go there and see what they are about." When he got down, five of them were sitting screaming and lamenting quite piteously, each out-doing the other. "What misfortune has happened then?" asked he. "Ah, dear Hans," said Elsie, "if we marry each other and have a child, and he is big, and we perhaps send him here to draw something to drink, then the pick-axe which has been left up there might dash his brains out if it were to fall down, so have we not reason to weep?" "Come," said Hans, "more understanding than this is not needed for my household, as thou art such a clever Elsie, I will have thee," and he seized her hand, took her upstairs with him, and married her.

After Hans had had her some time, he said, "Wife, I am going out to work and earn some money for us; go into the field and cut the corn that we may have some bread." "Yes, dear Hans, I will do that." After Hans had gone away, she cooked herself some good broth and took it into the field with her. When she came to the field she said to herself, "What shall I do; shall I shear first, or shall I eat first? Oh, I will eat first." Then she emptied her basin of broth, and when she was fully satisfied, she once more said, "What shall I do? Shall I shear first, or shall I sleep first? I will sleep first." Then she lay down among the corn and fell asleep. Hans had been at home for a long time, but Elsie did not come; then said he, "What a clever Elsie I have; she is so industrious that she does not even come home to eat." As, however, she still stayed away, and it was evening, Hans went out to see what she had cut, but nothing was cut, and she was lying among the corn asleep. Then Hans hastened home and brought a fowler's net with little bells and hung it round about her, and she still went on sleeping. Then he ran home, shut the house-door, and sat down in his chair and worked. At length, when it was quite dark, Clever Elsie awoke and when she got up there was a jingling all round about her, and the bells rang at each step which she took. Then she was alarmed, and became uncertain whether she really was Clever Elsie or not, and said, "Is it I, or is it not I?" But she knew not what answer to make to this, and stood for a time in doubt; at length she thought, "I will go home and ask if it be I, or if it be not I, they will be sure to know." She ran to the door of her own house, but it was shut; then she knocked at the window and cried, "Hans, is Elsie within?" "Yes," answered Hans, "she is within." Hereupon she was terrified, and said, "Ah, heavens! Then it is not I," and went to another door; but when the people heard the jingling of the bells they would not open it, and she could get in nowhere. Then she ran out of the village, and no one has seen her since.

THUMBLING

THERE was once a poor peasant who sat in the evening by the hearth and poked the fire, and his wife sat and span. Then said he, "How sad it is that we have no children! With us all is so quiet, and in other houses it is noisy and lively."

"Yes," replied the wife, and sighed, "even if we had only one, and it were quite small, and only as big as a thumb, I should be quite satisfied, and we would still love it with all our hearts." Now it so happened that the woman fell ill, and after seven months gave birth to a child, that was perfect in all its limbs, but no longer than a thumb. Then said they, "It is as we wished it to be, and it shall be our dear child;" and because of its size, they called it Thumbling. They did not let it want for food, but the child did not grow taller, but remained as it had been at the first; nevertheless it looked sensibly out of its eyes, and soon showed itself to be a wise and nimble creature, for everything it did turned out well.

One day the peasant was getting ready to go into the forest to cut wood, when he said as if to himself, "How I wish that there was any one who would bring the cart to me!" "Oh, father," cried Thumbling, "I will soon bring the cart, rely on that; it shall be in the forest at the appointed time." The man smiled and said, "How can that be done, thou art far too small to lead the horse by the reins?" "That's of no consequence, father, if my mother will only harness it, I will sit in the horse's ear, and call out to him how he is to go." "Well," answered the man, "for once we will try it."

When the time came, the mother harnessed the horse, and placed Thumbling in its ear, and then the little creature cried "Gee up, gee up!"

Then it went quite properly as if with its master, and

the cart went the right way into the forest. It so happened that just as he was turning a corner, and the little one was crying " Gee up," two strange men came towards him. " My word! " said one of them. " What is this? There is a cart coming, and a driver is calling to the horse, and still he is not to be seen! " " That can't be right," said the other, " we will follow the cart and see where it stops." The cart, however, drove right into the forest, and exactly to the place where the wood had been cut. When Thumbling saw his father, he cried to him, " Seest thou, father, here I am with the cart; now take me down." The father got hold of the horse with his left hand, and with the right took his little son out of the ear. Thumbling sat down quite merrily on a straw, but when the two strange men saw him, they did not know what to say for astonishment. Then one of them took the other aside and said, " Hark, the little fellow would make our fortune if we exhibited him in a large town, for money. We will buy him." They went to the peasant and said, "Sell us the little man. He shall be well treated with us." " No," replied the father, " he is the apple of my eye, and all the money in the world cannot buy him from me." Thumbling, however, when he heard of the bargain, had crept up the folds of his father's coat, placed himself on his shoulder, and whispered in his ear, " Father, do give me away, I will soon come back again." Then the father parted with him to the two men for a handsome bit of money. " Where wilt thou sit? " they said to him. " Oh, just set me on the rim of your hat, and then I can walk backwards and forwards and look at the country, and still not fall down." They did as he wished, and when Thumbling had taken leave of his father, they went away with him. They walked until it was dusk, and then the little fellow said, " Do take me down, I want to come down." The man took his hat off, and put the little fellow on the ground by the wayside, and he leapt and crept about a little between the sods, and then he suddenly slipped into a mouse-hole which he had sought out. " Good evening, gentlemen, just go home without me," he cried to them, and mocked them. They ran thither and stuck their sticks into the mouse-hole, but it was all lost labour Thumbling crept

still farther in, and as it soon became quite dark, they were
forced to go home with their vexation and their empty
purses.

When Thumbling saw that they were gone, he crept
back out of the subterranean passage. "It is so dangerous
to walk on the ground in the dark," said he; "how easily
a neck or a leg is broken!" Fortunately he knocked against
an empty snail-shell. "Thank God!" said he. "In that I
can pass the night in safety," and got into it. Not long
afterwards, when he was just going to sleep, he heard two
men go by, and one of them was saying, "How shall we
contrive to get hold of the rich pastor's silver and gold?"
"I could tell thee that," cried Thumbling, interrupting them.
"What was that?" said one of the thieves in a fright,
"I heard some one speaking." They stood still listening,
and Thumbling spoke again, and said, "Take me with you,
and I'll help you."

"But where art thou?" "Just look on the ground, and
observe from whence my voice comes," he replied. There
the thieves at length found him, and lifted him up. "Thou
little imp, how wilt thou help us?" they said. "A great
deal," said he, "I will creep into the pastor's room through
the iron bars, and will reach out to you whatever you
want to have." "Come then," they said, "and we will see
what thou canst do." When they got to the pastor's
house, Thumbling crept into the room, but instantly cried
out with all his might, "Do you want to have everything
that is here?" The thieves were alarmed, and said, "But do
speak softly, so as not to waken any one!" Thumbling,
however, behaved as if he had not understood this, and
cried again, "What do you want? Do you want to have
everything that is here?" The cook, who slept in the next
room, heard this and sat up in bed, and listened. The
thieves, however, had in their fright run some distance
away, but at last they took courage, and thought, "The
little rascal wants to mock us." They came back and
whispered to him, "Come, be serious, and reach something
out to us." Then Thumbling again cried as loudly as he
could, "I really will give you everything, only put your
hands in." The maid who was listening, heard this quite

distinctly, and jumped out of bed and rushed to the door.
The thieves took flight, and ran as if the Wild Huntsman
were behind them, but as the maid could not see anything,
she went to strike a light. When she came to the place
with it, Thumbling, unperceived, betook himself to the
granary, and the maid, after she had examined every corner
and found nothing, lay down in her bed again, and believed
that, after all, she had only been dreaming with open eyes
and ears.

Thumbling had climbed up among the hay and found a
beautiful place to sleep in; there he intended to rest until
day, and then go home again to his parents. But he had
other things to go through. Truly there is much affliction
and misery in this world! When day dawned, the maid
arose from her bed to feed the cows. Her first walk was
into the barn, where she laid hold of an armful of hay,
and precisely that very one in which poor Thumbling was
lying asleep. He, however, was sleeping so soundly that
he was aware of nothing, and did not awake until he was
in the mouth of a cow, who had picked him up with the
hay. "Ah, heavens!" cried he, "how have I got into the
fulling mill?" but he soon discovered where he was. Then
it was necessary to be careful not to let himself go between
the teeth and be dismembered, but he was nevertheless
forced to slip down into the stomach with the hay. "In
this little room the windows are forgotten," said he, "and
no sun shines in, neither will a candle be brought." His
quarters were especially unpleasing to him, and the worst
was, more and more hay was always coming in by the door,
and the space grew less and less. Then, at length in his
anguish, he cried as loud as he could, "Bring me no more
fodder, bring me no more fodder." The maid was just
milking the cow, and when she heard some one speaking,
and saw no one, and perceived that it was the same voice
that she had heard in the night, she was so terrified that
she slipped off her stool, and spilt the milk. She ran in
the greatest haste to her master, and said, "Oh, heavens,
pastor, the cow has been speaking!" "Thou art mad,"
replied the pastor; but he went himself to the byre to see
what was there. Hardly, however, had he set his foot

inside than Thumbling again cried, "Bring me no more fodder, bring me no more fodder." Then the pastor himself was alarmed, and thought that an evil spirit had gone into the cow, and ordered her to be killed. She was killed, but the stomach, in which Thumbling was, was thrown on the midden. Thumbling had great difficulty in working his way; however, he succeeded so far as to get some room, but, just as he was going to thrust his head out, a new misfortune occurred. A hungry wolf ran thither, and swallowed the whole stomach at one gulp. Thumbling did not lose courage. "Perhaps," thought he, "the wolf will listen to what I have got to say," and he called to him from out of his stomach, "Dear wolf, I know of a magnificent feast for thee."

"Where is it to be had?" said the wolf.

"In such and such a house; thou must creep into it through the kitchen-sink, and wilt find cakes, and bacon, and sausages, and as much of them as thou canst eat," and he described to him exactly his father's house. The wolf did not require to be told this twice, squeezed himself in at night through the sink, and ate to his heart's content in the larder. When he had eaten his fill, he wanted to go out again, but he had become so big that he could not go out by the same way. Thumbling had reckoned on this, and now began to make a violent noise in the wolf's body, and raged and screamed as loudly as he could. "Wilt thou be quiet," said the wolf, "thou wilt waken up the people!" "Eh, what," replied the little fellow, "thou hast eaten thy fill, and I will make merry likewise," and began once more to scream with all his strength. At last his father and mother were aroused by it, and ran to the room and looked in through the opening in the door. When they saw that a wolf was inside, they ran away, and the husband fetched his axe, and the wife the scythe. "Stay behind," said the man, when they entered the room. "When I have given him a blow, if he is not killed by it, thou must cut him down and hew his body to pieces." Then Thumbling heard his parents' voices, and cried, "Dear father, I am here; I am in the wolf's body." Said the father, full of joy, "Thank God, our dear child has found us again," and bade the woman take away her scythe.

that Thumbling might not be hurt with it. After that he raised his arm, and struck the wolf such a blow on his head that he fell down dead, and then they got knives and scissors and cut his body open, and drew the little fellow forth. "Ah," said the father, "what sorrow we have gone through for thy sake." "Yes, father, I have gone about the world a great deal. Thank heaven, I breathe fresh air again!" "Where hast thou been, then?" "Ah, father, I have been in a mouse's hole, in a cow's stomach, and then in a wolf's; now I will stay with you." "And we will not sell thee again, no, not for all the riches in the world," said his parents, and they embraced and kissed their dear Thumbling. They gave him to eat and to drink, and had some new clothes made for him, for his own had been spoiled on his journey.

THUMBLING AS JOURNEYMAN

A CERTAIN tailor had a son, who happened to be small, and no bigger than a Thumb, and on this account he was always called Thumbling. He had, however, some courage in him, and said to his father, "Father, I must and will go out into the world." "That's right, my son," said the old man, and took a long darning-needle and made a knob of sealing-wax on it at the candle, "and there is a sword for thee to take with thee on the way." Then the little tailor wanted to have one more meal with them, and hopped into the kitchen to see what his lady mother had cooked for the last time. It was, however, just dished up, and the dish stood on the hearth. Then he said, "Mother, what is there to eat to-day?" "See for thyself," said his mother. So Thumbling jumped on to the hearth, and peeped into the dish, but as he stretched his neck in too far the steam from the food caught hold of him, and carried him up the chimney. He rode about in the air on the steam for a while, until at length he sank down to the ground again. Now the little tailor was outside in the wide world, and he travelled about, and went to a master in his craft, but the food was not good enough for him. "Mistress, if you give us no better food," said Thumbling, "I will go away and early to-morrow morning I will write with chalk on the door of your house,

'Too many potatoes, too little meat! Farewell, Mr. Potato-King?'" "What wouldst thou have forsooth, grasshopper?" said the mistress, and grew angry, and seized a dish-cloth, and was just going to strike him; but my little tailor crept nimbly under a thimble, peeped out from beneath it, and put his tongue out at the mistress. She took up the thimble, and wanted to get hold of him, but little Thumbling hopped into the cloth, and while the mistress was opening it out and looking for him, he got into a crevice in the table. "Ho, ho, lady mistress," cried he, and thrust his head out, and when she began to strike him he leapt down into the drawer. At last, however, she caught him and drove him out of the house.

The little tailor journeyed on and came to a great forest, and there he fell in with a band of robbers who had a design to steal the King's treasure. When they saw the little tailor, they thought, "A little fellow like that can creep through a key-hole and serve as a picklock to us." "Hollo," cried one of them, "thou giant Goliath, wilt thou go to the treasure-chamber with us? Thou canst slip thyself in and throw out the money." Thumbling reflected a while, and at length he said "yes," and went with them to the treasure-chamber. Then he looked at the doors above and below, to see if there was any crack in them. It was not long before he espied one which was broad enough to let him in. He was therefore about to get in at once, but one of the two sentries who stood before the door, observed him, and said to the other, "What an ugly spider is creeping there; I will kill it." "Let the poor creature alone," said the other, "it has done thee no harm." Then Thumbling got safely through the crevice into the treasure-chamber, opened the window beneath which the robbers were standing, and threw out to them one thaler after another. When the little tailor was in the full swing of his work, he heard the King coming to inspect his treasure-chamber, and crept hastily into a hiding-place. The King noticed that several solid thalers were missing, but could not conceive who could have stolen them, for locks and bolts were in good condition, and all seemed well guarded. Then he went away again, and said to the sentries, "Be on the watch, some one is after the money." When therefore Thumbling recommenced his labours, they heard the money moving, and a sound of klink, klink, klink. They ran swiftly in to seize the thief, but the little tailor, who heard them coming, was still swifter, and leaped into a corner and covered himself with a thaler, so that nothing could be seen of him, and at the same time he mocked the sentries and cried, "Here am I!" The sentries ran thither, but as they got there, he had already hopped into another corner under a thaler, and was crying, "Ho, ho, here am I!" The watchmen sprang there in haste, but Thumbling had long ago got into a third corner, and was crying, "Ho, ho, here am I!" And thus he made fools of them, and drove them so long round about the treasure-chamber that they were weary and went away. Then by degrees he threw all the thalers out, despatching the last with all his might, then hopped nimbly upon it, and flew down with it through the window. The robbers paid him great compliments. "Thou art a valiant hero," said they; "wilt thou be our captain?"

Thumbling, however, declined, and said he wanted to see the world first. They now divided the booty, but the little tailor only asked for a kreuzer because he could not carry more.

Then he once more buckled on his sword, bade the robbers good-bye, and took to the road. First, he went to work with some masters, but he had no liking for that, and at last he hired himself as man-servant in an inn. The maids, however, could not endure him, for he saw all that they did secretly, without their seeing him, and he told their master and mistress what they had taken off the plates, and carried away out of the cellar, for themselves. Then said they, " Wait, and we will pay thee off! " and arranged with each other to play him a trick. Soon afterwards when one of the maids was mowing in the garden, and saw Thumbling jumping about and creeping up and down the plants, she mowed him up quickly with the grass, tied all in a great cloth, and secretly threw it to the cows. Now amongst them there was a great black one, who swallowed him down with it without hurting him. Down below, however, it pleased him ill, for it was quite dark, neither was any candle burning. When the cow was being milked he cried,

> Strip, strap, strull,
> Will the pail soon be full?"

But the noise of the milking prevented his being understood. After this the master of the house came into the cow-byre and said, "That cow shall be killed to-morrow." Then Thumbling was so alarmed that he cried out in a clear voice, "Let me out first, for I am shut up inside her." The master heard that quite well, but did not know from whence the voice came. "Where art thou?" asked he. "In the black one," answered Thumbling, but the master did not understand what that meant, and went out.

Next morning the cow was killed. Happily Thumbling did not meet with one blow at the cutting up and chopping; he got among the sausage-meat. And when the butcher came in and began his work, he cried out with all his might, "Don't chop too deep, don't chop too deep, I am amongst it." No one heard this because of the noise of the chopping-knife. Now poor Thumbling was in trouble, but trouble sharpens the wits, and he sprang out so adroitly between the blows that none of them touched him, and he got out with a whole skin. But still he could not get away, there was nothing for it, and he had to let himself be thrust into a black-pudding with the bits of bacon. His quarters there were rather confined, and besides that he was hung up in the chimney to be smoked, and there time did hang terribly heavy on his hands.

At length in winter he was taken down again, as the black-pudding had to be set before a guest. When the hostess was cutting it in slices, he took care not to stretch out his head too far lest a bit of it should be cut off; at last he saw his opportunity, cleared a passage for himself, and jumped out.

The little tailor, however, would not stay any longer in a house where he fared so ill, but at once set out on his journey again. But his liberty did not last long. In the open country he met with a fox who snapped him up in a fit of absence. "Hollo, Mr. Fox," cried the little tailor, "it is I who am sticking in your throat, set me at liberty again." "Thou art right," answered the fox. "Thou art next to nothing for me, but if thou wilt promise me the fowls in thy father's yard I will let thee go." "With all my heart," replied Thumbling. "Thou shalt have all the cocks and hens, that I promise thee." Then the fox let him go again, and himself carried him home. When the father once more saw his dear son, he willingly gave the fox all the fowls which he had. "For this I likewise bring thee a handsome bit of money," said Thumbling, and gave his father the kreuzer which he had earned on his travels.

"But why did the fox get the poor chickens to eat?" "Oh, you goose, your father would surely love his child far more than the fowls in the yard!"

THE SIX SWANS

ONCE upon a time, a certain King was hunting in a great forest, and he chased a wild beast so eagerly that none of his attendants could follow him. When evening drew near he stopped and looked around him, and then he saw that he had lost his way. He sought a way out, but could find none. Then he perceived an aged woman with a head which nodded perpetually, who came towards him, but she was a witch. "Good woman," said he to her, "can you not show me the way through the forest?" "Oh, yes, Lord King," she answered, "that I certainly can, but on one condition, and if you do not fulfil that, you will never get out of the forest and will die of hunger in it."

"What kind of condition is it?" asked the King.

"I have a daughter," said the old woman, "who is as beautiful as any one in the world, and well deserves to be your consort, and if you will make her your Queen, I will show you the way out of the forest." In the anguish of his heart the King consented, and the old woman led him to her little hut, where her daughter was sitting by the fire. She received the King as if she had been expecting him, and he saw that she was very beautiful, but still she did not please him, and he could not look at her without secret horror. After he had taken the maiden up on his horse, the old woman showed him the way, and the King reached his royal palace again, where the wedding was celebrated.

The King had already been married once, and had by his first wife, seven children, six boys and a girl, whom he loved better than anything else in the world. As he now feared that the step-mother might not treat them well, and even do them some injury, he took them to a lonely castle which stood in the midst of a forest. It lay so concealed, and the way was so difficult to find, that he himself would not have found it, if a wise woman had not given him a ball of yarn with wonderful properties. When he threw it down before him, it unrolled itself and showed him his path. The King, however, went so frequently away to his dear children that the Queen observed his absence; she was curious and wanted to know what he did when he was quite alone in the forest. She gave a great deal of money to his servants, and they betrayed the secret to her, and told her likewise of the ball which alone could point out the way. And now she knew no rest until she had learnt where the King kept the ball of yarn, and then she made little shirts of white silk, and as she had learnt the art of witchcraft from her mother, she sewed a charm inside them. And once when the King had ridden forth to hunt, she took the little shirts and went into the forest, and the ball showed her the way. The children, who saw from a distance that some one was approaching, thought that their dear father was coming to them, and full of joy, ran to meet him. Then she threw one of the little shirts over each of them, and no sooner had the shirts touched their bodies than they were changed into swans, and flew away over the forest. The Queen went home quite delighted, and thought she had got rid of her step-children, but the girl had not run out with her brothers, and the Queen knew nothing about her. Next day the King went to visit his children, but he found no one but the little girl. "Where are thy brothers?" asked the King. "Alas, dear father," she answered, "they have gone away and left me alone!" and she told him that she had seen from her little window how her brothers had flown away over the forest in the shape of swans, and she showed him the feathers, which they had let fall in the courtyard, and which she had picked up. The King mourned, but he did not think that the Queen had done this wicked deed, and as he feared that the girl would also be stolen away from him, he wanted to take her away with him. But she was afraid of her step-

mother, and entreated the King to let her stay just this one
night more in the forest castle.

The poor girl thought, "I can no longer stay here. I
will go and seek my brothers." And when night came,
she ran away, and went straight into the forest. She walked
the whole night long, and next day also without stopping,
until she could go no farther for weariness. Then she saw
a forest-hut, and went into it, and found a room with six
little beds, but she did not venture to get into one of them,
but crept under one, and lay down on the hard ground, intending to pass the night there. Just before sunset, however,
she heard a rustling, and saw six swans come flying in at
the window. They alighted on the ground and blew at
each other, and blew all the feathers off, and their swan's
skins stripped off like a shirt. Then the maiden looked at
them and recognized her brothers, was glad and crept forth
from beneath the bed. The brothers were not less delighted to see their little sister, but their joy was of short
duration. "Here canst thou not abide," they said to her.
"This is a shelter for robbers, if they come home and find
thee, they will kill thee." "But can you not protect me?"
asked the little sister. "No," they replied, "only for one
quarter of an hour each evening can we lay aside our
swan's skin and have during that time our human form, after
that, we are once more turned into swans." The little sister
wept and said, "Can you not be set free?" "Alas, no,"
they answered, "the conditions are too hard! For six years
thou mayest neither speak nor laugh, and in that time thou
must sew together six little shirts of starwort for us. And
if one single word falls from thy lips all thy work will be
lost." And when the brothers had said this, the quarter
of an hour was over, and they flew out of the window again
as swans.

The maiden, however, firmly resolved to deliver her
brothers, even if it should cost her her life. She left the
hut, went into the midst of the forest, seated herself on
a tree, and there passed the night. Next morning she went
out and gathered starwort and began to sew. She could
not speak to any one, and she had no inclination to laugh;
she sat there and looked at nothing but her work. When

she had already spent a long time there it came to pass that the King of the country was hunting in the forest, and his huntsmen come to the tree on which the maiden was sitting. They called to her and said, " Who art thou?" But she made no answer. " Come down to us," said they. " We will not do thee any harm." She only shook her head. As they pressed her further with questions she threw her golden necklace down to them, and thought to content them thus. They, however, did not cease, and then she threw her girdle down to them, and as this also was to no purpose, her garters, and by degrees everything that she had on that she could do without until she had nothing left but her shift. The huntsmen, however, did not let themselves be turned aside by that, but climbed the tree and fetched the maiden down and led her before the King. The King asked, " Who art thou? What art thou doing on the tree?" But she did not answer. He put the question in every language that he knew, but she remained as mute as a fish. As she was so beautiful, the King's heart was touched, and he was smitten with a great love for her. He put his mantle on her, took her before him on his horse, and carried her to his castle. Then he caused her to be dressed in rich garments, and she shone in her beauty like bright daylight, but no word could be drawn from her. He placed her by his side at table, and her modest bearing and courtesy pleased him so much that he said, " She is the one whom I wish to marry, and no other woman in the world." And after some days he united himself to her.

The King, however, had a wicked mother who was dissatisfied with this marriage and spoke ill of the young Queen. " Who knows," said she, " from whence the creature who can't speak, comes? She is not worthy of a king!" After a year had passed, when the Queen brought her first child into the world, the old woman took it away from her, and smeared her mouth with blood as she slept. Then she went to the King and accused the Queen of being a man-eater. The King would not believe it, and would not suffer any one to do her any injury. She, however, sat continually sewing at the shirts, and cared for nothing else. The next time, when she again bore a beautiful boy, the false step-mother used the same treachery, but the King could not bring himself to give credit to her words. He said, "She is too pious and good to do anything of that kind; if she were not dumb, and could defend herself, her innocence would come to light." But when the old woman stole away the newly-born child for the third time, and accused the Queen, who did not utter one word of defence, the King could do no otherwise than deliver her over to justice, and she was sentenced to suffer death by fire.

When the day came for the sentence to be executed, it was the last day of the six years during which she was not to speak or laugh, and she had delivered her dear brothers from the power of the enchantment. The six shirts were ready, only the left sleeve of the sixth was wanting. When, therefore, she was led to the stake, she laid the shirts on her arm, and when she stood on high and the fire was just going to be lighted, she looked around and six swans came flying through the air towards her. Then she saw that her deliverance was near, and her heart leapt with joy. The swans swept towards her and sank down so that she could throw the shirts over them, and as they were touched by them, their swan's skins fell off, and her brothers stood in their own bodily form before her, and were vigorous and handsome. The youngest only lacked his left arm, and had in the place of it a swan's wing on his shoulder. They embraced and kissed each other, and the Queen went to the King, who was greatly moved, and she began to speak and said, "Dearest husband, now I may speak and declare to thee that I am innocent, and falsely accused." And she told him of the treachery of the old woman who had taken away her three children and hidden them. Then to the great joy of the King they were brought thither, and as a punishment, the wicked step-mother was bound to the stake, and burnt to ashes. But the King and the Queen with their six brothers lived many years in happiness and peace.

LITTLE BRIAR-ROSE

A LONG time ago there were a King and Queen who said every day, "Ah, if only we had a child!" but they never had one. But it happened that once when the Queen was bathing, a frog crept out of the water on to the land, and said to her, "Your wish shall be fulfilled; before a year has gone by you shall have a daughter."

What the frog had said came true, and the Queen had a little girl who was so pretty that the King could not contain himself for joy, and ordered a great feast. He invited not only his kindred, friends and acquaintance, but also the Wise Women, in order that they might be kind and well-disposed towards the child. There were thirteen of them in his kingdom, but as he had only twelve golden plates for them to eat out of, one of them had to be left at home.

The feast was held with all manner of splendour, and when it came to an end the Wise Women bestowed their magic gifts upon the baby: one gave virtue, another beauty, a third riches, and so on with everything in the world that one can wish for.

When eleven of them had made their promises, suddenly the thirteenth came in. She wished to avenge herself for not having been invited, and without greeting, or even looking at any one, she cried with a loud voice, "The King's daughter shall in her fifteenth year prick herself with a spindle, and fall down dead." And, without saying a word more, she turned round and left the room.

They were all shocked; but the twelfth, whose good wish still remained unspoken, came forward, and as she could not undo the evil sentence, but only soften it, she said, "It shall not be death, but a deep sleep of a hundred years, into which the princess shall fall."

The King, who would fain keep his dear child from the misfortune, gave orders that every spindle in the whole kingdom should be burnt. Meanwhile the gifts of the Wise Women were plenteously fulfilled on the young girl, for she was so beautiful, modest, good-natured, and wise, that every one who saw her was bound to love her.

It happened that on the very day when she was fifteen years old the King and Queen were not at home, and the maiden was left in the palace quite alone. So she went round into all sorts of places, looked into rooms and bed-chambers just as she liked, and at last came to an old tower. She climbed up the narrow winding-staircase, and reached a little door. A rusty key was in the lock, and when she turned it the door sprang open, and there in a little room sat an old woman with a spindle, busily spinning her flax.

"Good day, old dame," said the King's daughter; "what are you doing there?" "I am spinning," said the old woman, and nodded her head. "What sort of thing is that, that rattles round so merrily?" said the girl, and she took the spindle and wanted to spin too. But scarcely had she touched the spindle when the magic decree was fulfilled, and she pricked her finger with it.

And, in the very moment when she felt the prick, she fell down upon the bed that stood there, and lay in a deep sleep. And this sleep extended over the whole palace; the King and Queen who had just come home, and had entered the great hall, began to go to sleep, and the whole court with them. The horses, too, went to sleep in the stable, the dogs in the yard, the pigeons upon the roof, the flies on the wall; even the fire that was flaming on the hearth became quiet and slept, the roast meat left off frizzling, and the cook, who was just going to pull the hair of the scullery boy, because he had forgotten something, let him go, and went to sleep. And the wind fell, and on the trees before the castle not a leaf moved again.

But round about the castle there began to grow a hedge of thorns, which every year became higher, and at last grew close up around the castle and all over it, so that there was nothing of it to be seen, not even the flag upon the roof. But the story of the beautiful sleeping "Briar-rose," for so the princess was named, went about the country, so that from time to time kings' sons came and tried to get through the thorny hedge into the castle.

But they found it impossible, for the thorns held fast together, as if they had hands, and the youths were caught in them, could not get loose again, and died a miserable death.

After long, long years a King's son came again to that country, and heard an old man talking about the thorn-hedge, and that a castle was said to stand behind it in which a wonderfully beautiful princess, named Briar-rose, had been asleep for a hundred years; and that the King and Queen and the whole court were asleep likewise. He had heard, too, from his grandfather, that many kings' sons had already come, and had tried to get through the thorny hedge, but they had remained sticking fast in it, and had died a pitiful death. Then the youth said, " I am not afraid, I will go and see the beautiful Briar-rose." The good old man might dissuade him as he would, he did not listen to his words.

But by this time the hundred years had just passed, and the day had come when Briar-rose was to awake again. When the King's son came near to the thorn-hedge, it was nothing but large and beautiful flowers, which parted from each other of their own accord, and let him pass unhurt, then they closed again behind him like a hedge. In the castle-yard he saw the horses and the spotted hounds lying asleep; on the roof sat the pigeons with their heads under their wings. And when he entered the house, the flies were asleep upon the wall, the cook in the kitchen was still holding out his hand to seize the boy, and the maid was sitting by the black hen which she was going to pluck.

He went on farther, and in the great hall he saw the whole of the court lying asleep, and up by the throne lay the King and Queen.

Then he went on still farther, and all was so quiet that a breath could be heard, and at last he came to the tower, and opened the door into the little room where Briar-rose was sleeping. There she lay, so beautiful that he could not turn his eyes away; and he stooped down and gave her a kiss. But as soon as he kissed her, Briar-rose opened her eyes and awoke, and looked at him quite sweetly.

Then they went down together, and the King awoke, and the Queen, and the whole court, and looked at each other in great astonishment. And the horses in the courtyard stood up and shook themselves; the hounds jumped up and wagged their tails; the pigeons upon the roof pulled out their heads from under their wings, looked round, and flew into the open country; the flies on the wall crept again; the fire in the kitchen burned up and flickered and cooked the meat; the joint began to turn and frizzle again, and the cook gave the boy such a box on the ear that he screamed, and the maid plucked the fowl ready for the spit.

And then the marriage of the King's son with Briar-rose was celebrated with all splendour, and they lived contented to the end of their days.

FUNDEVOGEL[1]

THERE was once a forester who went into the forest to hunt, and as he entered it he heard a sound of screaming as if a little child were there. He followed the sound, and at last came to a high tree, and at the top of this a little child was sitting, for the mother had fallen asleep under the tree with the child, and a bird of prey had seen it in her arms, had flown down, snatched it away, and set it on the high tree.

The forester climbed up, brought the child down, and thought to himself, "Thou wilt take him home with thee, and bring him up with thy Lina." He took it home, therefore, and the two children grew up together. The one, however, which he had found on a tree was called Fundevogel, because a bird had carried it away. Fundevogel and Lina loved each other so dearly that when they did not see each other they were sad.

The forester, however, had an old cook, who one evening took two pails and began to fetch water, and did not go once only, but many times, out to the spring. Lina saw this and said, "Hark you, old Sanna, why are you fetching so much water?" "If thou wilt never repeat it to any one, I will tell thee why." So Lina said, no, she would never repeat it to any one, and then the cook said, "Early to-

[1] I. e., Bird-foundling.

morrow morning, when the forester is out hunting, I will heat the water, and when it is boiling in the kettle, I will throw in Fundevogel, and will boil him in it."

Betimes next morning the forester got up and went out hunting, and when he was gone the children were still in bed. Then Lina said to Fundevogel, "If thou wilt never leave me, I too will never leave thee." Fundevogel said, "Neither now, nor ever will I leave thee." Then said Lina, "Then will I tell thee. Last night, old Sanna carried so many buckets of water into the house that I asked her why she was doing that, and she said that if I would promise not to tell any one she would tell me, and I said I would be sure not to tell any one, and she said that early to-morrow morning when father was out hunting, she would set on the kettle full of water, throw thee into it and boil thee; but we will get up quickly, dress ourselves, and go away together."

The two children therefore got up, dressed themselves quickly, and went away. When the water in the kettle was boiling, the cook went into the bed-room to fetch Fundevogel and throw him into it. But when she came in, and went to the beds, both the children were gone. Then she was terribly alarmed, and she said to herself, "What shall I say now when the forester comes home and sees that the children are gone? They must be followed instantly to get them back again."

Then the cook sent three servants after them, who were to run and overtake the children. The children, however, were sitting outside the forest, and when they saw from afar the three servants running, Lina said to Fundevogel, "Never leave me, and I will never leave thee." Fundevogel said, "Neither now, nor ever." Then said Lina, "Do thou become a rose-tree, and I the rose upon it." When the three servants came to the forest, nothing was there but a rose-tree and one rose on it, but the children were nowhere. Then said they, "There is nothing to be done here," and they went home and told the cook that they had seen nothing in the forest but a little rose-bush with one rose on it. Then the old cook scolded and said, "You simpletons, you should have cut the rose-bush in two, and have broken off the rose and brought it home with you; go, and do it at once." They had therefore to go out and look for the second time. The children, however, saw them coming from a distance. Then Lina said, " Fundevogel, never leave me and I will never leave thee." Fundevogel said, " Neither now, nor ever." Said Lina, " Then do thou become a church, and I'll be the chandelier in it." So when the three servants came, nothing was there but a church, with a chandelier in it. They said therefore to each other, " What can we do here, let us go home." When they got home, the cook asked if they had not found them; so they said no, they had found nothing but a church, and that there was a chandelier in it. And the cook scolded them and said, " You fools! why did you not pull the church to pieces, and bring the chandelier home with you?" And now the old cook herself got on her legs, and went with the three servants in pursuit of the children. The children, however, saw from afar that the three servants were coming, and the cook waddling after them. Then said Lina, " Fundevogel, never leave me, and I will never leave thee." Then said Fundevogel, " Neither now, nor ever." Said Lina, " Be a fishpond, and I will be the duck upon it." The cook, however, came up to them, and when she saw the pond she lay down by it, and was about to drink it up. But the duck swam quickly to her, seized her head in its beak and drew her into the water, and there the old witch had to drown. Then the children went home together and were heartily delighted, and if they are not dead, they are living still.

KING THRUSHBEARD

A KING had a daughter who was beautiful beyond all measure, but so proud and haughty withal that no suitor was good enough for her. She sent away one after the other, and ridiculed them as well.

Once the King made a great feast and invited thereto, from far and near, all the young men likely to marry. They were all marshalled in a row according to their rank and standing; first came the kings, then the grand-dukes, then the princes, the earls, the barons, and the gentry. Then the

King's daughter was led through the ranks, but to every one she had some objection to make; one was too fat, "The wine-cask," she said. Another was too tall, "Long and thin has little in." The third was too short, "Short and thick is never quick." The fourth was too pale, "As pale as death." The fifth too red, "A fighting-cock." The sixth was not straight enough, "A green log dried behind the stove."

So she had something to say against every one, but she made herself especially merry over a good king who stood quite high up in the row, and whose chin had grown a little crooked. "Well," she cried and laughed, "he has a chin like a thrush's beak!" and from that time he got the name of King Thrushbeard.

But the old King, when he saw that his daughter did nothing but mock the people, and despised all the suitors who were gathered there, was very angry, and swore that she should have for her husband the very first beggar that came to his doors.

A few days afterwards a fiddler came and sang beneath the windows, trying to earn a small alms. When the King heard him he said, "Let him come up." So the fiddler came in, in his dirty, ragged clothes, and sang before the King and his daughter, and when he had ended he asked for a trifling gift. The King said, "Your song has pleased me so well that I will give you my daughter there, to wife."

The King's daughter shuddered, but the King said, "I have taken an oath to give you to the very first beggar-man, and I will keep it." All she could say was in vain; the priest was brought, and she had to let herself be wedded to the fiddler on the spot. When that was done the King said, "Now it is not proper for you, a beggar-woman, to stay any longer in my palace, you may just go away with your husband."

The beggar-man led her out by the hand, and she was obliged to walk away on foot with him. When they came to a large forest she asked, "To whom does that beautiful forest belong?" "It belongs to King Thrushbeard; if you had taken him, it would have been yours." "Ah, unhappy girl that I am, if I had but taken King Thrushbeard!"

Afterwards they came to a meadow, and she asked again, "To whom does this beautiful green meadow belong?" "It belongs to King Thrushbeard; if you had taken him, it would have been yours." "Ah, unhappy girl that I am, if I had but taken King Thrushbeard!"

Then they came to a large town, and she asked again, "To whom does this fine large town belong?" "It belongs to King Thrushbeard; if you had taken him, it would have been yours." "Ah, unhappy girl that I am, if I had but taken King Thrushbeard!"

"It does not please me," said the fiddler, "to hear you always wishing for another husband; am I not good enough for you?" At last they came to a very little hut, and she said, "Oh, goodness! what a small house; to whom does this miserable, mean hovel belong?" The fiddler answered, "That is my house and yours, where we shall live together."

She had to stoop in order to go in at the low door. "Where are the servants?" said the King's daughter. "What servants?" answered the beggar-man; "you must yourself do what you wish to have done. Just make a fire at once, and set on water to cook my supper, I am quite tired." But the King's daughter knew nothing about lighting fires or cooking, and the beggar-man had to lend a hand himself to get anything fairly done. When they had finished their scanty meal they went to bed; but he forced her to get up quite early in the morning in order to look after the house.

For a few days they lived in this way as well as might be, and finished all their provisions. Then the man said, "Wife, we cannot go on any longer eating and drinking here and earning nothing. You must weave baskets." He went out, cut some willows, and brought them home. Then she began to weave, but the tough willows wounded her delicate hands.

"I see that this will not do," said the man; "you had better spin, perhaps you can do that better." She sat down and tried to spin, but the hard thread soon cut her soft fingers so that the blood ran down. "See," said the man, "you are fit for no sort of work; I have made a bad bargain with you. Now I will try to make a business with

pots and earthenware; you must sit in the market-place
and sell the ware." "Alas," thought she, "if any of the
people from my father's kingdom come to the market and
see me sitting there, selling, how they will mock me!" But
it was of no use, she had to yield unless she chose to die of
hunger.

For the first time she succeeded well, for the people were
glad to buy the woman's wares because she was good-look-
ing, and they paid her what she asked; many even gave her
the money and left the pots with her as well. So they lived
on what she had earned as long as it lasted, then the husband
bought a lot of new crockery. With this she sat down at
the corner of the market-place, and set it out round about
her ready for sale. But suddenly there came a drunken
hussar galloping along, and he rode right amongst the pots
so that they were all broken into a thousand bits. She
began to weep, and did not know what to do for fear.
"Alas! what will happen to me?" cried she; "what will
my husband say to this?"

She ran home and told him of the misfortune. "Who
would seat herself at a corner of the market-place with
crockery?" said the man; "leave off crying, I see very well
that you cannot do any ordinary work, so I have been to
our King's palace and have asked whether they cannot find
a place for a kitchen-maid, and they have promised me to
take you; in that way you will get your food for nothing."

The King's daughter was now a kitchen-maid, and had to
be at the cook's beck and call, and do the dirtiest work. In
both her pockets she fastened a little jar, in which she took
home her share of the leavings, and upon this they lived.

It happened that the wedding of the King's eldest son
was to be celebrated, so the poor woman went up and placed
herself by the door of the hall to look on. When all the
candles were lit, and people, each more beautiful than the
other, entered, and all was full of pomp and splendour, she
thought of her lot with a sad heart, and cursed the pride
and haughtiness which had humbled her and brought her
to so great poverty.

The smell of the delicious dishes which were being taken
in and out reached her, and now and then the servants threw

her a few morsels of them: these she put in her jars to take home.

All at once the King's son entered, clothed in velvet and silk, with gold chains about his neck. And when he saw the beautiful woman standing by the door he seized her by the hand, and would have danced with her; but she refused and shrank with fear, for she saw that it was King Thrushbeard, her suitor whom she had driven away with scorn. Her struggles were of no avail, he drew her into the hall; but the string by which her pockets were hung broke, the pots fell down, the soup ran out, and the scraps were scattered all about. And when the people saw it, there arose general laughter and derision, and she was so ashamed that she would rather have been a thousand fathoms below the ground. She sprang to the door and would have run away, but on the stairs a man caught her and brought her back; and when she looked at him it was King Thrushbeard again. He said to her kindly, "Do not be afraid, I and the fiddler who has been living with you in that wretched hovel are one. For love of you I disguised myself so; and I also was the hussar who rode through your crockery. This was all done to humble your proud spirit, and to punish you for the insolence with which you mocked me."

Then she wept bitterly and said, "I have done great wrong, and am not worthy to be your wife." But he said, "Be comforted, the evil days are past; now we will celebrate our wedding." Then the maids-in-waiting came and put on her the most splendid clothing, and her father and his whole court came and wished her happiness in her marriage with King Thrushbeard, and the joy now began in earnest. I wish you and I had been there too.

LITTLE SNOW-WHITE

ONCE upon a time in the middle of winter, when the flakes of snow were falling like feathers from the sky, a queen sat at a window sewing, and the frame of the window was made of black ebony. And whilst she was sewing and looking out of the window at the snow, she pricked her

finger with the needle, and three drops of blood fell upon
the snow. And the red looked pretty upon the white snow,
and she thought to herself, " Would that I had a child as
white as snow, as red as blood, and as black as the wood
of the window frame."

Soon after that she had a little daughter, who was as
white as snow, and as red as blood, and her hair was as
black as ebony; and she was therefore called Little Snow-
white. And when the child was born, the Queen died.

After a year had passed the King took to himself another
wife. She was a beautiful woman, but proud and haughty,
and she could not bear that any one else should surpass her
in beauty. She had a wonderful looking-glass, and when
she stood in front of it and looked at herself in it, and said—

> "Looking-glass, Looking-glass, on the wall,
>   Who in this land is the fairest of all?"

the looking-glass answered—

> "Thou, O Queen, art the fairest of all!"

Then she was satisfied, for she knew that the looking-glass
spoke the truth.

But Snow-white was growing up, and grew more and
more beautiful; and when she was seven years old she was
as beautiful as the day, and more beautiful than the Queen
herself. And once when the Queen asked her looking-glass—

> "Looking-glass, Looking-glass, on the wall,
>   Who in this land is the fairest of all?"

it answered—

> "Thou art fairer than all who are here, Lady Queen,
>   But more beautiful still is Snow-white, as I ween."

Then the Queen was shocked, and turned yellow and green
with envy. From that hour, whenever she looked at Snow-
white, her heart heaved in her breast, she hated the girl
so much.

And envy and pride grew higher and higher in her heart
like a weed, so that she had no peace day or night. She
called a huntsman, and said, " Take the child away into the

forest; I will no longer have her in my sight. Kill her, and bring me back her heart as a token." The huntsman obeyed, and took her away; but when he had drawn his knife, and was about to pierce Snow-white's innocent heart, she began to weep, and said, "Ah, dear huntsman, leave me my life! I will run away into the wild forest and never come home again."

And as she was so beautiful the huntsman had pity on her and said, "Run away, then, you poor child." "The wild beasts will soon have devoured you," thought he, and yet it seemed as if a stone had been rolled from his heart since it was no longer needful for him to kill her. And as a young boar just then came running by he stabbed it and cut out its heart and took it to the Queen as a proof that the child was dead. The cook had to salt this, and the wicked Queen ate it, and thought she had eaten the heart of Snow-white.

But now the poor child was all alone in the great forest, and so terrified that she looked at every leaf of every tree, and did not know what to do. Then she began to run, and ran over sharp stones and through thorns, and the wild beasts ran past her, but did her no harm.

She ran as long as her feet would go until it was almost evening; then she saw a little cottage and went into it to rest herself. Everything in the cottage was small, but neater and cleaner than can be told. There was a table on which was a white cover, and seven little plates, and on each plate a little spoon; moreover, there were seven little knives and forks, and seven little mugs. Against the wall stood seven little beds side by side, and covered with snow-white counterpanes.

Little Snow-white was so hungry and thirsty that she ate some vegetables and bread from each plate and drank a drop of wine out of each mug, for she did not wish to take all from one only. Then, as she was so tired, she laid herself down on one of the little beds, but none of them suited her; one was too long, another too short, but at last she found that the seventh one was right, and so she remained in it, said a prayer and went to sleep.

When it was quite dark the owners of the cottage came

back; they were seven dwarfs who dug and delved in the
mountains for ore. They lit their seven candles, and as it
was now light within the cottage they saw that some one
had been there, for everything was not in the same order
in which they had left it.

The first said, " Who has been sitting on my chair?"
The second, " Who has been eating off my plate?"
The third, " Who has been taking some of my bread?"
The fourth, " Who has been eating my vegetables?"
The fifth, "Who has been using my fork?"
The sixth, " Who has been cutting with my knife?"
The seventh, " Who has been drinking out of my mug?"

Then the first looked round and saw that there was a little
hole on his bed, and he said, " Who has been getting into
my bed?" The others came up and each called out, " Somebody has been lying in my bed too." But the seventh when
he looked at his bed saw little Snow-white, who was lying
asleep therein. And he called the others, who came running
up, and they cried out with astonishment, and brought their
seven little candles and let the light fall on little Snow-white.
" Oh, heavens! oh, heavens!" cried they, "what a lovely
child!" and they were so glad that they did not wake her
up, but let her sleep on in the bed. And the seventh dwarf
slept with his companions, one hour with each, and so got
through the night.

When it was morning little Snow-white awoke, and was
frightened when she saw the seven dwarfs. But they were
friendly and asked her what her name was. " My name
is Snow-white," she answered. " How have you come to
our house?" said the dwarfs. Then she told them that her
step-mother had wished to have her killed, but that the
huntsman had spared her life, and that she had run for the
whole day, until at last she had found their dwelling. The
dwarfs said, " If you will take care of our house, cook, make
the beds, wash, sew, and knit, and if you will keep everything
neat and clean, you can stay with us and you shall want for
nothing." " Yes," said Snow-white, " with all my heart,"
and she stayed with them. She kept the house in order for
them; in the mornings they went to the mountains and
looked for copper and gold, in the evenings they came back,

and then their supper had to be ready. The girl was alone the whole day, so the good dwarfs warned her and said, "Beware of your step-mother, she will soon know that you are here; be sure to let no one come in."

But the Queen, believing that she had eaten Snow-white's heart, could not but think that she was again the first and most beautiful of all; and she went to her looking-glass and said—

"Looking-glass, Looking-glass, on the wall,
Who in this land is the fairest of all?"

and the glass answered—

"Oh, Queen, thou art fairest of all I see,
But over the hills, where the seven dwarfs dwell,
Snow-white is still alive and well,
And none is so fair as she."

Then she was astounded, for she knew that the looking-glass never spoke falsely, and she knew that the huntsman had betrayed her, and that little Snow-white was still alive. And so she thought and thought again how she might kill her, for so long as she was not the fairest in the whole land, envy let her have no rest. And when she had at last thought of something to do, she painted her face, and dressed herself like an old pedler-woman, and no one could have known her. In this disguise she went over the seven mountains to the seven dwarfs, and knocked at the door and cried, "Pretty things to sell, very cheap, very cheap." Little Snow-white looked out of the window and called out, "Good-day, my good woman, what have you to sell?" "Good things, pretty things," she answered; "stay-laces of all colours," and she pulled out one which was woven of bright-coloured silk. "I may let the worthy old woman in," thought Snow-white, and she unbolted the door and bought the pretty laces. "Child," said the old woman, "what a fright you look; come, I will lace you properly for once." Snow-white had no suspicion, but stood before her, and let herself be laced with the new laces. But the old woman laced so quickly and laced so tightly that Snow-white lost her breath and fell down as if dead. "Now I am the most beautiful," said the Queen to herself, and ran away.

Not long afterwards, in the evening, the seven dwarfs came home, but how shocked they were when they saw their dear little Snow-white lying on the ground, and that she neither stirred nor moved, and seemed to be dead. They lifted her up, and, as they saw that she was laced too tightly, they cut the laces; then she began to breathe a little, and after a while came to life again. When the dwarfs heard what had happened they said, " The old pedler-woman was no one else than the wicked Queen; take care and let no one come in when we are not with you."

But the wicked woman when she had reached home went in front of the glass and asked—

> "Looking-glass, Looking-glass, on the wall,
> Who in this land is the fairest of all?"

and it answered as before—

> "Oh, Queen, thou art fairest of all I see,
> But over the hills, where the seven dwarfs dwell,
> Snow-white is still alive and well,
> And none is so fair as she."

When she heard that, all her blood rushed to her heart with fear, for she saw plainly that little Snow-white was again alive. " But now," she said, " I will think of something that shall put an end to you," and by the help of witchcraft, which she understood, she made a poisonous comb. Then she disguised herself and took the shape of another old woman. So she went over the seven mountains to the seven dwarfs, knocked at the door, and cried, " Good things to sell cheap, cheap ! " Little Snow-white looked out and said, " Go away; I cannot let any one come in." " I suppose you can look," said the old woman, and pulled the poisonous comb out and held it up. It pleased the girl so well that she let herself be beguiled, and opened the door. When they had made a bargain the old woman said, " Now I will comb you properly for once." Poor little Snow-white had no suspicion, and let the old woman do as she pleased, but hardly had she put the comb in her hair than the poison in it took effect, and the girl fell down senseless. " You paragon of beauty," said the wicked woman, " you are done for now," and she went away.

But fortunately it was almost evening, when the seven dwarfs came home. When they saw Snow-white lying as if dead upon the ground they at once suspected the step-mother, and they looked and found the poisoned comb. Scarcely had they taken it out when Snow-white came to herself, and told them what had happened. Then they warned her once more to be upon her guard and to open the door to no one.

The Queen, at home, went in front of the glass and said—

> "Looking-glass, Looking-glass, on the wall,
> Who in this land is the fairest of all?"

then it answered as before—

> "Oh, Queen, thou art fairest of all I see,
> But over the hills, where the seven dwarfs dwell,
> Snow-white is still alive and well,
> And none is so fair as she."

When she heard the glass speak thus she trembled and shook with rage. "Snow-white shall die," she cried, "even if it costs me my life!"

Thereupon she went into a quite secret, lonely room, where no one ever came, and there she made a very poison-ous apple. Outside it looked pretty, white with a red cheek, so that every one who saw it longed for it; but whoever ate a piece of it must surely die.

When the apple was ready she painted her face, and dressed herself up as a country-woman, and so she went over the seven mountains to the seven dwarfs. She knocked at the door. Snow-white put her head out of the window and said, "I cannot let any one in; the seven dwarfs have forbidden me." "It is all the same to me," answered the woman, "I shall soon get rid of my apples. There, I will give you one."

"No," said Snow-white, "I dare not take anything." "Are you afraid of poison?" said the old woman; "look, I will cut the apple in two pieces; you eat the red cheek, and I will eat the white." The apple was so cunningly made that only the red cheek was poisoned. Snow-white longed for the fine apple, and when she saw that the woman ate part of it she could resist no longer, and stretched out her hand and took the poisonous half. But hardly had she a bit of it in her mouth than she fell down dead. Then the Queen looked at her with a dreadful look, and laughed aloud and said, "White as snow, red as blood, black as ebony-wood! this time the dwarfs cannot wake you up again."

And when she asked of the Looking-glass at home—

> "Looking-glass, Looking-glass, on the wall,
> Who in this land is the fairest of all?"

it answered at last—

> "Oh, Queen, in this land thou art fairest of all."

Then her envious heart had rest, so far as an envious heart can have rest.

The dwarfs, when they came home in the evening, found Snow-white lying upon the ground; she breathed no longer and was dead. They lifted her up, looked to see whether they could find anything poisonous, unlaced her, combed her hair, washed her with water and wine, but it was all of no use; the poor child was dead, and remained dead. They laid her upon a bier, and all seven of them sat round it and wept for her, and wept three days long.

Then they were going to bury her, but she still looked as if she were living, and still had her pretty red cheeks. They said, "We could not bury her in the dark ground," and they had a transparent coffin of glass made, so that she could be seen from all sides, and they laid her in it, and wrote her name upon it in golden letters, and that she was a king's daughter. Then they put the coffin out upon the mountain, and one of them always stayed by it and watched it. And birds came too, and wept for Snow-white; first an owl, then a raven, and last a dove.

And now Snow-white lay a long, long time in the coffin, and she did not change, but looked as if she were asleep; for she was as white as snow, as red as blood, and her hair was as black as ebony.

It happened, however, that a king's son came into the forest, and went to the dwarfs' house to spend the night.

He saw the coffin on the mountain, and the beautiful Snow-white within it, and read what was written upon it in golden letters. Then he said to the dwarfs, "Let me have the coffin, I will give you whatever you want for it." But the dwarfs answered, "We will not part with it for all the gold in the world." Then he said, "Let me have it as a gift, for I cannot live without seeing Snow-white. I will honour and prize her as my dearest possession." As he spoke in this way the good dwarfs took pity upon him, and gave him the coffin.

And now the King's son had it carried away by his servants on their shoulders. And it happened that they stumbled over a tree-stump, and with the shock the poisonous piece of apple which Snow-white had bitten off came out of her throat. And before long she opened her eyes, lifted up the lid of the coffin, sat up, and was once more alive. "Oh, heavens, where am I?" she cried. The King's son, full of joy, said, "You are with me," and told her what had happened, and said, "I love you more than everything in the world; come with me to my father's palace, you shall be my wife."

And Snow-white was willing, and went with him, and their wedding was held with great show and splendour. But Snow-white's wicked step-mother was also bidden to the feast. When she had arrayed herself in beautiful clothes she went before the Looking-glass, and said—

> "Looking-glass, Looking-glass, on the wall,
> Who in this land is the fairest of all?"

the glass answered—

> "Oh, Queen, of all here the fairest art thou,
> But the young Queen is fairer by far as I trow."

Then the wicked woman uttered a curse, and was so wretched, so utterly wretched, that she knew not what to do. At first she would not go to the wedding at all, but she had no peace, and must go to see the young Queen. And when she went in she knew Snow-white; and she stood still with rage and fear, and could not stir. But iron slippers had already been put upon the fire, and they were brought in with tongs, and set before her. Then she was forced to put on the red-hot shoes, and dance until she dropped down dead.

RUMPELSTILTSKIN

ONCE there was a miller who was poor, but who had a beautiful daughter. Now it happened that he had to go and speak to the King, and in order to make himself appear important he said to him, "I have a daughter who can spin straw into gold." The King said to the miller, "That is an art which pleases me well; if your daughter is as clever as you say, bring her to-morrow to my palace, and I will try what she can do."

And when the girl was brought to him he took her into a room which was quite full of straw, gave her a spinning-wheel and a reel, and said, "Now set to work, and if by to-morrow morning early you have not spun this straw into gold during the night, you must die." Thereupon he himself locked up the room, and left her in it alone. So there sat the poor miller's daughter, and for her life could not tell what to do; she had no idea how straw could be spun into gold, and she grew more and more miserable, until at last she began to weep.

But all at once the door opened, and in came a little man, and said, "Good evening, Mistress Miller; why are you crying so?" "Alas!" answered the girl, "I have to spin straw into gold, and I do not know how to do it." "What will you give me," said the manikin, "if I do it for you?" "My necklace," said the girl. The little man took the necklace, seated himself in front of the wheel, and "whirr, whirr, whirr," three turns, and the reel was full; then he put another on, and whirr, whirr, whirr, three times round, and the second was full too. And so it went on until the morning, when all the straw was spun, and all the reels were full of gold. By daybreak the King was already there, and when he saw the gold he was astonished and delighted, but his heart became only more greedy. He had the miller's daughter taken into another room full of straw, which was much larger, and commanded her to spin that also in one night if she valued her life. The girl knew not how to help herself, and was crying, when the door again opened, and the little man appeared, and said, "What will you give me if I spin the straw into gold for you?" "The ring on my finger," answered the girl. The little man took the ring, again began to turn the wheel, and by morning had spun all the straw into glittering gold.

The King rejoiced beyond measure at the sight, but still he had not gold enough; and he had the miller's daughter taken into a still larger room full of straw, and said, "You must spin this, too, in the course of this night; but if you succeed, you shall be my wife." "Even if she be a miller's daughter," thought he, "I could not find a richer wife in the whole world."

When the girl was alone the manikin came again for the third time, and said, "What will you give me if I spin the straw for you this time also?" "I have nothing left that I could give," answered the girl. "Then promise me, if you should become Queen, your first child." "Who knows whether that will ever happen?" thought the miller's daughter; and, not knowing how else to help herself in this strait, she promised the manikin what he wanted, and for that he once more spun the straw into gold.

And when the King came in the morning, and found all as he had wished, he took her in marriage, and the pretty miller's daughter became a Queen.

A year after, she had a beautiful child, and she never gave a thought to the manikin. But suddenly he came into her room, and said, "Now give me what you promised." The Queen was horror-struck, and offered the manikin all the riches of the kingdom if he would leave her the child. But the manikin said, "No, something that is living is dearer to me than all the treasures in the world." Then the Queen began to weep and cry, so that the manikin pitied her. "I will give you three days' time," said he; "if by that time you find out my name, then shall you keep your child."

So the Queen thought the whole night of all the names that she had ever heard, and she sent a messenger over the country to inquire, far and wide, for any other names that there might be. When the manikin came the next day, she began with Caspar, Melchior, Balthazar, and said all the names she knew, one after another; but to every one the little man said, " That is not my name." On the second day she had inquiries made in the neighbourhood as to the names of the people there, and she repeated to the manikin the most uncommon and curious. " Perhaps your name is Shortribs, or Sheepshanks, or Laceleg?" but he always answered, " That is not my name."

On the third day the messenger came back again, and said, " I have not been able to find a single new name, but as I came to a high mountain at the end of the forest, where the fox and the hare bid each other good night, there I saw a little house, and before the house a fire was burning, and round about the fire quite a ridiculous little man was jumping: he hopped upon one leg, and shouted—

> " 'To-day I bake, to-morrow brew,
>   The next I'll have the young Queen's child.
> Ha! glad am I that no one knew
>   That Rumpelstiltskin I am styled."

You may think how glad the Queen was when she heard the name! And when soon afterwards the little man came in, and asked, " Now Mistress Queen, what is my name? " at first she said, " Is your name Conrad?" " No." " Is your name Harry?" " No."

" Perhaps your name is Rumpelstiltskin?"

" The devil has told you that! the devil has told you that! " cried the little man, and in his anger he plunged his right foot so deep into the earth that his whole leg went in; and then in rage he pulled at his left leg so hard with both hands that he tore himself in two.

THE THREE FEATHERS

THERE was once on a time a King who had three sons, of whom two were clever and wise, but the third did not speak much and was simple, and was called the Simpleton. When the King had become old and weak, and was thinking

of his end, he did not know which of his sons should inherit
the kingdom after him. Then he said to them, " Go forth,
and he who brings me the most beautiful carpet shall be
King after my death." And that there should be no dispute
amongst them, he took them outside his castle, blew three
feathers in the air, and said, " You shall go as they fly." One
feather flew to the east, the other to the west, but the
third flew straight up and did not fly far, but soon fell to
the ground. And now one brother went to the right, and
the other to the left, and they mocked Simpleton, who
was forced to stay where the third feather had fallen. He
sat down and was sad, then all at once he saw that there
was a trap-door close by the feather. He raised it up,
found some steps, and went down them, and then he came
to another door, knocked at it, and heard somebody inside
calling,

> "Little green maiden small,
> Hopping hither and thither,
> Hop to the door,
> And quickly see who is there."

The door opened, and he saw a great, fat toad sitting,
and round about her a crowd of little toads. The fat toad
asked what he wanted? He answered, " I should like to have
the prettiest and finest carpet in the world." Then she
called a young one and said,

> "Little green maiden small,
> Hopping hither and thither,
> Hop quickly and bring me
> The great box here."

The young toad brought the box, and the fat toad opened
it, and gave Simpleton a carpet out of it, so beautiful and
so fine, that on the earth above, none could have been woven
like it. Then he thanked her, and ascended again. The
two others had, however, looked on their youngest brother
as so stupid that they believed he would find and bring
nothing at all. " Why should we give ourselves a great
deal of trouble to search?" said they, and got some coarse
handkerchiefs from the first shepherds' wives whom they
met, and carried them home to the King. At the same time

Simpleton also came back, and brought his beautiful carpet, and when the King saw it he was astonished, and said, "If justice be done, the kingdom belongs to the youngest." But the two others let their father have no peace, and said that it was impossible that Simpleton, who in everything lacked understanding, should be King, and entreated him to make a new agreement with them. Then the father said, "He who brings me the most beautiful ring shall inherit the kingdom," and led the three brothers out, and blew into the air three feathers, which they were to follow. Those of the two eldest again went east and west, and Simpleton's feather flew straight up, and fell down near the door into the earth. Then he went down again to the fat toad, and told her that he wanted the most beautiful ring. She at once ordered her great box to be brought, and gave him a ring out of it, which sparkled with jewels, and was so beautiful that no goldsmith on earth would have been able to make it. The two eldest laughed at Simpleton for going to seek a golden ring. They gave themselves no trouble, but knocked the nails out of an old carriage-ring, and took it to the King; but when Simpleton produced his golden ring, his father again said, "The kingdom belongs to him." The two eldest did not cease from tormenting the King until he made a third condition, and declared that the one who brought the most beautiful woman home, should have the kingdom. He again blew the three feathers into the air, and they flew as before.

Then Simpleton without more ado went down to the fat toad, and said, "I am to take home the most beautiful woman!" "Oh," answered the toad. "the most beautiful woman! She is not at hand at the moment, but still thou shalt have her." She gave him a yellow turnip which had been hollowed out, to which six mice were harnessed. Then Simpleton said quite mournfully, "What am I to do with that?" The toad answered, "Just put one of my little toads into it." Then he seized one at random out of the circle, and put her into the yellow coach, but hardly was she seated inside it than she turned into a wonderfully beautiful maiden, and the turnip into a coach, and the six mice into horses. So he kissed her, and drove off quickly with the horses, and took her to the King. His brothers came afterwards; they had given themselves no trouble at all to seek beautiful girls, but had brought with them the first peasant women they chanced to meet. When the King saw them he said, "After my death the kingdom belongs to my youngest son." But the two eldest deafened the King's ears afresh with their clamour, "We cannot consent to Simpleton's being King," and demanded that the one whose wife could leap through a ring which hung in the centre of the hall should have the preference. They thought, "The peasant women can do that easily; they are strong enough, but the delicate maiden will jump herself to death." The aged King agreed likewise to this. Then the two peasant women jumped, and jumped through the ring, but were so stout that they fell, and their coarse arms and legs broke in two. And then the pretty maiden whom Simpleton had brought with him, sprang, and sprang through as lightly as a deer, and all opposition had to cease. So he received the crown, and has ruled wisely for a length of time.

THE GOLDEN GOOSE

THERE was a man who had three sons, the youngest of whom was called Dummling,[1] and was despised, mocked, and put down on every occasion.

It happened that the eldest wanted to go into the forest to hew wood, and before he went his mother gave him a beautiful sweet cake and a bottle of wine in order that he might not suffer from hunger or thirst.

When he entered the forest there met him a little grey-haired old man who bade him good-day, and said, "Do give me a piece of cake out of your pocket, and let me have a draught of your wine; I am so hungry and thirsty." But the prudent youth answered, "If I give you my cake and wine, I shall have none for myself; be off with you," and he left the little man standing and went on.

But when he began to hew down a tree, it was not long

[1] Simpleton.

before he made a false stroke, and the axe cut him in the arm, so that he had to go home and have it bound up. And this was the little grey man's doing.

After this the second son went into the forest, and his mother gave him, like the eldest, a cake and a bottle of wine. The little old grey man met him likewise, and asked him for a piece of cake and a drink of wine. But the second son, too, said with much reason, "What I give you will be taken away from myself; be off!" and he left the little man standing and went on. His punishment, however, was not delayed; when he had made a few strokes at the tree he struck himself in the leg, so that he had to be carried home.

Then Dummling said, "Father, do let me go and cut wood." The father answered, "Your brothers have hurt themselves with it, leave it alone, you do not understand anything about it." But Dummling begged so long that at last he said, "Just go then, you will get wiser by hurting yourself." His mother gave him a cake made with water and baked in the cinders, and with it a bottle of sour beer.

When he came to the forest the little old grey man met him likewise, and greeting him, said, "Give me a piece of your cake and a drink out of your bottle; I am so hungry and thirsty." Dummling answered, "I have only cinder-cake and sour beer; if that pleases you, we will sit down and eat." So they sat down, and when Dummling pulled out his cinder-cake, it was a fine sweet cake, and the sour beer had become good wine. So they ate and drank, and after that the little man said, "Since you have a good heart, and are willing to divide what you have, I will give you good luck. There stands an old tree, cut it down, and you will find something at the roots." Then the old man took leave of him.

Dummling went and cut down the tree, and when it fell there was a goose sitting in the roots with feathers of pure gold. He lifted her up, and taking her with him, went to an inn where he thought he would stay the night. Now the host had three daughters, who saw the goose and were curious to know what such a wonderful bird might be, and would have liked to have one of its golden feathers.

The eldest thought, "I shall soon find an opportunity of pulling out a feather," and as soon as Dummling had gone out she seized the goose by the wing, but her fingers and hand remained sticking fast to it.

The second came soon afterwards, thinking only of how she might get a feather for herself, but she had scarcely touched her sister than she was held fast.

At last the third also came with the like intent, and the others screamed out, "Keep away; for goodness' sake keep away!" But she did not understand why she was to keep away. "The others are there," she thought, "I may as well be there too," and ran to them; but as soon as she had touched her sister she remained sticking fast to her. So they had to spend the night with the goose.

The next morning Dummling took the goose under his arm and set out, without troubling himself about the three girls who were hanging to it. They were obliged to run after him continually, now left, now right, just as he was inclined to go.

In the middle of the fields the parson met them, and when he saw the procession he said, "For shame, you good-for-nothing girls, why are you running across the fields after this young man? is that seemly?" At the same time he seized the youngest by the hand in order to pull her away, but as soon as he touched her he likewise stuck fast, and was himself obliged to run behind.

Before long the sexton came by and saw his master, the parson, running on foot behind three girls. He was astonished at this and called out, "Hi! your reverence, whither away so quickly? do not forget that we have a christening to-day!" and running after him he took him by the sleeve, but was also held fast to it.

Whilst the five were trotting thus one behind the other, two labourers came with their hoes from the fields; the parson called out to them and begged that they would set him and the sexton free. But they had scarcely touched the sexton when they were held fast, and now there were seven of them running behind Dummling and the goose.

Soon afterwards he came to a city, where a king ruled who had a daughter who was so serious that no one could make her laugh. So he had put forth a decree that whosoever should be able to make her laugh should marry her. When Dummling heard this, he went with his goose and all her train before the King's daughter, and as soon as she saw the seven people running on and on, one behind the other, she began to laugh quite loudly, and as if she would never leave off. Thereupon Dummling asked to have her for his wife, and the wedding was celebrated. After the King's death Dummling inherited the kingdom, and lived a long time contentedly with his wife.

ALLERLEIRAUH

THERE was once on a time a King who had a wife with golden hair, and she was so beautiful that her equal was not to be found on earth. It came to pass that she lay ill, and as she felt that she must soon die, she called the King and said, "If thou wishest to marry again after my death, take no one who is not quite as beautiful as I am, and who has not just such golden hair as I have: this thou must promise me." And after the King had promised her this she closed her eyes and died.

For a long time the King could not be comforted, and had no thought of taking another wife. At length his councillors said, "There is no help for it, the King must marry again, that we may have a Queen." And now messengers were sent about far and wide, to seek a bride who equalled the late Queen in beauty. In the whole world, however, none was found, and even if one had been found, still there would have been no one who had such golden hair. So the messengers came home as they went.

Now the King had a daughter, who was just as beautiful as her dead mother, and had the same golden hair. When she was grown up the King looked at her one day, and saw that in every respect she was like his late wife, and suddenly felt a violent love for her. Then he spake to his councillors, "I will marry my daughter, for she is the counterpart of my late wife, otherwise I can find no bride who resembles her." When the councillors heard that, they were shocked, and said, "God has forbidden a father to marry his daughter, no good can come from such a crime, and the kingdom will be involved in the ruin."

The daughter was still more shocked when she became aware of her father's resolution, but hoped to turn him from his design. Then she said to him, "Before I fulfil your wish, I must have three dresses, one as golden as the sun, one as silvery as the moon, and one as bright as the stars; besides this, I wish for a mantle of a thousand different kinds of fur and hair joined together, and one of every kind of animal in your kingdom must give a bit of his skin for it." But she thought, "To get that will be quite impossible, and thus I shall divert my father from his wicked intentions." The King, however, did not give it up, and the cleverest maidens in his kingdom had to weave the three dresses, one as golden as the sun, one as silvery as the moon, and one as bright as the stars, and his huntsmen had to catch one of every kind of animal in the whole of his kingdom, and take from it a piece of its skin, and out of these was made a mantle of a thousand different kinds of fur. At length, when all was ready, the King caused the mantle to be brought, spread it out before her, and said, "The wedding shall be to-morrow."

When, therefore, the King's daughter saw that there was no longer any hope of turning her father's heart, she resolved to run away from him. In the night whilst every one was asleep, she got up, and took three different things from her treasures, a golden ring, a golden spinning-wheel, and a golden reel. The three dresses of the sun, moon, and stars she put into a nutshell, put on her mantle of all kinds of fur, and blackened her face and hands with soot. Then she commended herself to God, and went away, and walked the whole night until she reached a great forest. And as she was tired, she got into a hollow tree, and fell asleep.

The sun rose, and she slept on, and she was still sleeping when it was full day. Then it so happened that the

King to whom this forest belonged, was hunting in it. When his dogs came to the tree, they snuffed, and ran barking round about it. The King said to the huntsmen, "Just see what kind of wild beast has hidden itself in there." The huntsmen obeyed his order, and when they came back they said, "A wondrous beast is lying in the hollow tree; we have never before seen one like it. Its skin is fur of a thousand different kinds, but it is lying asleep." Said the King, "See if you can catch it alive, and then fasten it on the carriage, and we will take it with us." When the huntsmen laid hold of the maiden, she awoke full of terror, and cried to them, "I am a poor child, deserted by father and mother; have pity on me, and take me with you." Then said they "Allerleirauh, thou wilt be useful in the kitchen, come with us, and thou canst sweep up the ashes." So they put her in the carriage, and took her home to the royal palace. There they pointed out to her a closet under the stairs, where no daylight entered, and said, "Hairy animal, there canst thou live and sleep." Then she was sent into the kitchen, and there she carried wood and water, swept the hearth, plucked the fowls, picked the vegetables, raked the ashes, and did all the dirty work.

Allerleirauh lived there for a long time in great wretchedness. Alas, fair princess, what is to become of thee now! It happened, however, that one day a feast was held in the palace, and she said to the cook, "May I go up-stairs for a while, and look on? I will place myself outside the door." The cook answered, "Yes, go, but you must be back here in half-an-hour to sweep the hearth." Then she took her oil-lamp, went into her den, put off her fur-dress, and washed the soot off her face and hands, so that her full beauty once more came to light. And she opened the nut, and took out her dress which shone like the sun, and when she had done that she went up to the festival, and every one made way for her, for no one knew her, and thought no otherwise than that she was a king's daughter. The King came to meet her, gave his hand to her, and danced with her, and thought in his heart, "My eyes have never yet seen any one so beautiful!" When the dance was over she curtsied, and when the King looked round again she had vanished, and none knew whither. The guards who stood outside the palace were called and questioned, but no one had seen her.

She had, however, run into her little den, had quickly taken off her dress, made her face and hands black again, put on the fur-mantle, and again was Allerleirauh. And now when she went into the kitchen, and was about to get to her work and sweep up the ashes, the cook said, " Leave that alone till morning, and make me the soup for the King; I, too, will go upstairs awhile, and take a look; but let no hairs fall in, or in future thou shalt have nothing to eat." So the cook went away, and Allerleirauh made the soup for the King, and made bread soup and the best she could, and when it was ready she fetched her golden ring from her little den, and put it in the bowl in which the soup was served. When the dancing was over, the King had his soup brought and ate it, and he liked it so much that it seemed to him he had never tasted better. But when he came to the bottom of the bowl, he saw a golden ring lying, and could not conceive how it could have got there. Then he ordered the cook to appear before him. The cook was terrified when he heard the order, and said to Allerleirauh, " Thou hast certainly let a hair fall into the soup, and if thou hast, thou shalt be beaten for it." When he came before the King the latter asked who had made the soup? The cook replied, " I made it." But the King said, " That is not true, for it was much better than usual, and cooked differently." He answered, " I must acknowledge that I did not make it, it was made by the rough animal." The King said, " Go and bid it come up here."

When Allerleirauh came, the King said, " Who art thou?" " I am a poor girl who no longer has any father or mother." He asked further, " Of what use art thou in my palace?" She answered, " I am good for nothing but to have boots thrown at my head." He continued, " Where didst thou get the ring which was in the soup?" She answered, " I know nothing about the ring." So the King could learn nothing, and had to send her away again.

After a while, there was another festival, and then, as before, Allerleirauh begged the cook for leave to go and look on. He answered, "Yes, but come back again in half-an-hour, and make the King the bread soup which he so much likes." Then she ran into her den, washed herself quickly, and took out of the nut the dress which was as silvery as the moon, and put it on. Then she went up and was like a princess, and the King stepped forward to meet her, and rejoiced to see her once more, and as the dance was just beginning they danced it together. But when it was at end, she again disappeared so quickly that the King could not observe where she went. She, however, sprang into her den, and once more made herself a hairy animal, and went into the kitchen to prepare the bread soup. When the cook had gone up-stairs, she fetched the little golden spinning-wheel, and put it in the bowl so that the soup covered it. Then it was taken to the King, who ate it, and liked it as much as before, and had the cook brought, who this time likewise was forced to confess that Allerleirauh had prepared the soup. Allerleirauh again came before the King, but she answered that she was good for nothing else but to have boots thrown at her head, and that she knew nothing at all about the little golden spinning-wheel.

When, for the third time, the King held a festival, all happened just as it had done before. The cook said, "Faith, rough-skin, thou art a witch, and always puttest something in the soup which makes it so good that the King likes it better than that which I cook," but as she begged so hard, he let her go up at the appointed time. And now she put on the dress which shone like the stars, and thus entered the hall. Again the King danced with the beautiful maiden, and thought that she never yet had been so beautiful. And whilst she was dancing, he contrived, without her noticing it, to slip a golden ring on her finger, and he had given orders that the dance should last a very long time. When it was ended, he wanted to hold her fast by her hands, but she tore herself loose, and sprang away so quickly through the crowd that she vanished from his sight. She ran as fast as she could into her den beneath the stairs, but as she had been too long and had stayed more than half-an-hour she could not take off her pretty dress, but only threw over it her fur-mantle, and in her haste she did not make herself quite black, but one finger remained white. Then Allerleirauh ran into the kitchen, and cooked the bread soup for the King, and as the cook was away, put her golden reel into it. When the King found the reel at the bottom of it, he caused Allerleirauh to be summoned, and then he espied the white finger, and saw the ring which he had put on it during the dance. Then he grasped her by the hand, and held her fast, and when she wanted to release herself and run away, her fur-mantle opened a little, and the star-dress shone forth. The King clutched the mantle and tore it off. Then her golden hair shone forth, and she stood there in full splendour, and could no longer hide herself. And when she had washed the soot and ashes from her face, she was more beautiful than any one who had ever been seen on earth. But the King said, " Thou art my dear bride, and we will never more part from each other." Thereupon the marriage was solemnized, and they lived happily until their death.

THE WOLF AND THE FOX

THE wolf had the fox with him, and whatsoever the wolf wished, that the fox was compelled to do, for he was the weaker, and he would gladly have been rid of his master. It chanced that once as they were going through the forest, the wolf said, " Red-fox, get me something to eat, or else I will eat thee thyself." Then the fox answered, " I know a farm-yard where there are two young lambs; if thou art inclined, we will fetch one of them." That suited the wolf, and they went thither, and the fox stole the little lamb, took it to the wolf, and went away. The wolf devoured it, but was not satisfied with one; he wanted the other as well, and went to get it. As, however, he did it so awkwardly, the mother of the little lamb heard him, and began to cry out terribly, and to bleat so that the farmer came running there. They found the wolf, and beat him so mercilessly, that he went to the fox limping and howling. "Thou hast misled me finely," said he; "I wanted to fetch the other lamb, and the country folks surprised me, and have beaten me to a jelly." The fox replied, "Why art thou such a glutton?"

Next day they again went into the country, and the greedy wolf once more said, "Red-fox, get me something to eat, or I will eat thee thyself." Then answered the fox, "I know a farm-house where the wife is baking pancakes to-night; we will get some of them for ourselves." They went there, and the fox slipped round the house, and peeped and sniffed about until he discovered where the dish was, and then drew down six pancakes and carried them to the wolf. "There is something for thee to eat," said he to him, and then went his way. The wolf swallowed down the pancakes in an instant, and said, "They make one want more," and went thither and tore the whole dish down so that it broke in pieces. This made such a great noise that the woman came out, and when she saw the wolf she called the people, who hurried there, and beat him as long as their sticks would hold together, till with two lame legs, and howling loudly, he got back to the fox in the forest. "How abominably thou hast misled me!" cried he, "the peasants caught me, and tanned my skin for me." But the fox replied, "Why art thou such a glutton?"

On the third day, when they were out together, and the wolf could only limp along painfully, he again said, "Red-fox, get me something to eat, or I will eat thee thyself." The fox answered, "I know a man who has been killing, and the salted meat is lying in a barrel in the cellar; we will get that." Said the wolf, "I will go when thou dost, that thou mayest help me if I am not able to get away." "I am willing," said the fox, and showed him the by-paths and ways by which at length they reached the cellar. There was meat in abundance, and the wolf attacked it instantly and thought, "There is plenty of time before I need leave off!" The fox liked it also, but looked about everywhere, and often ran to the hole by which they had come in, and tried if his body was still thin enough to slip through it. The wolf said, "Dear fox, tell me why thou art running here and there so much and jumping in and out?"

"I must see that no one is coming," replied the crafty fellow. "Don't eat too much!" Then said the wolf, "I shall not leave until the barrel is empty." In the meantime the farmer, who had heard the noise of the fox's jumping, came into the cellar. When the fox saw him he was out of the hole at one bound. The wolf wanted to follow him, but he had made himself so fat with eating that he could no longer get through, but stuck fast. Then came the farmer with a cudgel and struck him dead, but the fox bounded into the forest, glad to be rid of the old glutton.

HANS IN LUCK

HANS had served his master for seven years, so he said to him, "Master, my time is up; now I should be glad to go back home to my mother; give me my wages." The master answered, "You have served me faithfully and honestly; as the service was so shall the reward be;" and he gave Hans a piece of gold as big as his head. Hans pulled his handkerchief out of his pocket, wrapped up the lump in it, put it on his shoulder, and set out on the way home.

As he went on, always putting one foot before the other, he saw a horseman trotting quickly and merrily by on a lively horse. "Ah!" said Hans quite loud, "what a fine thing it is to ride! There you sit as on a chair; you stumble over no stones, you save your shoes, and get on, you don't know how."

The rider, who had heard him, stopped and called out, "Hollo! Hans, why do you go on foot then?"

"I must," answered he, "for I have this lump to carry home; it is true that it is gold, but I cannot hold my head straight for it, and it hurts my shoulder."

"I will tell you what," said the rider, "we will exchange: I will give you my horse, and you can give me your lump."

"With all my heart," said Hans, "but I can tell you, you will have to crawl along with it."

The rider got down, took the gold, and helped Hans up;

then gave him the bridle tight in his hands and said, " If you want to go at a really good pace, you must click your tongue and call out, " Jup! Jup!"

Hans was heartily delighted as he sat upon the horse and rode away so bold and free. After a little while he thought that it ought to go faster, and began to click with his tongue and call out, " Jup! Jup!" The horse put himself into a sharp trot, and before Hans knew where he was, he was thrown off and lying in a ditch which separated the field from the highway. The horse would have gone off too if it had not been stopped by a countryman, who was coming along the road and driving a cow before him.

Hans got his limbs together and stood up on his legs again, but he was vexed, and said to the countryman, " It is a poor joke, this riding, especially when one gets hold of a mare like this, that kicks and throws one off, so that one has a chance of breaking one's neck. Never again will I mount it. Now I like your cow, for one can walk quietly behind her, and have, over and above, one's milk, butter and cheese every day without fail. What would I not give to have such a cow." " Well," said the countryman, " if it would give you so much pleasure, I do not mind giving the cow for the horse." Hans agreed with the greatest delight; the countryman jumped upon the horse, and rode quickly away.

Hans drove his cow quietly before him, and thought over his lucky bargain. " If only I have a morsel of bread—and that can hardly fail me—I can eat butter and cheese with it as often as I like; if I am thirsty, I can milk my cow and drink the milk. Good heart, what more can I want?"

When he came to an inn he made a halt, and in his great content ate up what he had with him—his dinner and supper —and all he had, and with his last few farthings had half a glass of beer. Then he drove his cow onwards along the road to his mother's village.

As it drew nearer mid-day, the heat was more oppressive, and Hans found himself upon a moor which it took about an hour to cross. He felt it very hot and his tongue clave to the roof of his mouth with thirst. " I can find a cure for this," thought Hans; " I will milk the cow now and refresh myself with the milk." He tied her to a withered tree, and as he had no pail he put his leather cap underneath; but try as he would, not a drop of milk came. And as he set himself to work in a clumsy way, the impatient beast at last gave him such a blow on his head with its hind foot, that he fell on the ground, and for a long time could not think where he was.

By good fortune a butcher just then came along the road with a wheel-barrow, in which lay a young pig. "What sort of a trick is this?" cried he, and helped the good Hans up. Hans told him what had happened. The butcher gave him his flask and said, "Take a drink and refresh yourself. The cow will certainly give no milk, it is an old beast; at the best it is only fit for the plough, or for the butcher." "Well, well," said Hans, as he stroked his hair down on his head, "who would have thought it? Certainly it is a fine thing when one can kill a beast like that at home; what meat one has! But I do not care much for beef, it is not juicy enough for me. A young pig like that now is the thing to have; it tastes quite different; and then there are the sausages!"

"Hark ye, Hans," said the butcher, "out of love for you I will exchange, and will let you have the pig for the cow." "Heaven repay you for your kindness!" said Hans as he gave up the cow, whilst the pig was unbound from the barrow, and the cord by which it was tied was put in his hand.

Hans went on, and thought to himself how everything was going just as he wished; if he did meet with any vexation it was immediately set right. Presently there joined him a lad who was carrying a fine white goose under his arm. They said good morning to each other, and Hans began to tell of his good luck, and how he had always made such good bargains. The boy told him that he was taking the goose to a christening-feast. "Just lift her," added he, and laid hold of her by the wings; "how heavy she is— she has been fattened up for the last eight weeks. Whoever has a bit of her when she is roasted will have to wipe the fat from both sides of his mouth." "Yes," said Hans, as he weighed her in one hand, "she is a good weight, but my pig is no bad one."

Meanwhile the lad looked suspiciously from one side to

the other, and shook his head. "Look here," he said at length, "it may not be all right with your pig. In the village through which I passed, the Mayor himself had just had one stolen out of its sty. I fear—I fear that you have got hold of it there. They have sent out some people and it would be a bad business if they caught you with the pig; at the very least, you would be shut up in the dark hole."

The good Hans was terrified. "Goodness!" he said, "help me out of this fix; you know more about this place than I do, take my pig and leave me your goose." "I shall risk something at that game," answered the lad, "but I will not be the cause of your getting into trouble." So he took the cord in his hand, and drove away the pig quickly along a by-path.

The good Hans, free from care, went homewards with the goose under his arm. "When I think over it properly," said he to himself, "I have even gained by the exchange: first there is the good roast-meat, then the quantity of fat which will drip from it, and which will give me dripping for my bread for a quarter of a year, and lastly the beautiful white feathers; I will have my pillow stuffed with them, and then indeed I shall go to sleep without rocking. How glad my mother will be!"

As he was going through the last village, there stood a scissors-grinder with his barrow; as his wheel whirred he sang—

> "I sharpen scissors and quickly grind,
> My coat blows out in the wind behind."

Hans stood still and looked at him; at last he spoke to him and said, "All's well with you, as you are so merry with your grinding." "Yes," answered the scissors-grinder, "the trade has a golden foundation. A real grinder is a man who as often as he puts his hand into his pocket finds gold in it. But where did you buy that fine goose?"

"I did not buy it, but exchanged my pig for it."

"And the pig?"

"That I got for a cow."

"And the cow?"

"I took that instead of a horse."

"And the horse?"

"For that I gave a lump of gold as big as my head."

"And the gold?"

"Well, that was my wages for seven years' service."

"You have known how to look after yourself each time," said the grinder. "If you can only get on so far as to hear the money jingle in your pocket whenever you stand up, you will have made your fortune."

"How shall I manage that?" said Hans. "You must be a grinder, as I am; nothing particular is wanted for it but a grindstone, the rest finds itself. I have one here; it is certainly a little worn, but you need not give me anything for it but your goose; will you do it?"

"How can you ask?" answered Hans. "I shall be the luckiest fellow on earth; if I have money whenever I put my hand in my pocket, what need I trouble about any longer?" and he handed him the goose and received the grindstone in exchange. "Now," said the grinder, as he took up an ordinary heavy stone that lay by him, "here is a strong stone for you into the bargain; you can hammer well upon it, and straighten your old nails. Take it with you and keep it carefully."

Hans loaded himself with the stones and went on with a contented heart; his eyes shone with joy. "I must have been born with a caul," he cried; "everything I want happens to me just as if I were a Sunday-child."

Meanwhile, as he had been on his legs since daybreak, he began to feel tired. Hunger also tormented him, for in his joy at the bargain by which he got the cow he had eaten up all his store of food at once. At last he could only go on with great trouble, and was forced to stop every minute; the stones, too, weighed him down dreadfully. Then he could not help thinking how nice it would be if he had not to carry them just then.

He crept like a snail to a well in a field, and there he thought that he would rest and refresh himself with a cool draught of water, but in order that he might not injure the stones in sitting down, he laid them carefully by his side on the edge of the well. Then he sat down on it, and was about to stoop and drink, when he made a slip, pushed against the stones, and both of them fell into the water. When Hans saw them with his own eyes sinking to the bottom, he jumped for joy, and then knelt down, and with tears in his eyes thanked God for having shown him this favour also, and delivered him in so good a way, and without his having any need to reproach himself, from those heavy stones which had been the only things that troubled him.

"There is no man under the sun so fortunate as I," he cried out. With a light heart and free from every burden he now ran on until he was with his mother at home.

THE GOOSE-GIRL

THERE was once upon a time an old Queen whose husband had been dead for many years, and she had a beautiful daughter. When the princess grew up she was betrothed to a prince who lived at a great distance. When the time came for her to be married, and she had to journey forth into the distant kingdom, the aged Queen packed up for her many costly vessels of silver and gold, and trinkets also of gold and silver; and cups and jewels—in short, everything which appertained to a royal dowry, for she loved her child with all her heart. She likewise sent her maid in waiting, who was to ride with her, and hand her over to the bridegroom, and each had a horse for the journey, but the horse of the King's daughter was called Falada, and could speak. So when the hour of parting had come, the aged mother went into her bedroom, took a small knife and cut her finger with it until it bled, then she held a white handkerchief to it into which she let three drops of blood fall, gave it to her daughter and said, "Dear child, preserve this carefully, it will be of service to you on your way."

So they took a sorrowful leave of each other; the princess put the piece of cloth in her bosom, mounted her horse, and then went away to her bridegroom. After she had ridden for a while she felt a burning thirst, and said to her waiting-maid, "Dismount, and take my cup which thou hast brought with thee for me, and get me some water from the stream, for I should like to drink." "If you are thirsty,"

said the waiting-maid, " get off your horse yourself, and
lie down and drink out of the water, I don't choose to be
your servant." So in her great thirst the princess alighted,
bent down over the water in the stream and drank, and was
not allowed to drink out of the golden cup. Then she said,
" Ah, Heaven ! " and the three drops of blood answered, " If
thy mother knew this, her heart would break." But the
King's daughter was humble, said nothing, and mounted
her horse again. She rode some miles further, but the day
was warm, the sun scorched her, and she was thirsty once
more, and when they came to a stream of water, she again
cried to her waiting-maid, " Dismount and give me some
water in my golden cup," for she had long ago forgotten
the girl's ill words. But the waiting-maid said still more
haughtily, " If you wish to drink, drink as you can, I don't
choose to be your maid." Then in her great thirst the
King's daughter alighted, bent over the flowing stream, wept
and said, " Ah, Heaven ! " and the drops of blood again
replied, " If thy mother knew this, her heart would break."
And as she was thus drinking and leaning right over the
stream, the handkerchief with the three drops of blood
fell out of her bosom, and floated away with the water
without her observing it, so great was her trouble. The
waiting-maid, however, had seen it, and she rejoiced to
think that she had now power over the bride, for since the
princess had lost the drops of blood, she had become weak
and powerless. So now when she wanted to mount her
horse again, the one that was called Falada, the waiting-
maid said, " Falada is more suitable for me, and my nag
will do for thee," and the princess had to be content with
that. Then the waiting-maid, with many hard words, bade
the princess exchange her royal apparel for her own shabby
clothes; and at length she was compelled to swear by the
clear sky above her, that she would not say one word of
this to any one at the royal court, and if she had not taken
this oath she would have been killed on the spot. But Falada
saw all this, and observed it well.

The waiting-maid now mounted Falada, and the true
bride the bad horse, and thus they travelled onwards, until
at length they entered the royal palace. There were great

rejoicings over her arrival, and the prince sprang forward to meet her, lifted the waiting-maid from her horse, and thought she was his consort. She was conducted upstairs, but the real princess was left standing below. Then the old King looked out of the window and saw her standing in the courtyard, and how dainty and delicate and beautiful she was, and instantly went to the royal apartment, and asked the bride about the girl she had with her who was standing down below in the courtyard, and who she was? " I picked her up on my way for a companion; give the girl something to work at, that she may not stand idle." But the old King had no work for her, and knew of none, so he said, " I have a little boy who tends the geese, she may help him." The boy was called Conrad, and the true bride had to help him to tend the geese. Soon afterwards the false bride said to the young King, " Dearest husband, I beg you to do me a favour." He answered, " I will do so most willingly." " Then send for the knacker, and have the head of the horse on which I rode here cut off, for it vexed me on the way." In reality, she was afraid that the horse might tell how she had behaved to the King's daughter. Then she succeeded in making the King promise that it should be done, and the faithful Falada was to die; this came to the ears of the real princess, and she secretly promised to pay the knacker a piece of gold if he would perform a small service for her. There was a great dark-looking gateway in the town, through which morning and evening she had to pass with the geese: would he be so good as to nail up Falada's head on it, so that she might see him again, more than once. The knacker's man promised to do that, and cut off the head, and nailed it fast beneath the dark gateway.

Early in the morning, when she and Conrad drove out their flock beneath this gateway, she said in passing,

> "Alas, Falada, hanging there!"

Then the head answered,

> "Alas, young Queen, how ill you fare!
> If this your tender mother knew,
> Her heart would surely break in two."

Then they went still further out of the town, and drove
their geese into the country. And when they had come
to the meadow, she sat down and unbound her hair which
was like pure gold, and Conrad saw it and delighted in its
brightness, and wanted to pluck out a few hairs. Then
she said,

> "Blow, blow, thou gentle wind, I say,
> Blow Conrad's little hat away,
> And make him chase it here and there,
> Until I have braided all my hair,
> And bound it up again."

And there came such a violent wind that it blew Conrad's
hat far away across country, and he was forced to run
after it. When he came back she had finished combing
her hair and was putting it up again, and he could not get
any of it. Then Conrad was angry, and would not speak
to her, and thus they watched the geese until the evening,
and then they went home.

Next day when they were driving the geese out through
the dark gateway, the maiden said,

> "Alas, Falada, hanging there!"

Falada answered,

> "Alas, young Queen, how ill you fare!
> If this your tender mother knew,
> Her heart would surely break in two."

And she sat down again in the field and began to comb out
her hair, and Conrad ran and tried to clutch it, so she said
in haste,

> "Blow, blow, thou gentle wind, I say,
> Blow Conrad's little hat away,
> And make him chase it here and there,
> Until I have braided all my hair,
> And bound it up again."

Then the wind blew, and blew his little hat off his head
and far away, and Conrad was forced to run after it, and
when he came back, her hair had been put up a long time,
and he could get none of it, and so they looked after their
geese till evening came.

But in the evening after they had got home, Conrad went

to the old King, and said, " I won't tend the geese with
that girl any longer! " " Why not? " inquired the aged
King. " Oh, because she vexes me the whole day long."
Then the aged King commanded him to relate what it was
that she did to him. And Conrad said, " In the morning
when we pass beneath the dark gateway with the flock, there
is a sorry horse's head on the wall, and she says to it,

> "Alas, Falada, hanging there!"

And the head replies,

> "Alas, young Queen, how ill you fare!
> If this your tender mother knew,
> Her heart would surely break in two."

And Conrad went on to relate what happened on the goose
pasture, and how when there he had to chase his hat.

The aged King commanded him to drive his flock out
again next day, and as soon as morning came, he placed
himself behind the dark gateway, and heard how the maiden
spoke to the head of Falada, and then he too went into the
country, and hid himself in the thicket in the meadow.
There he soon saw with his own eyes the goose-girl and
the goose-boy bringing their flock, and how after a while
she sat down and unplaited her hair, which shone with
radiance. And soon she said,

> "Blow, blow, thou gentle wind, I say,
> Blow Conrad's little hat away,
> And make him chase it here and there,
> Until I have braided all my hair,
> And bound it up again."

Then came a blast of wind and carried off Conrad's hat,
so that he had to run far away, while the maiden quietly
went on combing and plaiting her hair, all of which the
King observed. Then, quite unseen, he went away, and
when the goose-girl came home in the evening, he called
her aside, and asked why she did all these things. " I may
not tell you that, and I dare not lament my sorrows to
any human being, for I have sworn not to do so by the heaven
which is above me; if I had not done that, I should have lost
my life." He urged her and left her no peace, but he could

draw nothing from her. Then said he, " If thou wilt not tell me anything, tell thy sorrows to the iron-stove there," and he went away. Then she crept into the iron-stove, and began to weep and lament, and emptied her whole heart, and said, " Here am I deserted by the whole world, and yet I am a King's daughter, and a false waiting-maid has by force brought me to such a pass that I have been compelled to put off my royal apparel, and she has taken my place with my bridegroom, and I have to perform menial service as a goose-girl. If my mother did but know that, her heart would break."

The aged King, however, was standing outside by the pipe of the stove, and was listening to what she said, and heard it. Then he came back again, and bade her come out of the stove. And royal garments were placed on her, and it was marvellous how beautiful she was! The aged King summoned his son, and revealed to him that he had got the false bride who was only a waiting-maid, but that the true one was standing there, as the sometime goose-girl. The young King rejoiced with all his heart when he saw her beauty and youth, and a great feast was made ready to which all the people and all good friends were invited. At the head of the table sat the bridegroom with the King's daughter at one side of him, and the waiting-maid on the other, but the waiting-maid was blinded, and did not recognize the princess in her dazzling array. When they had eaten and drunk, and were merry, the aged King asked the waiting-maid as a riddle, what a person deserved who had behaved in such and such a way to her master, and at the same time related the whole story, and asked what sentence such an one merited? Then the false bride said, " She deserves no better fate than to be stripped entirely naked, and put in a barrel which is studded inside with pointed nails, and two white horses should be harnessed to it, which will drag her along through one street after another, till she is dead." " It is thou," said the aged King, " and thou hast pronounced thine own sentence, and thus shall it be done unto thee." And when the sentence had been carried out, the young King married his true bride, and both of them reigned over their kingdom in peace and happiness.

THE PEASANT'S WISE DAUGHTER

THERE was once a poor peasant who had no land, but only a small house, and one daughter. Then said the daughter, "We ought to ask our lord the King for a bit of newly-cleared land." When the King heard of their poverty, he presented them with a bit of land, which she and her father dug up, and intended to sow with a little corn and grain of that kind. When they had dug nearly the whole of the field, they found in the earth a mortar made of pure gold. "Listen," said the father to the girl, "as our lord the King has been so gracious and presented us with the field, we ought to give him this mortar in return for it." The daughter, however, would not consent to this, and said, "Father, if we have the mortar without having the pestle as well, we shall have to get the pestle, so you had much better say nothing about it." He would, however, not obey her, but took the mortar and carried it to the King, said that he had found it in the cleared land, and asked if he would accept it as a present. The King took the mortar, and asked if he had found nothing besides that? "No," answered the countryman. Then the King said that he must now bring him the pestle. The peasant said they had not found that, but he might just as well have spoken to the wind; he was put in prison, and was to stay there until he produced the pestle. The servants had daily to carry him bread and water, which is what people get in prison, and they heard how the man cried out continually, "Ah! if I had but listened to my daughter! Alas, alas, if I had but listened to my daughter!" Then the servants went to the King and told him how the prisoner was always crying, "Ah! if I had but listened to my daughter!" and would neither eat nor drink. So he commanded the servants to bring the prisoner before him, and then the King asked the peasant why he was always crying, "Ah! if I had but listened to my daughter!" and what it was that his daughter had said. "She told me that I ought not to take the mortar to you, for I should have to produce the pestle as well." "If you have a daughter who is as wise as that, let her come here." She was therefore obliged to appear before the King, who asked her if she really was so wise, and said he would set her a riddle, and if she could guess that, he would marry her. She at once said yes, she would guess it. Then said the King, "Come to me not clothed, not naked, not riding, not walking, not in the road, and not out of the road, and if thou canst do that I will marry thee." So she went away, put off everything she had on, and then she was not clothed, and took a great fishing-net, and seated herself in it and wrapped it entirely round and round her, and then she was not naked, and she hired an ass, and tied the fisherman's net to its tail, so that it was forced to drag her along, and that was neither riding nor walking. The ass had also to drag her in the ruts, so that she only touched the ground with her great toe, and that was neither being in the road nor out of the road. And when she arrived in that fashion, the King said she had guessed the riddle and fulfilled all the conditions. Then he ordered her father to be released from the prison, took her to wife, and gave into her care all the royal possessions.

Now when some years had passed, the King was once drawing up his troops on parade, when it happened that some peasants who had been selling wood stopped with their waggons before the palace; some of them had oxen yoked to them, and some horses. There was one peasant who had three horses, one of which was delivered of a young foal, and it ran away and lay down between two oxen which were in front of the waggon. When the peasants came together, they began to dispute, to beat each other and make a disturbance, and the peasant with the oxen wanted to keep the foal, and said one of the oxen had given birth to it, and the other said his horse had had it, and that it was his. The quarrel came before the King, and he gave the verdict that the foal should stay where it had been found, and so the peasant with the oxen, to whom it did not belong, got it. Then the other went away, and wept and lamented over his foal. Now he had heard how gracious his lady the Queen was because she herself had sprung from poor peasant folks, so he went to her and begged her to see if she could not help him to get his foal back again. Said she, "Yes, I will tell thee what to do, if thou wilt promise me not to betray me. Early to-morrow morning, when the King parades the guard, place thyself there in the middle of the road by which he must pass, take a great fishing-net and pretend to be fishing; go on fishing too, and empty out the net as if thou hadst got it full"—and then she told him also what he was to say if he was questioned by the King. The next day, therefore, the peasant stood there, and fished on dry ground. When the King passed by, and saw that, he sent his messenger to ask what the stupid man was about? He answered, "I am fishing." The messenger asked how he could fish when there was no water whatever there? The peasant said, "It is as easy for me to fish on dry land as it is for an ox to have a foal." The messenger went back and took the answer to the King, who ordered the peasant to be brought to him and told him that this was not his own idea, and he wanted to know whose it was? The peasant must confess that at once. The peasant, however, would not do so, and said always, God forbid he should! the idea was his own. They laid him, however, on a heap of straw, and beat him and tormented him so long that at last he admitted that he had got the idea from the Queen.

When the King reached home again, he said to his wife, "Why hast thou behaved so falsely to me? I will not have thee any longer for a wife; thy time is up, go back to the place from whence thou camest—to thy peasant's hut." One favour, however, he granted her; she might take with her the one thing that was dearest and best in her eyes; and thus was she dismissed. She said, "Yes, my dear husband, if you command this, I will do it," and she embraced him and kissed him, and said she would take leave of him. Then she ordered a powerful sleeping draught to be brought to drink farewell to him; the King took a long draught, but she took only a little. He soon fell into a deep sleep, and when she perceived that, she called a servant and took a fair white linen cloth and wrapped the King in it, and the servant was forced to carry him into a carriage that stood before the door, and she drove with him to her own little house. She laid him in her own little bed, and he slept one day and one night without awakening, and when he awoke he looked round and said, "Good God! where am I?" He called his attendants, but none of them were there. At length his wife came to his bedside and said, "My dear lord and King, you told me I might bring away with me from the palace that which was dearest and most precious in my eyes—I have nothing more precious and dear than yourself, so I have brought you with me." Tears rose to the King's eyes and he said, "Dear wife, thou shalt be mine and I will be thine," and he took her back with him to the royal palace and was married again to her, and at the present time they are very likely still living.

THE SPIRIT IN THE BOTTLE

THERE was once a poor woodcutter who toiled from early morning till late night. When at last he had laid by some money he said to his boy, "You are my only child, I will spend the money which I have earned with the sweat of my brow on your education; if you learn some honest trade you can support me in my old age, when my limbs have grown stiff and I am obliged to stay at home." Then the boy went to a High School and learned diligently so that his masters praised him, and he remained there a long time. When he had worked through two classes, but was still not yet perfect in everything, the little pittance which the father had earned was all spent, and the boy was obliged to return home to him. "Ah," said the father, sorrowfully, "I can give you no more, and in these hard times I cannot earn a farthing more than will suffice for our daily bread." "Dear father," said the son, "don't trouble yourself about it; if it is God's will it will turn to my advantage. I shall soon accustom myself to it." When the father wanted to go into the forest to earn money by helping to pile and stack wood and also to chop it, the son said, "I will go with you and help you." "Nay, my son," said the father, "that would be hard for you; you are not accustomed to rough work, and will not be able to bear it, besides I have only one axe and no money left wherewith to buy another." "Just go to the neighbour," answered the son, "he will lend you his axe until I have earned one for myself." The father then borrowed an axe of the neighbour, and next morning at break of day they went into the forest together. The son helped his father and was quite merry and brisk about it. But when the sun was right over their heads, the father said, "We will rest, and have our dinner, and then we shall work

as well again." The son took his bread in his hands, and said,
"Just you rest, father, I am not tired; I will walk up and down
a little in the forest, and look for birds' nests." "Oh, you
fool," said the father, "why should you want to run about
there? Afterwards you will be tired, and no longer able to
raise your arm; stay here, and sit down beside me." The
son, however, went into the forest, ate his bread, was very
merry, peered in among the green branches to see if he could
discover a bird's nest anywhere. So he went up and down to
see if he could find a bird's nest, until at last he came to a
great dangerous-looking oak, which certainly was already
many hundred years old, and which five men could not have
spanned. He stood still and looked at it, and thought, "Many
a bird must have built its nest in that." Then all at once it
seemed to him that he heard a voice. He listened and became
aware that some one was crying in a very smothered voice,
"Let me out, let me out!" He looked around, but could discover nothing; nevertheless, he fancied that the voice came
out of the ground. Then he cried, "Where art thou?" The
voice answered, "I am down here amongst the roots of the
oak-tree. Let me out! Let me out!" The scholar began to
loosen the earth under the tree, and search among the roots,
until at last he found a glass bottle in a little hollow. He
lifted it up and held it against the light, and then saw a
creature shaped like a frog springing up and down in it. "Let
me out! Let me out!" it cried anew, and the scholar thinking
no evil, drew the cork out of the bottle. Immediately a spirit
ascended from it, and began to grow, and grew so fast that in
a very few moments he stood before the scholar, a terrible
fellow as big as half the tree by which he was standing.
"Knowest thou," he cried in an awful voice, "what thy wages
are for having let me out?" "No," replied the scholar fear-
lessly, "how should I know that?" "Then I will tell thee,"
cried the spirit; "I must strangle thee for it." "Thou shouldst
have told me that sooner," said the scholar, "for I should then
have left thee shut up, but my head shall stand fast for all
thou canst do; more persons than one must be consulted about
that." "More persons here, more persons there," said the
spirit. "Thou shalt have the wages thou hast earned. Dost
thou think that I was shut up there for such a long time as a

favour? No, it was a punishment for me. I am the mighty Mercurius. Who so releases me, him must I strangle." "Softly," answered the scholar, "not so fast. I must first know that thou wert really shut up in that little bottle, and that thou art the right spirit. If indeed thou canst get in again, I will believe, and then thou mayst do as thou wilt with me." The spirit said haughtily, "That is a very trifling feat," drew himself together, and made himself as small and slender as he had been at first, so that he crept through the same open-ing, and right through the neck of the bottle in again. Scarcely was he within than the scholar thrust the cork he had drawn back into the bottle, and threw it among the roots of the oak into its old place, and the spirit was betrayed.

And now the scholar was about to return to his father, but the spirit cried very piteously, "Ah, do let me out! Ah, do let me out!" "No," answered the scholar, "not a second time! He who has once tried to take my life shall not be set free by me, now that I have caught him again." "If thou wilt set me free," said the spirit, "I will give thee so much that thou wilt have plenty all the days of thy life." "No," answered the scholar, "thou wouldst cheat me as thou didst the first time." "Thou art playing away thy own good luck," said the spirit; "I will do thee no harm, but will reward thee richly." The scholar thought, "I will venture it, perhaps he will keep his word, and anyhow he shall not get the better of me." Then he took out the cork, and the spirit rose up from the bottle as he had done before, stretched himself out and became as big as a giant. "Now thou shalt have thy reward," said he, and handed the scholar a little bag just like a plaster, and said, "If thou spreadest one end of this over a wound it will heal, and if thou rubbest steel or iron with the other end it will be changed into silver." "I must just try that," said the scholar, and went to a tree, tore off the bark with his axe, and rubbed it with one end of the plaster. It immediately closed together and was healed. "Now, it is all right," he said to the spirit, "and we can part." The spirit thanked him for his release, and the scholar thanked the spirit for his present, and went back to his father.

"Where hast thou been racing about?" said the father; "why hast thou forgotten thy work? I said at once that thou wouldst never get on with anything." "Be easy, father, I will make it up." "Make it up indeed," said the father angrily, "there's no art in that." "Take care, father, I will soon hew that tree there, so that it will split." Then he took his plaster, rubbed the axe with it, and dealt a mighty blow, but as the iron had changed into silver, the edge turned: "Hollo, father, just look what a bad axe you've given me, it has become quite crooked." The father was shocked and said, "Ah, what hast thou done? now I shall have to pay for that, and have not the wherewithal, and that is all the good I have got by thy work." "Don't get angry," said the son, "I will soon pay for the axe." "Oh, thou blockhead," cried the father, "wherewith wilt thou pay for it? Thou hast nothing but what I give thee. These are students' tricks that are sticking in thy head, but thou hast no idea of wood-cutting." After a while the scholar said, "Father, I can really work no more, we had better take a holiday." "Eh, what!" answered he. "Dost thou think I will sit with my hands lying in my lap like thee? I must go on working, but thou mayst take thyself off home." "Father, I am here in this wood for the first time, I don't know my way alone. Do go with me." As his anger had now abated, the father at last let himself be persuaded and went home with him. Then he said to the son, "Go and sell thy damaged axe, and see what thou canst get for it, and I must earn the difference, in order to pay the neighbour." The son took the axe, and carried it into town to a goldsmith, who tested it, laid it in the scales, and said, "It is worth four hundred thalers, I have not so much as that by me." The son said, "Give me what you have, I will lend you the rest." The goldsmith gave him three hundred thalers, and remained a hundred in his debt. The son thereupon went home and said, "Father, I have got the money, go and ask the neighbour what he wants for the axe." "I know that already," answered the old man, "one thaler six groschen." "Then give him two thalers, twelve groschen, that is double and enough; see, I have money in plenty," and he gave the father a hundred thalers, and said, "You shall never know want, live as comfortably as you like." "Good heavens!" said the father, "how hast thou come by these riches?" The scholar then told how all had come to pass, and how he, trusting in his luck, had made such a good hit. But with the money that was left, he went back to the High School and went on learning more, and as he could heal all wounds with his plaster, he became the most famous doctor in the whole world.

BEARSKIN

THERE was once a young fellow who enlisted as a soldier, conducted himself bravely, and was always the foremost when it rained bullets. So long as the war lasted, all went well, but when peace was made, he received his dismissal, and the captain said he might go where he liked. His parents were dead, and he had no longer a home, so he went to his brothers and begged them to take him in, and keep him until war broke out again. The brothers, however, were hard-hearted and said, "What can we do with thee? thou art of no use; go and make a living for thyself." The soldier had nothing left but his gun; he took that on his shoulder, and went forth into the world. He came to a wide heath, on which nothing was to be seen but a circle of trees; under these trees he sat sorrowfully down, and began to think over his fate. "I have no money," thought he, "I have learnt no trade but that of fighting, and now that they have made peace they don't want me any longer; so I see beforehand that I shall have to starve." All at once he heard a rustling, and when he looked round, a strange man stood before him, who wore a green coat and looked right stately, but had a hideous cloven foot. "I know already what thou art in need of," said the man; "gold and possessions shalt thou have, as much as thou canst make away with, do what thou wilt, but first I must know if thou art fearless, that I may not bestow my money in vain." "A soldier and fear—how can those two things go together?" he answered; "thou canst put me to the proof." "Very well, then," answered the man, "look behind thee." The soldier turned round, and saw a large bear, which came growling towards him. "Oho!" cried the soldier, "I will tickle thy nose for thee, so that thou shalt soon lose thy fancy for growling," and he aimed at the bear and shot it through the muzzle; it fell down and never stirred again. "I see quite well," said the stranger, "that thou art not wanting in courage, but there is still another condition which thou wilt have to fulfil." "If it does not endanger my salvation," replied the soldier, who knew very well who was standing beside him. "If it does, I'll have nothing to do with it." "Thou wilt look to that for thyself," answered Greencoat; "thou shalt for the next seven years neither wash thyself, nor comb thy beard, nor thy hair, nor cut thy nails, nor say one paternoster. I will give thee a coat and a cloak, which during this time thou must wear. If thou diest during these seven years, thou art mine; if thou remainest alive, thou art free, and rich to boot, for all the rest of thy life." The soldier thought of the great extremity in which he now found himself, and as he so often had gone to meet death, he resolved to risk it now also, and agreed to the terms. The Devil took off his green coat, gave it to the soldier, and said, "If thou hast this coat on thy back and puttest thy hand into the pocket, thou wilt always find it full of money." Then he pulled the skin off the bear and said, "This shall be thy cloak, and thy bed also, for thereon shalt thou sleep, and in no other bed shalt thou lie, and because of this apparel shalt thou be called Bearskin." After this the Devil vanished.

The soldier put the coat on, felt at once in the pocket, and found that the thing was really true. Then he put on the bearskin, and went forth into the world, and enjoyed himself, refraining from nothing that did him good and his money harm. During the first year his appearance was passable, but during the second he began to look like a monster. His hair covered nearly the whole of his face, his beard was like a piece of coarse felt, his fingers had claws, and his face was so covered with dirt that if cress had been sown on it, it would have come up. Whosoever saw him, ran away, but as he everywhere gave the poor money to pray that he might not die during the seven years, and as he paid well for everything he still always found shelter. In the fourth year, he entered an inn where the landlord would not receive him, and would not even let him have a place in the stable, because he was afraid the horses would be scared. But as Bearskin thrust his hand into his pocket and pulled out a handful of ducats, the host let himself be persuaded and gave him a room in an outhouse. Bearskin was, however, obliged to promise not to let himself be seen, lest the inn should get a bad name.

As Bearskin was sitting alone in the evening, and wishing from the bottom of his heart that the seven years were over, he heard a loud lamenting in a neighbouring room. He had a compassionate heart, so he opened the door, and saw an old man weeping bitterly, and wringing his hands. Bearskin went nearer, but the man sprang to his feet and tried to escape from him. At last when the man perceived that Bearskin's voice was human he let himself be prevailed on, and by kind words Bearskin succeeded so far that the old man revealed the cause of his grief. His property had dwindled away by degrees, he and his daughters would have to starve, and he was so poor that he could not pay the innkeeper, and was to be put in prison. "If that is your only trouble," said Bearskin, "I have plenty of money." He caused the innkeeper to be brought thither, paid him and put a purse full of gold into the poor old man's pocket besides.

When the old man saw himself set free from all his troubles he did not know how to be grateful enough. "Come with me," said he to Bearskin; "my daughters are all miracles of beauty, choose one of them for thyself as a wife. When she hears what thou hast done for me, she will not refuse thee. Thou dost in truth look a little strange, but she will soon put thee to rights again." This pleased Bearskin well, and he went. When the eldest saw him she was so terribly alarmed at his face that she screamed and ran away. The second stood still and looked at him from head to foot, but then she said, "How can I accept a husband who no longer has a human form? The shaven bear that once was here and passed itself off for a man pleased me far better, for at any rate it wore a hussar's dress and white gloves. If it were nothing but ugliness, I might get used to that." The youngest, however, said, "Dear father, that must be a good man to have helped you out of your trouble, so if you have promised him a bride for doing it, your promise must be kept." It was a pity that Bearskin's face was covered with dirt and with hair, for if not they might have seen how delighted he was when he heard these words. He took a ring from his finger, broke it in two, and gave her one half, the other he kept for himself. He wrote his name, however, on her half, and hers on his, and begged her to keep her piece carefully, and then he took his leave and said, " I must still wander about for three years, and if I do not return then, thou art free, for I shall be dead. But pray to God to preserve my life."

The poor betrothed bride dressed herself entirely in black, and when she thought of her future bridegroom, tears came into her eyes. Nothing but contempt and mockery fell to her lot from her sisters. " Take care," said the eldest, " if thou givest him thy hand, he will strike his claws into it." " Beware ! " said the second. " Bears like sweet things, and if he takes a fancy to thee, he will eat thee up." " Thou must always do as he likes," began the elder again, " or else he will growl." And the second continued, " but the wedding will be a merry one, for bears dance well." The bride was silent, and did not let them vex her. Bearskin, however, travelled about the world from one place to another, did good where he was able, and gave generously to the poor that they might pray for him.

At length, as the last day of the seven years dawned, he went once more out on to the heath, and seated himself beneath the circle of trees. It was not long before the wind whistled, and the Devil stood before him and looked angrily at him; then he threw Bearskin his old coat, and asked for his own green one back. " We have not got so far as that yet," answered Bearskin, " thou must first make me clean." Whether the Devil liked it or not, he was forced to fetch water, and wash Bearskin, comb his hair, and cut his nails. After this, he looked like a brave soldier, and was much handsomer that he had ever been before.

When the Devil had gone away, Bearskin was quite light-hearted. He went into the town, put on a magnificent velvet coat, seated himself in a carriage drawn by four white horses, and drove to his bride's house. No one recognized him, the father took him for a distinguished general, and led him into the room where his daughters

were sitting. He was forced to place himself between the
two eldest, they helped him to wine, gave him the best
pieces of meat, and thought that in all the world they had
never seen a handsomer man. The bride, however, sat
opposite to him in her black dress, and never raised her
eyes, nor spoke a word. When at length he asked the
father if he would give him one of his daughters to wife,
the two eldest jumped up, ran into their bedrooms to put
on splendid dresses, for each of them fancied she was the
chosen one. The stranger, as soon as he was alone with
his bride, brought out his half of the ring, and threw it in
a glass of wine which he reached across the table to her.
She took the wine, but when she had drunk it, and found
the half ring lying at the bottom, her heart began to beat.
She got the other half, which she wore on a ribbon round
her neck, joined them, and saw that the two pieces fitted
exactly together. Then said he, "I am thy betrothed bridegroom, whom thou sawest as Bearskin, but through God's
grace I have again received my human form, and have
once more become clean." He went up to her, embraced her,
and gave her a kiss. In the mean time the two sisters came
back in full dress, and when they saw that the handsome
man had fallen to the share of the youngest, and heard
that he was Bearskin, they ran out full of anger and rage.
One of them drowned herself in the well, the other hanged
herself on a tree. In the evening, some one knocked at the
door, and when the bridegroom opened it, it was the Devil
in his green coat, who said, "Seest thou, I have now got
two souls in the place of thy one!"

THE WILLOW-WREN AND THE BEAR

ONCE in summer-time the bear and the wolf were walking
in the forest, and the bear heard a bird singing so beautifully that he said, "Brother wolf, what bird is it that
sings so well?" "That is the King of the birds," said the
wolf, "before whom we must bow down." It was, however,
in reality the willow-wren (*zaunkönig*). 'If that's the
case," said the bear, "I should very much like to see his

royal palace; come, take me thither." "That is not done quite as you seem to think," said the wolf; "you must wait until the Queen comes." Soon afterwards, the Queen arrived with some food in her beak, and the lord King came too, and they began to feed their young ones. The bear would have liked to go at once, but the wolf held him back by the sleeve, and said, "No, you must wait until the lord and lady Queen have gone away again." So they observed the hole in which was the nest, and trotted away. The bear, however, could not rest until he had seen the royal palace, and when a short time had passed, again went to it. The King and Queen had just flown out, so he peeped in and saw five or six young ones lying in it. "Is that the royal palace?" cried the bear; "it is a wretched palace, and you are not King's children; you are disreputable children!" When the young wrens heard that, they were frightfully angry, and screamed, "No, that we are not! Our parents are honest people! Bear, thou wilt have to pay for that!"

The bear and the wolf grew uneasy, and turned back and went into their holes. The young willow-wrens, however, continued to cry and scream, and when their parents again brought food they said, "We will not so much as touch one fly's leg, no, not if we were dying of hunger, until you have settled whether we are respectable children or not; the bear has been here and has insulted us!" Then the old King said, "Be easy, he shall be punished," and he at once flew with the Queen to the bear's cave, and called in, "Old Growler, why hast thou insulted my children? Thou shalt suffer for it—we will punish thee by a bloody war." Thus war was announced to the bear, and all four-footed animals were summoned to take part in it, oxen, asses, cows, deer, and every other animal the earth contained. And the willow-wren summoned everything which flew in the air, not only birds, large and small, but midges, and hornets, bees and flies had to come.

When the time came for the war to begin, the willow-wren sent out spies to discover who was the enemy's commander-in-chief. The gnat, who was the most crafty, flew into the forest where the enemy was assembled, and hid herself beneath a leaf of the tree where the watchword was to be given. There stood the bear, and he called the fox before him and said, "Fox, thou art the most cunning of all animals, thou shalt be general and lead us." "Good," said the fox, "but what signal shall we agree upon?" No one knew that, so the fox said, "I have a fine long bushy tail, which almost looks like a plume of red feathers. When I lift my tail up quite high, all is going well, and you must charge; but if I let it hang down, run away as fast as you can." When the gnat had heard that, she flew away again, and revealed everything, with the greatest minuteness, to the willow-wren. When day broke, and the battle was to begin, all the four-footed animals came running up with such a noise that the earth trembled. The willow-wren also came flying through the air with his army with such a humming, and whirring, and swarming that every one was uneasy and afraid, and on both sides they advanced against each other. But the willow-wren sent down the hornet, with orders to get beneath the fox's tail, and sting it with all his might. When the fox felt the first sting, he started so that he drew up one leg, with the pain, but he bore it, and still kept his tail high in the air; at the second sting, he was forced to put it down for a moment: at the third, he could hold out no longer, and screamed out and put his tail between his legs. When the animals saw that, they thought all was lost, and began to fly, each into his hole and the birds had won the battle.

Then the King and Queen flew home to their children and cried, "Children, rejoice, eat and drink to your heart's content, we have won the battle!" But the young wrens said, "We will not eat yet, the bear must come to the nest, and beg for pardon and say that we are honourable children, before we will do that." Then the willow-wren flew to the bear's hole and cried, "Growler, thou art to come to the nest to my children, and beg their pardon, or else every rib of thy body shall be broken." So the bear crept thither in the greatest fear, and begged their pardon. And now at last the young wrens were satisfied, and sat down together and ate and drank and made merry till quite late into the night.

WISE FOLKS

ONE day a peasant took his good hazel-stick out of the corner and said to his wife, "Trina, I am going across country, and shall not return for three days. If during that time the cattle-dealer should happen to call and want to buy our three cows, you may strike a bargain at once, but not unless you can get two hundred thalers for them; nothing less, do you hear?" "For heaven's sake just go in peace," answered the woman, "I will manage that." "You, indeed," said the man. "You once fell on your head when you were a little child, and that affects you even now; but let me tell you this, if you do anything foolish, I will make your back black and blue, and not with paint, I assure you, but with the stick which I have in my hand, and the colouring shall last a whole year, you may rely on that." And having said that, the man went on his way.

Next morning the cattle-dealer came, and the woman had no need to say many words to him. When he had seen the cows and heard the price, he said, "I am quite willing to give that; honestly speaking, they are worth it. I will take the beasts away with me at once." He unfastened their chains and drove them out of the byre, but just as he was going out of the yard-door, the woman clutched him by the sleeve and said, "You must give me the two hundred thalers now, or I cannot let the cows go." "True," answered the man, "but I have forgotten to buckle on my money-belt. Have no fear, however, you shall have security for my paying. I will take two cows with me and leave one, and then you will have a good pledge." The woman saw the force of this, and let the man go away with the cows, and thought to herself, "How pleased Hans will be when he finds how cleverly I have managed it!" The peasant came home on the third day as he had said he would, and at once inquired if the cows were sold? "Yes, indeed, dear Hans," answered the woman, "and as you said, for two hundred thalers. They are scarcely worth so much, but the man took them without making any objection." "Where is the money?" asked the peasant. "Oh, I have not got the money," replied the woman; "he had happened to forget his money-belt, but he will soon bring it, and he left good security behind him." "What kind of security?" asked the man. "One of the three cows, which he shall not have until he has paid for the other two. I have managed very cunningly, for I have kept the smallest, which eats the least." The man was enraged and lifted up his stick, and was just going to give her the beating he had promised her. Suddenly he let the stick fall and said, "You are the stupidest goose that ever waddled on God's earth, but I am sorry for you. I will go out into the highways and wait for three days to see if I find any one who is still stupider than you. If I succeed in doing so, you shall go scot-free, but if I do not find him, you shall receive your well-deserved reward without any discount."

He went out into the great highways, sat down on a stone, and waited for what would happen. Then he saw a peasant's waggon coming towards him, and a woman was standing upright in the middle of it, instead of sitting on the bundle of straw which was lying beside her, or walking near the oxen and leading them. The man thought to himself, "That is certainly one of the kind I am in search of," and jumped up and ran backwards and forwards in front of the waggon like one who is not very wise. "What do you want, my friend?" said the woman to him; "I don't know you, where do you come from?" "I have fallen down from Heaven," replied the man, "and don't know how to get back again, couldn't you drive me up?" "No," said the woman, "I don't know the way, but if you come from Heaven you can surely tell me how my husband, who has been there these three years, is. You must have seen him?" "Oh, yes, I have seen him, but all men can't get on well. He keeps sheep, and the sheep give him a great deal to do. They run up the mountains and lose their way in the wilderness, and he has to run after them and drive them together again. His clothes are all torn to pieces too, and will soon fall off his body. There is no tailor there, for Saint Peter won't let any of them in, as you know by the story." "Who would have thought it?" cried the woman, "I tell you what, I will fetch his Sunday coat which is still hanging at home

in the cupboard, he can wear that and look respectable.
You will be so kind as to take it with you." "That won't
do very well," answered the peasant; "people are not allowed to take clothes into Heaven, they are taken away from
one at the gate." "Then hark you," said the woman, "I sold
my fine wheat yesterday and got a good lot of money for it,
I will send that to him. If you hide the purse in your
pocket, no one will know that you have it." "If you can't
manage it any other way," said the peasant, "I will do you
that favour." "Just sit still where you are," said she, "and
I will drive home and fetch the purse, I shall soon be back
again. I do not sit down on the bundle of straw, but stand
up in the waggon, because it makes it lighter for the cattle."
She drove her oxen away, and the peasant thought, "That
woman has a perfect talent for folly, if she really brings
the money, my wife may think herself fortunate, for she
will get no beating." It was not long before she came in
a great hurry with the money, and with her own hands put
it in his pocket. Before she went away, she thanked him
again a thousand times for his courtesy.

When the woman got home again, she found her son
who had come in from the field. She told him what un-
looked-for things had befallen her, and then added, "I am
truly delighted at having found an opportunity of sending
something to my poor husband. Who would ever have
imagined that he could be suffering for want of anything
up in Heaven?" The son was full of astonishment.
"Mother," said he, "it is not every day that a man comes
from Heaven in this way, I will go out immediately, and
see if he is still to be found; he must tell me what it is like
up there, and how the work is done." He saddled the horse
and rode off with all speed. He found the peasant who was
sitting under a willow-tree, and was just going to count
the money in the purse. "Have you seen the man who has
fallen down from Heaven?" cried the youth to him. "Yes,"
answered the peasant, "he has set out on his way back there,
and has gone up that hill, from whence it will be rather
nearer; you could still catch him up, if you were to ride
fast." "Alas," said the youth, "I have been doing tiring
work all day, and the ride here has completely worn me out;

you know the man, be so kind as to get on my horse, and go and persuade him to come here." "Aha!" thought the peasant, "here is another who has no wick in his lamp!" "Why should I not do you this favour?" said he, and mounted the horse and rode off in a quick trot. The youth remained sitting there till night fell, but the peasant never came back. "The man from Heaven must certainly have been in a great hurry, and would not turn back," thought he, "and the peasant has no doubt given him the horse to take to my father." He went home and told his mother what had happened, and that he had sent his father the horse so that he might not have to be always running about. "Thou hast done well," answered she, "thy legs are younger than his, and thou canst go on foot."

When the peasant got home, he put the horse in the stable beside the cow which he had as a pledge, and then went to his wife and said, "Trina, as your luck would have it, I have found two who are still sillier fools than you; this time you escape without a beating, I will store it up for another occasion." Then he lighted his pipe, sat down in his grandfather's chair, and said, "It was a good stroke of business to get a sleek horse and a great purse full of money into the bargain, for two lean cows. If stupidity always brought in as much as that I would be quite willing to hold it in honour." So thought the peasant, but you no doubt prefer the simple folks.

THE SHROUD

THERE was once a mother who had a little boy of seven years old, who was so handsome and loveable that no one could look at him without liking him, and she herself worshipped him above everything in the world. Now it so happened that he suddenly became ill, and God took him to himself; and for this the mother could not be comforted, and wept both day and night. But soon afterwards, when the child had been buried, it appeared by night in the places where it had sat and played during its life, and if the mother wept, it wept also, and when morning came it disappeared.

As, however, the mother would not stop crying, it came one night, in the little white shroud in which it had been laid in its coffin, and with its wreath of flowers round its head, and stood on the bed at her feet, and said, " Oh, mother, do stop crying, or I shall never fall asleep in my coffin, for my shroud will not dry because of all thy tears, which fall upon it." The mother was afraid when she heard that, and wept no more. The next night the child came again, and held a little light in its hand, and said, " Look, mother, my shroud is nearly dry, and I can rest in my grave." Then the mother gave her sorrow into God's keeping, and bore it quietly and patiently, and the child came no more, but slept in its little bed beneath the earth.

THE TWO KINGS' CHILDREN

THERE was once on a time a King who had a little boy of whom it had been foretold that he should be killed by a stag when he was sixteen years of age, and when he had reached that age the huntsmen once went hunting with him. In the forest, the King's son was separated from the others, and all at once he saw a great stag which he wanted to shoot, but could not hit. At length he chased the stag so far that they were quite out of the forest, and then suddenly a great tall man was standing there instead of the stag, and said, " It is well that I have thee, I have already ruined six pairs of glass skates with running after thee, and have not been able to get thee." Then he took the King's son with him, and dragged him through a great lake to a great palace, and then he had to sit down to table with him and eat something. When they had eaten something together the King said, " I have three daughters, thou must keep watch over the eldest for one night, from nine in the evening till six in the morning, and every time the clock strikes, I will come myself and call, and if thou then givest me no answer, to-morrow morning thou shalt be put to death, but if thou always givest me an answer, thou shalt have her to wife."

When the young folks went to the bed-room there stood

a stone image of St. Christopher, and the King's daughter said to it, "My father will come at nine o'clock, and every hour till it strikes three; when he calls, give him an answer instead of the King's son." Then the stone image of St. Christopher nodded its head quite quickly, and then more and more slowly till at last it stood still. The next morning the King said to him, "Thou hast done the business well, but I cannot give my daughter away, thou must now watch a night by my second daughter, and then I will consider with myself, whether thou canst have my eldest daughter to wife, but I shall come every hour myself, and when I call thee, answer me, and if I call thee and thou dost not reply, thy blood shall flow." Then they both went into the sleeping-room, and there stood a still larger stone image of St. Christopher, and the King's daughter said to it, "If my father calls do you answer him." Then the great stone image of St. Christopher again nodded its head quite quickly and then more and more slowly, until at last it stood still again. And the King's son lay down on the threshold, put his hand under his head and slept. The next morning the King said to him, "Thou hast done the business really well, but I cannot give my daughter away; thou must now watch a night by the youngest princess, and then I will consider with myself whether thou canst have my second daughter to wife, but I shall come every hour myself, and when I call thee answer me, and if I call thee and thou answerest not, thy blood shall flow for me."

Then they once more went to the sleeping-room together, and there was a much greater and much taller image of St. Christopher than the two first had been. The King's daughter said to it, "When my father calls, do thou answer." Then the great tall stone image of St. Christopher nodded quite half an hour with its head, until at length the head stood still again. And the King's son lay down on the threshold of the door and slept. The next morning the King said, "Thou hast indeed watched well, but I cannot give thee my daughter now; I have a great forest, if thou cuttest it down for me between six o'clock this morning and six at night, I will think about it." Then he gave him a glass axe, a glass wedge, and a glass mallet. When he got into the wood, he began to cut, but the axe broke in two, then he took the wedge, and struck it once with the mallet, and it became as short and as small as sand. Then he was much troubled and believed he would have to die, and sat down and wept.

Now when it was noon the King said, " One of you girls must take him something to eat." " No," said the two eldest, " we will not take it to him; the one by whom he last watched, can take him something." Then the youngest was forced to go and take him something to eat. When she got into the forest, she asked him how he was getting on? " Oh," said he, " I am getting on very badly." Then she said he was to come and just eat a little. " Nay," said he, " I cannot do that, I shall still have to die, so I will eat no more." Then she spoke so kindly to him and begged him just to try, that he came and ate something. When he had eaten something she said, " I will comb thy hair a while, and then thou wilt feel happier."

So she combed his hair, and he became weary and fell asleep, and then she took her handkerchief and made a knot in it, and struck it three times on the earth, and said, " Earthworkers, come forth." In a moment, numbers of little earthmen came forth, and asked what the King's daughter commanded? Then said she, " In three hours' time the great forest must be cut down, and the whole of the wood laid in heaps." So the little earth-men went about and got together the whole of their kindred to help them with the work. They began at once, and when the three hours were over, all was done, and they came back to the King's daughter and told her so. Then she took her white handkerchief again and said, " Earth-workers, go home." On this they all disappeared.

When the King's son awoke, he was delighted, and she said, " Come home when it has struck six o'clock." He did as she told him, and then the King asked, " Hast thou made away with the forest?" "Yes," said the King's son. When they were sitting at table, the King said, " I cannot yet give thee my daughter to wife, thou must still do something more for her sake." So he asked what it was to be, then? " I have a great fish-pond," said the King. " Thou must go to it to-morrow morning and clear it of all mud until it is as bright as a mirror, and fill it with every kind of fish." The next morning the King gave him a glass shovel and said, "The fish-pond must be done by six o'clock." So he went away, and when he came to the fish-pond he stuck his shovel in the mud and it broke in two, then he stuck his hoe in the mud, and broke it also. Then he was much troubled. At noon the youngest daughter brought him something to eat, and asked him how he was getting on? So the King's son said everything was going very ill with him, and he would certainly have to lose his head. "My tools have broken to pieces again." "Oh," said she, "thou must just come and eat something, and then thou wilt be in another frame of mind." "No," said he, "I cannot eat, I am far too unhappy for that!" Then she gave him many good words until at last he came and ate something. Then she combed his hair again, and he fell asleep, so once more she took her handkerchief, tied a knot in it, and struck the ground thrice with the knot, and said, "Earth-workers, come forth." In a moment a great many little earth-men came and asked what she desired, and she told them that in three hours' time they must have the fish-pond entirely cleaned out, and it must be so clear that people could see themselves reflected in it, and every kind of fish must be in it. The little earth-men went away and summoned all their kindred to help them, and in two hours it was done. Then they returned to her and said, "We have done as thou hast commanded." The King's daughter took the handkerchief and once more struck thrice on the ground with it, and said, "Earth-workers, go home again." Then they all went away.

When the King's son awoke the fish-pond was done. Then the King's daughter went away also, and told him that when it was six he was to come to the house. When he arrived at the house the King asked, "Hast thou got the fish-pond done?" "Yes," said the King's son. That was very good.

When they were again sitting at table the King said, "Thou hast certainly done the fish-pond, but I cannot give thee my daughter yet; thou must just do one thing more." "What is that, then?" asked the King's son. The King said he had a great mountain on which there was nothing but briars which must all be cut down, and at the top of it the youth must build up a great castle, which must be as strong as could be conceived, and all the furniture and fittings belonging to a castle must be inside it. And when he arose next morning the King gave him a glass axe and a glass gimlet with him, and he was to have all done by six o'clock. As he was cutting down the first briar with the axe, it broke off short, and so small that the pieces flew all round about, and he could not use the gimlet either. Then he was quite miserable, and waited for his dearest to see if she would not come and help him in his need. When it was mid-day she came and brought him something to eat. He went to meet her and told her all, and ate something, and let her comb his hair and fell asleep. Then she once more took the knot and struck the earth with it, and said, "Earth-workers, come forth!" Then came once again numbers of earth-men, and asked what her desire was. Then said she, "In the space of three hours they must cut down the whole of the briars, and a castle must be built on the top of the mountain that must be as strong as any one could conceive, and all the furniture that pertains to a castle must be inside it. They went away, and summoned their kindred to help them and when the time was come, all was ready. Then they came to the King's daughter and told her so, and the King's daughter took her handkerchief and struck thrice on the earth with it, and said "Earth-workers, go home," on which they all disappeared. When therefore the King's son awoke and saw everything done, he was as happy as a bird in air.

When it had struck six, they went home together. Then said the King, "Is the castle ready?" "Yes," said the King's son. When they sat down to table, the King said, "I cannot give away my youngest daughter until the two eldest are married." Then the King's son and the King's daughter were quite troubled, and the King's son had no idea what to do. But he went by night to the King's daughter and ran away with her. When they had got a little distance away, the King's daughter peeped round and saw her father behind her. "Oh," said she, "what are we to do? My father is behind us, and will take us back with him. I will at once change thee into a briar, and myself into a rose, and I will shelter myself in the midst of the bush." When the father reached the place, there stood a briar with one rose on it, then he was about to gather the rose, when the thorn came and pricked his finger so that he was forced to go home again. His wife asked why he had not brought their daughter back with him? So he said he had nearly got up to her, but that all at once he had lost sight of her, and a briar with one rose was growing on the spot.

Then said the Queen, "If thou hadst but gathered the rose, the briar would have been forced to come too." So he went back again to fetch the rose, but in the meantime the two were already far over the plain, and the King ran after them. Then the daughter once more looked round and saw her father coming, and said, "Oh, what shall we do now? I will instantly change thee into a church and myself into a priest, and I will stand up in the pulpit, and preach." When the King got to the place, there stood a church, and in the pulpit was a priest preaching. So he listened to the sermon, and then went home again.

Then the Queen asked why he had not brought their daughter with him, and he said, "Nay, I ran a long time after her, and just as I thought I should soon overtake her, a church was standing there and a priest was in the pulpit preaching." "Thou shouldst just have brought the priest," said his wife, "and then the church would soon have come. It is no use to send thee, I must go there myself." When she had walked for some time, and could see the two in the distance, the King's daughter peeped round and saw her mother coming, and said, "Now we are undone, for my mother is coming herself: I will immediately change thee into a fish-pond and myself into a fish."

When the mother came to the place, there was a large fish-pond, and in the midst of it a fish was leaping about and peeping out of the water, and it was quite merry. She wanted to catch the fish but she could not. Then she was very angry, and drank up the whole pond in order to catch the fish, but it made her so ill that she was forced to vomit, and vomited the whole pond out again. Then she cried, "I see very well that nothing can be done now," and said

that now they might come back to her. Then the King's
daughter went back again, and the Queen gave her daughter
three walnuts, and said, " With these thou canst help thyself
when thou art in thy greatest need." So the young folks
went once more away together. And when they had walked
quite ten miles they arrived at the castle from whence the
King's son came, and close by it was a village. When they
reached it, the King's son said, " Stay here, my dearest, I
will just go to the castle, and then will I come with a carriage and with attendants to fetch thee."

When he got to the castle they all rejoiced greatly at
having the King's son back again, and he told them he had
a bride who was now in the village, and they must go with
the carriage to fetch her. Then they harnessed the horses
at once, and many attendants seated themselves outside the
carriage. When the King's son was about to get in, his
mother gave him a kiss, and he forgot everything which had
happened, and also what he was about to do. On this his
mother ordered the horses to be taken out of the carriage
again, and every one went back into the house. But the
maiden sat in the village and watched and watched, and
thought he would come and fetch her, but no one came.
Then the King's daughter took service in the mill which
belonged to the castle, and was obliged to sit by the pond
every afternoon and clean the tubs. And the Queen came
one day on foot from the castle, and went walking by the
pond, and saw the well-grown maiden sitting there, and said,
" What a fine strong girl that is ! She pleases me well ! "
Then she and all with her looked at the maid, but no one
knew her. So a long time passed by during which the
maiden served the miller honourably and faithfully. In the
meantime, the Queen had sought a wife for her son, who
came from quite a distant part of the world. When the bride
came, they were at once to be married. And many people
hurried together, all of whom wanted to see everything.
Then the girl said to the miller that he might be so good
as to give her leave to go also. So the miller said, " Yes,
do go there." When she was about to go, she opened one
of the three walnuts, and a beautiful dress lay inside it. She
put it on, and went into the church and stood by the altar.

Suddenly came the bride and bridegroom, and seated themselves before the altar, and when the priest was just going to bless them, the bride peeped half round and saw the maiden standing there. Then she stood up again, and said she would not be given away until she also had as beautiful a dress as that lady there. So they went back to the house again, and sent to ask the lady if she would sell that dress. No, she would not sell it, but the bride might perhaps earn it. Then the bride asked her how she was to do this? Then the maiden said if she might sleep one night outside the King's son's door, the bride might have what she wanted. So the bride said, " Yes, she was to do that." But the servants were ordered to give the King's son a sleeping drink, and then the maiden laid herself down on the threshold and lamented all night long. She had had the forest cut down for him, she had had the fish-pond cleaned out for him, she had had the castle built for him, she had changed him into a briar, and then into a church, and at last into a fish-pond, and yet he had forgotten her so quickly. The King's son did not hear one word of it, but the servants had been awakened, and had listened to it, and had not known what it could mean. The next morning when they were all up, the bride put on the dress, and went away to the church with the bridegroom. In the meantime the maiden opened the second walnut, and a still more beautiful dress was inside it. She put it on, and went and stood by the altar in the church, and everything happened as it had happened the time before. And the maiden again lay all night on the threshold which led to the chamber of the King's son, and the servant was once more to give him a sleeping-drink. The servant, however, went to him and gave him something to keep him awake, and then the King's son went to bed, and the miller's maiden bemoaned herself as before on the threshold of the door, and told of all that she had done. All this the King's son heard, and was sore troubled, and what was passed came back to him. Then he wanted to go to her, but his mother had locked the door. The next morning, however, he went at once to his beloved, and told her everything which had happened to him, and prayed her not to be angry with him for having forgotten her. Then the King's daughter opened the third walnut, and within it was a still more magnificent dress, which she put on, and went with her bridegroom to church, and numbers of children came who gave them flowers, and offered them gay ribbons to bind about their feet, and they were blessed by the priest, and had a merry wedding. But the false mother and the bride had to depart. And the mouth of the person who last told all this is still warm.

THE SEVEN SWABIANS

Seven Swabians were once together. The first was Master Schulz; the second, Jackli; the third, Marli; the fourth, Jergli; the fifth, Michal; the sixth, Hans; the seventh, Veitli: all seven had made up their minds to travel about the world to seek adventures, and perform great deeds. But in order that they might go in security and with arms in their hands, they thought it would be advisable that they should have one solitary, but very strong, and very long spear made for them. This spear all seven of them took in their hands at once; in front walked the boldest and bravest, and that was Master Schulz; all the others followed in a row, and Veitli was the last. Then it came to pass one day in the hay-making month (July), when they had walked a long distance, and still had a long way to go before they reached the village where they were to pass the night, that as they were in a meadow in the twilight a great beetle or hornet flew by them from behind a bush, and hummed in a menacing manner. Master Schulz was so terrified that he all but dropped the spear, and a cold perspiration broke out over his whole body. "Hark! hark!" cried he to his comrades. "Good heavens! I hear a drum." Jackli, who was behind him holding the spear, and who perceived some kind of a smell, said, "Something is most certainly going on, for I taste powder and matches." At these words Master Schulz began to take to flight, and in a trice jumped over a hedge, but as he just happened to jump on to the teeth of a rake which had been left lying there after the hay-making, the handle of it struck against his face and gave him a tremendous blow. "Oh dear! Oh dear!" screamed Master Schulz. "Take me prisoner; I surrender! I surrender!" The other six all leapt over, one on the top of the other, crying, "If you surrender, I surrender too! If you surrender, I surrender too!" At length, as no enemy was there to bind and take them away, they saw that they had been mistaken, and in order that the story might not be known, and they be treated as fools and ridiculed, they all swore to each other to hold their peace about it until one of them accidentally spoke of it.

Then they journeyed onwards. The second danger which they survived cannot be compared with the first. Some days afterwards, their path led them through a fallow-field where a hare was sitting sleeping in the sun. Her ears were standing straight up, and her great glassy eyes were wide open. All of them were alarmed at the sight of the horrible wild beast, and they consulted together as to what it would be the least dangerous to do. For if they were to run away, they knew that the monster would pursue and swallow them whole. So they said, "We must go through a great and dangerous struggle. Boldly ventured, is half won," and all seven grasped the spear, Master Schulz in front, and Veitli behind. Master Schulz was always trying to keep the spear back, but Veitli had become quite brave while behind, and wanted to dash forward and cried,

> "Strike home, in every Swabian's name,
> Or else I wish ye may be lame."

But Hans knew how to meet this, and said,

> "Thunder and lightning, it's fine to prate,
> But for dragon-hunting thou'rt aye too late."

Michal cried,

> "Nothing is wanting, not even a hair,
> Be sure the Devil himself is there."

Then it was Jergli's turn to speak,

> "If it be not, it's at least his mother,
> Or else it's the Devil's own step-brother."

And now Marli had a bright thought, and said to Veitli,

> "Advance, Veitli, advance, advance,
> And I behind will hold the lance."

Veitli, however, did not attend to that, and Jackli said,

> "'Tis Schulz's place the first to be,
> No one deserves that honour but he."

Then Master Schulz plucked up his courage, and said, gravely,

> "Then let us boldly advance to the fight,
> And thus we shall show our valour and might."

Hereupon they all together set on the dragon. Master Schulz crossed himself, and prayed for God's assistance, but as all this was of no avail, and he was getting nearer and nearer to the enemy, he screamed "Oho! Oho! ho! ho! ho!" in the greatest anguish. This awakened the hare, which in great alarm darted swiftly away. When Master Schulz saw her thus flying from the field of battle, he cried in his joy.

> "Quick, Veitli, quick, look there, look there,
> The monster's nothing but a hare!"

But the Swabian allies went in search of further adventures, and came to the Moselle, a mossy, quiet, deep river, over which there are few bridges, and which in many places people have to cross in boats. As the seven Swabians did not know this, they called to a man who was working on the opposite side of the river, to know how people contrived to get across. The distance and their way of speaking made the man unable to understand what they wanted, and he said "What? what?" in the way people speak in the neighbourhood of Treves. Master Schulz thought he was saying, "Wade, wade through the water," and as he was the first, began to set out and went into the Moselle. It was not long before he sank in the mud and the deep waves which drove against him, but his hat was blown on the opposite shore by the wind, and a frog sat down beside it and croaked "Wat, wat, wat." The other six on the opposite side heard that, and said, "Oho, comrades, Master Schulz is calling us; if he can wade across, why cannot we?" So they all jumped into the water

together in a great hurry, and were drowned, and thus
one frog took the lives of all six of them, and not one
of the Swabian allies ever reached home again.

ONE-EYE, TWO-EYES, AND THREE-EYES

THERE was once a woman who had three daughters, the
eldest of whom was called One-eye, because she had only
one eye in the middle of her forehead, and the second, Two-
eyes, because she had two eyes like other folks, and the
youngest, Three-eyes, because she had three eyes; and
her third eye was also in the centre of her forehead.
However, as Two-eyes saw just as other human beings did,
her sisters and her mother could not endure her. They
said to her, "Thou, with thy two eyes, art no better than
the common people; thou dost not belong to us!" They
pushed her about, and threw old clothes to her, and gave
her nothing to eat but what they left, and did everything
that they could to make her unhappy. It came to pass
that Two-eyes had to go out into the fields and tend the goat,
but she was still quite hungry, because her sisters had given
her so little to eat. So she sat down on a ridge and began
to weep, and so bitterly that two streams ran down from her
eyes. And once when she looked up in her grief, a woman
was standing beside her, who said, "Why art thou weeping,
little Two-eyes?" Two-eyes answered, "Have I not reason
to weep, when I have two eyes like other people, and my
sisters and mother hate me for it, and push me from one
corner to another, throw old clothes at me, and give me
nothing to eat but the scraps they leave? To-day they have
given me so little that I am still quite hungry." Then the
wise woman said, "Wipe away thy tears, Two-eyes, and I
will tell thee something to stop thee ever suffering from hunger again; just say to thy goat,

> "Bleat, my little goat, bleat,
> Cover the table with something to eat,"

and then a clean well-spread little table will stand before
thee, with the most delicious food upon it of which thou

mayest eat as much as thou art inclined for, and when
thou hast had enough, and hast no more need of the little
table, just say,

> "Bleat, bleat, my little goat, I pray,
> And take the table quite away,"

and then it will vanish again from thy sight." Hereupon
the wise woman departed. But Two-eyes thought, "I
must instantly make a trial, and see if what she said is
true, for I am far too hungry," and she said,

> "Bleat, my little goat, bleat,
> Cover the table with something to eat,"

and scarcely had she spoken the words than a little table,
covered with a white cloth, was standing there, and on it
was a plate with a knife and fork, and a silver spoon; and
the most delicious food was there also, warm and smoking
as if it had just come out of the kitchen. Then Two-eyes
said the shortest prayer she knew, "Lord God, be with us
always, Amen," and helped herself to some food, and
enjoyed it. And when she was satisfied, she said, as the
wise woman had taught her,

> "Bleat, bleat, my little goat, I pray,
> And take the table quite away,"

and immediately the little table and everything on it was
gone again. "This is a delightful way of keeping house!"
thought Two-eyes, and was quite glad and happy.

In the evening, when she went home with her goat, she
found a small earthenware dish, with some food, which her
sisters had set ready for her, but she did not touch it.
Next day she again went out with her goat, and left the
few bits of broken bread which had been handed to her,
lying untouched. The first and second time that she did
this, her sisters did not remark it at all, but as it happened
every time, they did observe it, and said, "There is something wrong about Two-eyes, she always leaves her food
untasted, and she used to eat up everything that was given
her; she must have discovered other ways of getting food."
In order that they might learn the truth, they resolved to

send One-eye with Two-eyes when she went to drive her
goat to the pasture, to observe what Two-eyes did when
she was there, and whether any one brought her anything
to eat and drink. So when Two-eyes set out the next
time, One-eye went to her and said, "I will go with you to
the pasture, and see that the goat is well taken care of,
and driven where there is food." But Two-eyes knew what
was in One-eye's mind, and drove the goat into high grass
and said, "Come, One-eye, we will sit down, and I will
sing something to you." One-eye sat down and was tired
with the unaccustomed walk and the heat of the sun, and
Two-eyes sang constantly,

> "One eye, wakest thou?
> One eye, sleepest thou?"

until One-eye shut her one eye, and fell asleep, and as
soon as Two-eyes saw that One-eye was fast asleep, and
could discover nothing, she said,

> "Bleat, my little goat, bleat,
> Cover the table with something to eat,"

and seated herself at her table, and ate and drank until
she was satisfied, and then she again cried,

> "Bleat, bleat, my little goat, I pray,
> And take the table quite away,"

and in an instant all was gone. Two-eyes now awakened
One-eye, and said, "One-eye, you want to take care of the
goat, and go to sleep while you are doing it, and in the
meantime the goat might run all over the world. Come, let
us go home again." So they went home, and again Two-eyes
let her little dish stand untouched, and One-eye could not
tell her mother why she would not eat it, and to excuse
herself said, "I fell asleep when I was out."

Next day the mother said to Three-eyes, "This time thou
shalt go and observe if Two-eyes eats anything when she is
out, and if any one fetches her food and drink, for she must
eat and drink in secret." So Three-eyes went to Two-eyes,
and said, "I will go with you and see if the goat is taken
proper care of, and driven where there is food." But Two-

eyes knew what was in Three-eyes' mind, and drove the goat into high grass and said, " We will sit down, and I will sing something to you, Three-eyes." Three-eyes sat down and was tired with the walk and with the heat of the sun, and Two-eyes began the same song as before, and sang,

> " Three eyes, are you waking?"

but then, instead of singing,

> " Three eyes, are you sleeping?"

as she ought to have done, she thoughtlessly sang,

> " Two eyes, are you sleeping?"

and sang all the time,

> " Three eyes, are you waking?
> Two eyes, are you sleeping?"

Then two of the eyes which Three-eyes had, shut and fell asleep, but the third, as it had not been named in the song, did not sleep. It is true that Three-eyes shut it, but only in her cunning, to pretend it was asleep too, but it blinked, and could see everything very well. And when Two-eyes thought that Three-eyes was fast asleep she used her little charm,

> " Bleat, my little goat, bleat,
> Cover the table with something to eat,"

and ate and drank as much as her heart desired, and then ordered the table to go away again,

> " Bleat, bleat, my little goat, I pray,
> And take the table quite away,"

and Three-eyes had seen everything. Then Two-eyes came to her, waked her and said, " Have you been asleep, Three-eyes? You are a good care-taker! Come, we will go home." And when they got home, Two-eyes again did not eat, and Three-eyes said to the mother, " Now, I know why that high-minded thing there does not eat. When she is out, she says to the goat,

> "Bleat, my little goat, bleat,
> Cover the table with something to eat,"

and then a little table appears before her covered with
the best of food, much better than any we have here, and
when she has eaten all she wants, she says,

> "Bleat, bleat, my little goat, I pray,
> And take the table quite away,"

and all disappears. I watched everything closely. She put
two of my eyes to sleep by using a certain form of words,
but luckily the one in my forehead kept awake." Then the
envious mother cried, "Dost thou want to fare better than
we do? The desire shall pass away," and she fetched a
butcher's knife, and thrust it into the heart of the goat,
which fell down dead.

When Two-eyes saw that, she went out full of trouble,
seated herself on the ridge of grass at the edge of the field
and wept bitter tears. Suddenly the wise woman once
more stood by her side, and said, "Two-eyes, why art thou
weeping?" "Have I not reason to weep?" she answered.
"The goat which covered the table for me every day when
I spoke your charm, has been killed by my mother, and now
I shall again have to bear hunger and want." The wise
woman said, "Two-eyes, I will give thee a piece of good
advice; ask thy sisters to give thee the entrails of the
slaughtered goat, and bury them in the ground in front of
the house, and thy fortune will be made." Then she vanished, and Two-eyes went home and said to her sisters,
"Dear sisters, do give me some part of my goat; I don't
wish for what is good, but give me the entrails." Then they
laughed and said, "If that's all you want, you can have it."
So Two-eyes took the entrails and buried them quietly in
the evening, in front of the house-door, as the wise woman
had counselled her to do.

Next morning, when they all awoke, and went to the house-
door, there stood a strangely magnificent tree with leaves
of silver, and fruit of gold hanging among them, so that
in all the wide world there was nothing more beautiful or
precious. They did not know how the tree could have come
there during the night, but Two-eyes saw that it had grown
up out of the entrails of the goat, for it was standing on
the exact spot where she had buried them. Then the mother

said to One-eye, "Climb up, my child, and gather some of the fruit of the tree for us." One-eye climbed up, but when she was about to get hold of one of the golden apples, the branch escaped from her hands, and that happened each time, so that she could not pluck a single apple, let her do what she might. Then said the mother, "Three-eyes, do you climb up; you with your three eyes can look about you better than One-eye. One-eye slipped down, and Three-eyes climbed up. Three-eyes was not more skilful, and might search as she liked, but the golden apples always escaped her. At length the mother grew impatient, and climbed up herself, but could get hold of the fruit no better than One-eye and Three-eyes, for she always clutched empty air. Then said Two-eyes, "I will just go up, perhaps I may succeed better." The sisters cried, "You indeed, with your two eyes, what can you do?" But Two-eyes climbed up, and the golden apples did not get out of her way, but came into her hand of their own accord, so that she could pluck them one after the other, and brought a whole apronful down with her. The mother took them away from her, and instead of treating poor Two-eyes any better for this, she and One-eye and Three-eyes were only envious, because Two-eyes alone had been able to get the fruit, and they treated her still more cruelly.

It so befell that once when they were all standing together by the tree, a young knight came up. "Quick, Two-eyes," cried the two sisters, "creep under this, and don't disgrace us!" and with all speed they turned an empty barrel which was standing close by the tree over poor Two-eyes, and they pushed the golden apples which she had been gathering, under it too. When the knight came nearer he was a handsome lord, who stopped and admired the magnificent gold and silver tree, and said to the two sisters, "To whom does this fine tree belong? Any one who would bestow one branch of it on me might in return for it ask whatsoever he desired." Then One-eye and Three-eyes replied that the tree belonged to them, and that they would give him a branch. They both took great trouble, but they were not able to do it, for the branches and fruit both moved away from them every time. Then said the knight,

"It is very strange that the tree should belong to you, and that you should still not be able to break a piece off." They again asserted that the tree was their property. Whilst they were saying so, Two-eyes rolled out a couple of golden apples from under the barrel to the feet of the knight, for she was vexed with One-eye and Three-eyes, for not speaking the truth. When the knight saw the apples he was astonished, and asked where they came from. One-eye and Three-eyes answered that they had another sister, who was not allowed to show herself, for she had only two eyes like any common person. The knight, however, desired to see her, and cried, "Two-eyes, come forth." Then Two-eyes, quite comforted, came from beneath the barrel, and the knight was surprised at her great beauty, and said, "Thou, Two-eyes, canst certainly break off a branch from the tree for me." "Yes," replied Two-eyes, "that I certainly shall be able to do, for the tree belongs to me." And she climbed up, and with the greatest ease broke off a branch with beautiful silver leaves and golden fruit, and gave it to the knight. Then said the knight, "Two-eyes, what shall I give thee for it?" "Alas!" answered Two-eyes, "I suffer from hunger and thirst, grief and want, from early morning till late night; if you would take me with you, and deliver me from these things, I should be happy." So the knight lifted Two-eyes on to his horse, and took her home with him to his father's castle, and there he gave her beautiful clothes and meat and drink to her heart's content, and as he loved her so much he married her, and the wedding was solemnized with great rejoicing. When Two-eyes was thus carried away by the handsome knight, her two sisters grudged her good fortune in downright earnest. "The wonderful tree, however, still remains with us," thought they, "and even if we can gather no fruit from it, still every one will stand still and look at it, and come to us and admire it. Who knows what good things may be in store for us?" But next morning, the tree had vanished, and all their hopes were at an end. And when Two-eyes looked out of the window of her own little room to her great delight it was standing in front of it, and so it had followed her.

Two-eyes lived a long time in happiness. Once two poor women came to her in her castle, and begged for alms. She looked in their faces, and recognized her sisters, One-eye, and Three-eyes, who had fallen into such poverty that they had to wander about and beg their bread from door to door. Two-eyes, however, made them welcome, and was kind to them, and took care of them, so that they both with all their hearts repented the evil that they had done their sister in their youth.

SNOW-WHITE AND ROSE-RED

THERE was once a poor widow who lived in a lonely cottage. In front of the cottage was a garden wherein stood two rose-trees, one of which bore white and the other red roses. She had two children who were like the two rose-trees, and one was called Snow-white and the other Rose-red. They were as good and happy, as busy and cheerful, as ever two children in the world were, only Snow-white was more quiet and gentle than Rose-Red. Rose-Red liked better to run about in the meadows and fields seeking flowers and catching butterflies; but Snow-white sat at home with her mother, and helped her with her house-work, or read to her when there was nothing to do.

The two children were so fond of each other that they always held each other by the hand when they went out together, and when Snow-white said, "We will not leave each other," Rose-red answered, "Never so long as we live," and their mother would add, "What one has she must share with the other."

They often ran about the forest alone and gathered red berries, and no beasts did them any harm, but came close to them trustfully. The little hare would eat a cabbage-leaf out of their hands, the roe grazed by their side, the stag leapt merrily by them, and the birds sat still upon the boughs, and sang whatever they knew.

No mishap overtook them; if they had stayed too late in the forest and night came on, they laid themselves down near one another upon the moss, and slept until morning came, and their mother knew this and had no distress on their account.

Once when they had spent the night in the wood and the dawn had roused them, they saw a beautiful child in a shining white dress sitting near their bed. He got up and looked quite kindly at them, but said nothing and went away into the forest. And when they looked round they found that they had been sleeping quite close to a precipice, and would certainly have fallen into it in the darkness if they had gone only a few paces further. And their mother told them that it must have been the angel who watches over good children.

Snow-white and Rose-red kept their mother's little cottage so neat that it was a pleasure to look inside it. In the summer Rose-red took care of the house, and every morning laid a wreath of flowers by her mother's bed before she awoke, in which was a rose from each tree. In the winter Snow-white lit the fire and hung the kettle on the wrekin. The kettle was of copper and shone like gold, so brightly was it polished. In the evening, when the snowflakes fell, the mother said, "Go, Snow-white, and bolt the door," and then they sat round the hearth, and the mother took her spectacles and read aloud out of a large book, and the two girls listened as they sat and span. And close by them lay a lamb upon the floor, and behind them upon a perch sat a white dove with its head hidden beneath its wings.

One evening, as they were thus sitting comfortably together, some one knocked at the door, as if he wished to be let in. The mother said, "Quick, Rose-red, open the door, it must be a traveller who is seeking shelter." Rose-red went and pushed back the bolt, thinking that it was a poor man, but it was not; it was a bear that stretched his broad, black head within the door.

Rose-red screamed and sprang back, the lamb bleated, the dove fluttered, and Snow-white hid herself behind her mother's bed. But the bear began to speak and said, "Do not be afraid, I will do you no harm! I am half-frozen, and only want to warm myself a little beside you."

"Poor bear," said the mother, "lie down by the fire, only take care that you do not burn your coat." Then she cried, "Snow-white, Rose-red, come out, the bear will do you no

harm, he means well." So they both came out, and by-and-by
the lamb and dove came nearer, and were not afraid of him.
The bear said, "Here, children, knock the snow out of my
coat a little;" so they brought the broom and swept the bear's
hide clean; and he stretched himself by the fire and growled
contentedly and comfortably. It was not long before they
grew quite at home, and played tricks with their clumsy guest.
They tugged his hair with their hands, put their feet upon
his back and rolled him about, or they took a hazel-switch
and beat him, and when he growled they laughed. But the
bear took it all in good part, only when they were too
rough he called out, "Leave me alive, children,

> "Snowy-white, Rosy-red,
> Will you beat your lover dead?"

When it was bed-time, and the others went to bed, the
mother said to the bear, "You can lie there by the hearth,
and then you will be safe from the cold and the bad weather."
As soon as day dawned the two children let him out, and
he trotted across the snow into the forest.

Henceforth the bear came every evening at the same time,
laid himself down by the hearth, and let the children amuse
themselves with him as much as they liked; and they
got so used to him that the doors were never fastened until
their black friend had arrived.

When spring had come and all outside was green, the bear
said one morning to Snow-white, "Now I must go away, and
cannot come back for the whole summer." "Where are you
going, then, dear bear?" asked Snow-white. "I must go into
the forest and guard my treasures from the wicked dwarfs.
In the winter, when the earth is frozen hard, they are obliged
to stay below and cannot work their way through; but now,
when the sun has thawed and warmed the earth, they break
through it, and come out to pry and steal; and what once gets
into their hands, and in their caves, does not easily see daylight again."

Snow-white was quite sorry for his going away, and as she
unbolted the door for him, and the bear was hurrying out,
he caught against the bolt and a piece of his hairy coat was
torn off, and it seemed to Snow-white as if she had seen gold

shining through it, but she was not sure about it. The bear ran away quickly, and was soon out of sight behind the trees.

A short time afterwards the mother sent her children into the forest to get fire-wood. There they found a big tree which lay felled on the ground, and close by the trunk something was jumping backwards and forwards in the grass, but they could not make out what it was. When they came nearer they saw a dwarf with an old withered face and a snow-white beard a yard long. The end of the beard was caught in a crevice of the tree, and the little fellow was jumping backwards and forwards like a dog tied to a rope, and did not know what to do.

He glared at the girls with his fiery red eyes and cried, "Why do you stand there? Can you not come here and help me?" "What are you about there, little man?" asked Rose-red. "You stupid, prying goose!" answered the dwarf; "I was going to split the tree to get a little wood for cooking. The little bit of food that one of us wants gets burnt up directly with thick logs; we do not swallow so much as you coarse, greedy folk. I had just driven the wedge safely in, and everything was going as I wished; but the wretched wood was too smooth and suddenly sprang asunder, and the tree closed so quickly that I could not pull out my beautiful white beard; so now it is tight in and I cannot get away, and the silly, sleek, milk-faced things laugh! Ugh! how odious you are!"

The children tried very hard, but they could not pull the beard out, it was caught too fast. "I will run and fetch some one," said Red-rose. "You senseless goose!" snarled the dwarf; "why should you fetch some one? You are already two too many for me; can you not think of something better?" "Don't be too impatient," said Snow-white, "I will help you," and she pulled her scissors out of her pocket, and cut off the end of the beard.

As soon as the dwarf felt himself free he laid hold of a bag which lay amongst the roots of the tree, and which was full of gold, and lifted it up, grumbling to himself, "Uncouth people, to cut off a piece of my fine beard. Bad luck to you!" and then he swung the bag upon his back, and went off without even once looking at the children.

Some time after that Snow-white and Rose-red went to catch a dish of fish. As they came near the brook they saw something like a large grasshopper jumping towards the water, as if it were going to leap in. They ran to it and found it was the dwarf. "Where are you going?" said Rose-red; "you surely don't want to go into the water?" "I am not such a fool!" cried the dwarf; "don't you see that the accursed fish wants to pull me in?" The little man had been sitting there fishing, and unluckily the wind had twisted his beard with the fishing-line; just then a big fish bit, and the feeble creature had not the strength to pull it out; the fish kept the upper hand and pulled the dwarf towards him. He held on to all the reeds and rushes, but it was of little good, he was forced to follow the movements of the fish, and was in urgent danger of being dragged into the water.

The girls came just in time; they held him fast and tried to free his beard from the line, but all in vain, beard and line were entangled fast together. Nothing was left but to bring out the scissors and cut the beard, whereby a small part of it was lost.

When the dwarf saw that he screamed out, "Is that civil, you toad-stool, to disfigure one's face? Was it not enough to clip off the end of my beard? Now you have cut off the best part of it. I cannot let myself be seen by my people. I wish you had been made to run the soles off your shoes!" Then he took out a sack of pearls which lay in the rushes, and without saying a word more he dragged it away and disappeared behind a stone.

It happened that soon afterwards the mother sent the two children to the town to buy needles and thread, and laces and ribbons. The road led them across a heath upon which huge pieces of rock lay strewn here and there. Now they noticed a large bird hovering in the air, flying slowly round and round above them; it sank lower and lower, and at last settled near a rock not far off. Directly afterwards they heard a loud, piteous cry. They ran up and saw with horror that the eagle had seized their old acquaintance the dwarf, and was going to carry him off.

The children, full of pity, at once took tight hold of the little man, and pulled against the eagle so long that at last he let his booty go. As soon as the dwarf had recovered from his first fright he cried with his shrill voice, "Could you not have done it more carefully? You dragged at my brown coat so that it is all torn and full of holes, you help-less clumsy creatures!" Then he took up a sack full of precious stones and slipped away again under the rock into his hole. The girls, who by this time were used to his thanklessness, went on their way and did their business in the town.

As they crossed the heath again on their way home they surprised the dwarf, who had emptied out his bag of precious stones in a clean spot, and had not thought that any one would come there so late. The evening sun shone upon the brilliant stones; they glittered and sparkled with all colours so beauti-fully that the children stood still and looked at them. "Why do you stand gaping there?" cried the dwarf, and his ashen-grey face became copper-red with rage. He was going on with his bad words when a loud growling was heard, and a black bear came trotting towards them out of the forest. The dwarf sprang up in a fright, but he could not get to his cave, for the bear was already close. Then in the dread of his heart he cried, "Dear Mr. Bear, spare me, I will give you all my treasures; look, the beautiful jewels lying there! Grant me my life; what do you want with such a slender little fellow as I? you would not feel me between your teeth. Come, take these two wicked girls, they are tender mor-sels for you, fat as young quails; for mercy's sake eat them!" The bear took no heed of his words, but gave the wicked creature a single blow with his paw, and he did not move again.

The girls had run away, but the bear called to them, "Snow-white and Rose-red, do not be afraid; wait, I will come with you." Then they knew his voice and waited, and when he came up to them suddenly his bearskin fell off, and he stood there a handsome man, clothed all in gold. "I am a King's son," he said, "and I was bewitched by that wicked dwarf, who had stolen my treasures; I have had to run about the forest as a savage bear until I was freed by his death. Now he has got his well-deserved punishment."

Snow-white was married to him, and Rose-red to his

brother, and they divided between them the great treasure which the dwarf had gathered together in his cave. The old mother lived peacefully and happily with her children for many years. She took the two rose-trees with her, and they stood before her window, and every year bore the most beautiful roses, white and red.

TALES FROM
HANS CHRISTIAN ANDERSEN

INTRODUCTORY NOTE

HANS CHRISTIAN ANDERSEN *was born in Odense, Denmark, April 2, 1805. He was the son of a poor cobbler who died when Hans was eleven; and after a meager schooling he went to Copenhagen at the age of fourteen in the hope of finding employment in the theater. Here after much discouragement and hardship he finally found patrons who kept him from starving, and arranged for his regular education at the government's expense. His literary career began in 1829 with his humorous extravaganza, "A Journey on Foot from Holm Canal to the East Point of Amager," which was followed by plays, poems, and descriptions of travel, and in 1835 by his first novel, "The Improvisatore," which was an immediate success. In the same year he found his real forte in the first volume of his "Fairy Tales" (Eventyr), but neither he nor the general public recognized this at first. Those critics who condescended to consider them at all were troubled about their lack of clear moral teaching and their colloquial style; but children liked them from the beginning.*

While the Tales, added to year by year, were gradually finding their public, Andersen continued his writing of novels in his "O. T." and "Only a Fiddler"; of plays in his "Mulatto" and many others; of travels in his "Author's Bazaar," "In Sweden," and "In Spain"; of poetry in his epic, "Ahasuerus," and many lyrics. His reputation spread far beyond Denmark and in the many countries he visited he was enthusiastically received. He died full of honors in August, 1875.

As a man Andersen was vain and sentimental, and he suffered more from his mortified vanity than from his actual hardships. The stories which have made his name a household word he underestimated, and strove after a dramatic success for which he was temperamentally unfitted.

Oddly enough, he was not particularly fond of children, though he had an extraordinary capacity for amusing them; and it was this gift that led a friend to suggest his writing down the stories which he invented for their entertainment. Many of the tales are based on folk-lore, many are purely his own imaginings, but all are told with a quaintness, humor, and fancy that have given the author a place by himself in letters.

CONTENTS

ANDERSEN'S TALES—

FOLK-LORE AND FABLE

ANDERSEN'S TALES

THE UGLY DUCKLING

IT WAS so glorious out in the country; it was summer; the
corn-fields were yellow, the oats were green, the hay had
been put up in stacks in the green meadows, and the stork
went about on his long red legs, and chattered Egyptian, for
this was the language he had learned from his good mother.
All around the fields and meadows were great forests, and in
the midst of these forests lay deep lakes. Yes, it was right
glorious out in the country. In the midst of the sunshine
there lay an old farm, with deep canals about it, and from the
wall down to the water grew great burdocks, so high that
little children could stand upright under the loftiest of them.
It was just as wild there as in the deepest wood, and here
sat a Duck upon her nest; she had to hatch her ducklings;
but she was almost tired out before the little ones came;
and then she so seldom had visitors. The other ducks liked
better to swim about in the canals than to run up to sit
down under a burdock, and cackle with her.

At last one egg-shell after another burst open. "Piep!
Piep!" it cried, and in all the eggs there were little creatures
that stuck out their heads.

"Quack! quack!" they said; and they all came quacking
out as fast as they could, looking all around them under the
green leaves; and the mother let them look as much as they
chose, for green is good for the eye.

"How wide the world is!" said all the young ones, for
they certainly had much more room now than when they
were in the eggs.

"D'ye think this is all the world?" said the mother.
"That stretches far across the other side of the garden, quite
into the parson's field; but I have never been there yet. I

hope you are all together," and she stood up. "No, I have not all. The largest egg still lies there. How long is that to last? I am really tired of it." And she sat down again.

"Well, how goes it?" asked an old Duck who had come to pay her a visit.

"It lasts a long time with that one egg," said the Duck who sat there. "It will not burst. Now, only look at the others; are they not the prettiest little ducks one could possibly see? They are all like their father: the rogue, he never comes to see me."

"Let me see the egg which will not burst," said the old visitor. "You may be sure it is a turkey's egg. I was once cheated in that way, and had much anxiety and trouble with the young ones, for they are afraid of the water. Must I say it to you, I could not get them to venture in. I quacked and I clacked, but it was no use. Let me see the egg. Yes, that's a turkey's egg. Let it lie there, and teach the other children to swim."

"I think I will sit on it a little longer," said the Duck. "I've sat so long now that I can sit a few days more."

"Just as you please," said the old Duck; and she went away.

At last the great egg burst. "Piep! piep!" said the little one, and crept forth. It was very large and very ugly. The Duck looked at it.

"It's a very large duckling," said she; "none of the others look like that: can it really be a turkey chick? Well, we shall soon find out. It must go into the water, even if I have to thrust it in myself."

The next day, it was bright, beautiful weather; the sun shone on all the green trees. The Mother-Duck went down to the canal with all her family. Splash! she jumped into the water. "Quack! quack!" she said, and one duckling after another plunged in. The water closed over their heads, but they came up in an instant, and swam capitally; their legs went of themselves, and they were all in the water. The ugly gray Duckling swam with them.

"No, it's not a turkey," said she; "look how well it can use its legs, and how straight it holds itself. It is my own child! On the whole it's quite pretty, if one looks at it rightly. Quack! quack! come with me, and I'll lead you out into the great world, and present you in the duck-yard; but keep close to me, so that no one may tread on you, and take care of the cats!"

And so they came into the duck-yard. There was a terrible riot going on in there, for two families were quarreling about an eel's head, and the cat got it after all.

"See, that's how it goes in the world!" said the Mother-Duck; and she whetted her beak, for she too wanted the eel's head. "Only use your legs," she said. "See that you can bustle about, and bow your heads before the old Duck yonder. She's the grandest of all here; she's of Spanish blood—that's why she's so fat; and d'ye see? she has a red rag round her leg; that's something particularly fine, and the greatest distinction a duck can enjoy: it signifies that one does not want to lose her, and that she's to be known by the animals and by men too. Shake yourselves— don't turn in your toes; a well-brought-up duck turns its toes quite out, just like father and mother,—so! Now bend your necks and say 'Quack!'"

And they did so: but the other ducks round about looked at them, and said quite boldly,—

"Look there! now we're to have these hanging on, as if there were not enough of us already! And—fie!—how that Duckling yonder looks; we won't stand that!" And one duck flew up at it, and bit it in the neck.

"Let it alone," said the mother; "it does no harm to any one."

"Yes, but it's too large and peculiar," said the Duck who had bitten it; "and therefore it must be put down."

"Those are pretty children that the mother has there," said the old Duck with the rag round her leg. "They're all pretty but that one; that was rather unlucky. I wish she could bear it over again."

"That cannot be done, my lady," replied the Mother-Duck. "It is not pretty, but it has a really good disposition, and swims as well as any other; yes, I may even say it, swims better. I think it will grow up pretty, and become smaller in time; it has lain too long in the egg, and therefore is not properly shaped." And then she pinched it in the neck, and smoothed its feathers. "Moreover it is a drake," she said, "and therefore it is not of so much consequence. I think he will be very strong: he makes his way already."

"The other ducklings are graceful enough," said the old Duck. "Make yourself at home; and if you find an eel's head, you may bring it me."

And now they were at home. But the poor Duckling which had crept last out of the egg, and looked so ugly, was bitten and pushed and jeered, as much by the ducks as by the chickens.

"It is too big!" they all said. And the turkey-cock, who had been born with the spurs, and therefore thought himself an emperor, blew himself up like a ship in full sail, and bore straight down upon it; then he gobbled and grew quite red in the face. The poor Duckling did not know where it should stand or walk; it was quite melancholy because it looked ugly, and was the butt of the whole duck-yard.

So it went on the first day; and afterwards it became worse and worse. The poor Duckling was hunted about by every one; even its brothers and sisters were quite angry with it, and said, "If the cat would only catch you, you ugly creature!" And the mother said, "If you were only far away!" And the ducks bit it, and the chickens beat it, and the girl who had to feed the poultry kicked at it with her foot.

Then it ran and flew over the fence, and the little birds in the bushes flew up in fear.

"That is because I am so ugly!" thought the Duckling; and it shut its eyes, but flew on further; and so it came out into the great moor, where the wild ducks lived. Here it lay the whole night long; and it was weary and downcast.

Towards morning the wild ducks flew up, and looked at their new companion.

"What sort of a one are you?" they asked; and the Duckling turned in every direction, and bowed as well as it could. "You are remarkably ugly!" said the Wild Ducks. "But that is nothing to us, so long as you do not marry into our family."

Poor thing! it certainly did not think of marrying, and only hoped to obtain leave to lie among the reeds and drink some of the swamp water.

Thus it lay two whole days; then came thither two wild geese, or, properly speaking, two wild ganders. It was not long since each had crept out of an egg, and that's why they were so saucy.

"Listen, comrade," said one of them. "You're so ugly that I like you. Will you go with us, and become a bird of passage? Near here, in another moor, there are a few sweet lovely wild geese, all unmarried, and all able to say 'Rap?' You've a chance of making your fortune, ugly as you are."

"Piff! paff!" resounded through the air; and the two ganders fell down dead in the swamp, and the water became blood red. "Piff! paff!" it sounded again, and the whole flock of wild geese rose up from the reeds. And then there was another report. A great hunt was going on. The sportsmen were lying in wait all round the moor, and some were even sitting up in the branches of the trees, which spread far over the reeds. The blue smoke rose up like clouds among the dark trees, and was wafted far away across the water; and the hunting dogs came—splash, splash!—into the swamp, and the rushes and the reeds bent down on every side. That was a fright for the poor Duckling! It turned its head, and put it under its wing; but at that moment a frightful great dog stood close by the Duckling. His tongue hung far out of his mouth, and his eyes gleamed horrible and ugly; he thrust out his nose close against the Duckling, showed his sharp teeth, and—splash, splash!—on he went, without seizing it.

"O, Heaven be thanked!" sighed the Duckling. "I am so ugly, that even the dog does not like to bite me!"

And so it lay quite quiet, while the shots rattled through the reeds and gun after gun was fired. At last, late in the day, all was still; but the poor Duckling did not dare to rise up; it waited several hours before it looked round, and then hastened away out of the moor as fast as it could. It ran on over field and meadow; there was such a storm raging that it was difficult to get from one place to another.

Towards evening the Duck came to a little miserable peasant's hut. This hut was so dilapidated that it did not itself know on which side it should fall; and that's why it remained standing. The storm whistled round the Duckling in such a way that the poor creature was obliged to sit down, to stand against it; and the wind blew worse and worse. Then the Duckling noticed that one of the hinges of the door had given way, and the door hung so slanting that the Duckling could slip through the crack into the room; and that is what it did.

Here lived a woman, with her Cat and her Hen. And the Cat, whom she called Sonnie, could arch his back and purr, he could even give out sparks; but for that one had to stroke his fur the wrong way. The Hen had quite little short legs, and therefore she was called Chickabiddy Shortshanks; she laid good eggs, and the woman loved her as her own child.

In the morning the strange Duckling was at once noticed, and the Cat began to purr and the Hen to cluck.

"What's this?" said the woman, and looked all round; but she could not see well, and therefore she thought the Duckling was a fat duck that had strayed. "This is a rare prize!" she said. "Now I shall have duck's eggs. I hope it is not a drake. We must try that."

And so the Duckling was admitted on trial for three weeks; but no eggs came. And the Cat was master of the house, and the Hen was the lady, and always said "We and the world!" for she thought they were half the world, and by far the better half. The Duckling thought one might have a different opinion, but the Hen would not allow it.

"Can you lay eggs?" she asked.

"No."

"Then will you hold your tongue!"

And the Cat said, "Can you curve your back, and purr, and give out sparks?"

"No."

"Then you will please have no opinion of your own when sensible folks are speaking."

And the Duckling sat in a corner and was melancholy; then the fresh air and the sunshine streamed in; and it was seized with such a strange longing to swim on the water, that it could not help telling the Hen of it.

"What are you thinking of?" cried the Hen. "You have

nothing to do, that's why you have these fancies. Lay eggs, or purr, and they will pass over."

"But it is so charming to swim on the water!" said the Duckling, "so refreshing to let it close above one's head, and to dive down to the bottom."

"Yes, that must be a mighty pleasure, truly," quoth the Hen. "I fancy you must have gone crazy. Ask the Cat about it,—he's the cleverest animal I know,—ask him if he likes to swim on the water, or to dive down: I won't speak about myself. Ask our mistress, the old woman; no one in the world is cleverer than she. Do you think she has any desire to swim, and to let the water close above her head?"

"You don't understand me," said the Duckling.

"We don't understand you? Then pray who is to understand you? You surely don't pretend to be cleverer than the Cat and the woman—I won't say anything of myself. Don't be conceited, child, and thank your Maker for all the kindness you have received. Did you not get into a warm room, and have you not fallen into company from which you may learn something? But you are a chatterer, and it is not pleasant to associate with you. You may believe me, I speak for your good. I tell you disagreeable things, and by that one may always know one's true friends! Only take care that you learn to lay eggs, or to purr, and give out sparks!"

"I think I will go out into the wide world," said the Duckling.

"Yes, do go," replied the Hen.

And so the Duckling went away. It swam on the water, and dived, but it was slighted by every creature because of its ugliness.

Now came the autumn. The leaves in the forest turned yellow and brown; the wind caught them so that they danced about, and up in the air it was very cold. The clouds hung low, heavy with hail and snow-flakes, and on the fence stood the raven, crying, "Croak! croak!" for mere cold; yes, it was enough to make one feel cold to think of this. The poor little Duckling certainly had not a good time. One evening—the sun was just setting in his beauty—there came a whole flock of great, handsome birds out of the bushes; they were dazzlingly white, with long, flexible necks; they were swans.

They uttered a very peculiar cry, spread forth their glorious great wings, and flew away from that cold region to warmer lands, to fair open lakes. They mounted so high, so high! and the ugly Duckling felt quite strangely as it watched them. It turned round and round in the water like a wheel, stretched out its neck towards them, and uttered such a strange, loud cry as frightened itself. O! it could not forget those beautiful, happy birds; and so soon as it could see them no longer, it dived down to the very bottom, and when it came up again, it was quite beside itself. It knew not the name of those birds, and knew not whither they were flying; but it loved them more than it had ever loved any one. It was not at all envious of them. How could it think of wishing to possess such loveliness as they had? It would have been glad if only the ducks would have endured its company—the poor, ugly creature!

And the winter grew cold, very cold! The Duckling was forced to swim about in the water, to prevent the surface from freezing entirely; but every night the hole in which it swam about became smaller and smaller. It froze so hard that the icy covering crackled again; and the Duckling was obliged to use its legs continually to prevent the hole from freezing up. At last it became exhausted, and lay quite still, and thus froze fast into the ice.

Early in the morning a peasant came by, and when he saw what had happened, he took his wooden shoe, broke the ice-crust to pieces, and carried the Duckling home to his wife. Then it came to itself again. The children wanted to play with it; but the Duckling thought they wanted to hurt it, and in its terror fluttered up into the milk-pan, so that the milk spurted down into the room. The woman clasped her hands, at which the Duckling flew down into the butter-tub, and then into the meal barrel and out again. How it looked then! The woman screamed, and struck at it with the fire-tongs; the children tumbled over one another in their efforts to catch the Duckling; and they laughed and they screamed! —well it was that the door stood open, and the poor creature was able to slip out between the shrubs into the newly-fallen snow—there it lay quite exhausted.

But it would be too melancholy if I were to tell all the

misery and care which the Duckling had to endure in the hard winter. It lay out on the moor among the reeds, when the sun began to shine again and the larks to sing: it was a beautiful spring.

Then all at once the Duckling could flap its wings: they beat the air more strongly than before, and bore it strongly away; and before it well knew how all this happened, it found itself in a great garden, where the elder-trees smelt sweet, and bent their long green branches down to the canal that wound through the region. O, here it was so beautiful, such a gladness of spring! and from the thicket came three glorious white swans; they rustled their wings, and swam lightly on the water. The Duckling knew the splendid creatures, and felt oppressed by a peculiar sadness.

"I will fly away to them, to the royal birds; and they will beat me, because I, that am so ugly, dare to come near them. But it is all the same. Better be killed by *them* than to be pursued by ducks, and beaten by fowls, and pushed about by the girl who takes care of the poultry yard, and to suffer hunger in winter!" And it flew out into the water, and swam towards the beautiful swans: these looked at it, and came sailing down upon it with outspread wings. "Kill me!" said the poor creature, and bent its head down upon the water, expecting nothing but death. But what was this that it saw in the clear water? It beheld its own image; and, lo! it was no longer a clumsy dark-gray bird, ugly and hateful to look at, but a—swan!

It matters nothing if one is born in a duck-yard, if one has only lain in a swan's egg.

It felt quite glad at all the need and misfortune it had suffered, now it realized its happiness in all the splendor that surrounded it. And the great swans swam round it, and stroked it with their beaks.

Into the garden came little children, who threw bread and corn into the water; and the youngest cried, "There is a new one!" and the other children shouted joyously, "Yes, a new one has arrived!" And they clapped their hands and danced about, and ran to their father and mother; and bread and cake were thrown into the water; and they all said, "The new one is the most beautiful of all! so young and handsome!" and the old swans bowed their heads before him.

Then he felt quite ashamed, and hid his head under his wings, for he did not know what to do; he was so happy, and yet not at all proud. He thought how he had been persecuted and despised; and now he heard them saying that he was the most beautiful of all birds. Even the elder-tree bent its branches straight down into the water before him, and the sun shown warm and mild. Then his wings rustled, he lifted his slender neck, and cried rejoicingly from the depths of his heart,—

"I never dreamed of so much happiness when I was the Ugly Duckling!"

THE SWINEHERD

THERE was once a poor Prince; he had a kingdom that was very small; still it was quite large enough to marry upon; and he wished to marry.

It was certainly rather cool of him to say to the Emperor's daughter, "Will you have me?" But so he did; for his name was renowned far and wide; and there were a hundred Princesses who would have answered, "Thank you." But see what she said. Now we will hear.

By the grave of the Prince's father there grew a rose-tree, —a most beautiful rose-tree; it blossomed only once in every five years, and even then bore only one flower, but that was a rose that smelt so sweet as to make one forget all cares and sorrows.

And furthermore, the Prince had a nightingale, who could sing in such a manner that it seemed as though all sweet melodies dwelt in her little throat. So the Princess was to have the rose and the nightingale; and they were accordingly put into large silver caskets, and sent to her.

The Emperor had them brought into a large hall, where the Princess was playing at "making calls," with the ladies of the court; they never did anything else, and when she saw the caskets with the presents, she clapped her hands for joy.

"Ah, if it were but a little pussy-cat!" exclaimed she; then out came the beautiful rose.

"O, how prettily it is made!" said all the court-ladies.

"It is more than pretty," said the Emperor; "it is charming!"

But the Princess touched it and was almost ready to cry.

"Fie, papa!" said she, "it is not made at all; it is natural!"

"Fie!" cried all the court-ladies; "it is natural!"

"Let us see what is in the other casket, before we get into a bad humor," proposed the Emperor. So the Nightingale came forth, and sang so delightfully that at first no one could say anything ill-humored of it.

"*Superbe! charmant!*" exclaimed the ladies; for they all used to chatter French, each one worse than her neighbor.

"How much the bird reminds me of the musical box that belonged to our blessed Empress!" remarked an old Knight. "Ah yes! it is the very same tone, the same execution."

"Yes! yes!" said the Emperor, and he wept like a little child.

"I will still hope that it is not a real bird," said the Princess.

"Yet it is a real bird," said those who had brought it.

"Well, then let the bird fly," returned the Princess; and she positively refused to see the Prince.

However, he was not to be discouraged; he daubed his face over brown and black; pulled his cap over his ears, and knocked at the door.

"Good day, Emperor!" said he. "Can I have employment at the palace?"

"O there are so many that want a place!" said the Emperor; "well, let me see, I want some one to take care of the pigs, for we have a great many of them."

So the Prince was appointed "Imperial Swineherd." He had a dirty little room close by the pig-sty; and there he sat the whole day, and worked. By the evening, he had made a pretty little saucepan. Little bells were hung all around it; and when the pot was boiling, these bells tinkled in the most charming manner, and played the old melody:—

> "Ah! thou dearest Augustine!
> All is gone, gone, gone!"

But what was still more curious, whoever held his finger in the smoke of this saucepan, immediately smelt all the dishes that were cooking on every hearth in the city: this, you see, was something quite different from the rose.

Now the Princess happened to walk that way; and when she heard the tune, she stood quite still, and seemed pleased; for she could play "Dearest Augustine;" it was the only piece she knew, and she played it with one finger.

"Why, there is my piece!" said the Princess; "that Swineherd must certainly have been well educated! Here! Go in and ask him the price of the instrument."

And so one of the court-ladies must run in; however, she drew on wooden slippers first.

"What will you take for the saucepan?" inquired the lady.

"I will have ten kisses from the Princess," said the Swineherd.

"Mercy on us!" said the lady.

"Yes, I cannot sell it for less," said the swineherd.

"Well, what does he say?" asked the Princess.

"I cannot tell you really," replied the lady; "it is too bad!"

"Then you can whisper it!" So the lady whispered it.

"He is an impudent fellow!" said the Princess, and she walked on; but when she had gone a little way, the bells tinkled so prettily,—

> "Ah! thou dearest Augustine!
> All is gone, gone, gone!"

"Stay," said the Princess. "Ask him if he will have ten kisses from the ladies of my court."

"No, thank you!" answered the swineherd: "ten kisses from the Princess, or I keep the saucepan myself."

"That must not be, either!" said the Princess; "but do you all stand before me, that no one may see us."

And the court-ladies placed themselves in front of her, and spread out their dresses; and so the Swineherd got ten kisses, and she got the saucepan.

It was delightful! the saucepan was kept boiling all the evening, and the whole of the following day. They knew perfectly well what was cooking at every fire throughout the city, from the chamberlain's to the cobbler's; the court-ladies danced, and clapped their hands.

"We know who has soup and who has pancakes for dinner to-day, who has cutlets, and who has eggs. How interesting!"

And "How interesting!" said the Lord Steward's wife.

"Yes, but keep my secret, for I am an Emperor's daughter."

"Mercy on us," said they all.

The Swineherd—that is to say the Prince, for no one knew that he was other than an ill-favored swineherd—let not a day pass without working at something; he at last constructed a rattle, which, when it was swung round, played all the waltzes and jig-tunes which have ever been heard since the creation of the world.

"Ah, that is *superbe!*" said the Princess when she passed by; "I have never heard prettier compositions! Go in and ask him the price of the instrument; but I won't kiss him!"

"He will have a hundred kisses from the Princess!" said the court-lady who had been in to ask.

"I think he is crazy!" said the Princess, and walked on; but when she had gone a little way, she stopped again. "One must encourage art," said she; "I am the Emperor's daughter. Tell him, he shall, as on yesterday, have ten kisses from me, and may take the rest from the ladies of the court."

"O! but we should not like that at all!" said the court-ladies.

"What are you muttering?" asked the Princess; "if I can kiss him, surely you can! Remember, I give you your food and wages." So the court-ladies were obliged to go to him again.

"A hundred kisses from the Princess!" said he, "or else let every one keep his own."

"Stand round!" said she; and all the ladies stood round her whilst the kissing was going on.

"What can be the reason for such a crowd close by the pig-sty?" said the Emperor, who happened just then to step out on the balcony. He rubbed his eyes and put on his spectacles. "They are ladies of the court; there is some play going on. I must go down and see what they are about!" So he pulled up his slippers at the heel, for he had trodden them down.

Heh there! what a hurry he is in.

As soon as he had got into the court-yard, he moved very softly, and the ladies were so much engrossed with counting the kisses, that all might go on fairly, that they did not perceive the Emperor. He rose on his tiptoes.

"What is all this?" said he, when he saw what was going on, and he boxed the Princess's ears with his slipper, just as the Swineherd was taking the eighty-sixth kiss.

"Off with you!" cried the Emperor, for he was very angry; and both Princess and Swineherd were thrust out of the city.

The Princess now stood and wept, the Swineherd scolded, and the rain poured down.

"O how miserable I am!" said the Princess. "If I had but married the handsome young Prince! Ah! how unfortunate I am!"

And the Swineherd went behind a tree, washed the black-and-brown color from his face, threw off his dirty clothes, and stepped forth in his princely robes; he looked so noble that the Princess could not help bowing before him.

"I am come to despise thee," said he. "Thou wouldst not have an honourable prince! thou couldst not prize the rose and the nightingale, but thou wast ready to kiss the Swineherd for the sake of a trumpery plaything. Now thou hast thy deserts!"

He then went back to his own little kingdom, and shut the door of his palace in her face. Now she might well sing,

"Ah! thou dearest Augustine!
All is gone, gone, gone!"

THE EMPEROR'S NEW CLOTHES

MANY years ago there lived an Emperor, who was so excessively fond of grand new clothes that he spent all his money upon them, that he might be very fine. He did not care about his soldiers, nor about the theatre, and only liked to drive out and show his new clothes. He had a coat for every hour of the day; and just as they say of a king, " He is in council," so they always said of him, " The Emperor is in the wardrobe."

In the great city in which he lived it was always very merry; every day came many strangers; one day two rogues came: they gave themselves out as weavers, and declared they could weave the finest stuff any one could imagine. Not only were their colors and patterns, they said, uncommonly beautiful, but the clothes made of the stuff possessed the wonderful quality that they became invisible to any one who was unfit for the office he held, or was incorrigibly stupid.

" Those would be capital clothes! " thought the Emperor. " If I wore those, I should be able to find out what men in my empire are not fit for the places they have; I could tell the clever from the dunces. Yes, the stuff must be woven for me directly! "

And he gave the two rogues a great deal of cash in hand, that they might begin their work at once.

As for them, they put up two looms, and pretended to be working; but they had nothing at all on their looms. They at once demanded the finest silk and the costliest gold; this they put into their own pockets, and worked at the empty looms till late into the night.

" I should like to know how far they have got on with the stuff," thought the Emperor. But he felt quite uncomfortable when he thought that those who were not fit for their offices could not see it. He believed, indeed, that he had nothing to fear for himself, but yet he preferred first to send some one else to see how matters stood. All the people in the city knew what peculiar power the stuff possessed, and all were anxious to see how bad or how stupid their neighbors were.

"I will send my honest old Minister to the weavers," thought the Emperor. "He can judge best how the stuff looks, for he has sense, and no one understands his office better than he."

Now the good old Minister went out into the hall where the two rogues sat working at the empty looms.

"Mercy on us!" thought the old Minister, and he opened his eyes wide. "I cannot see anything at all!" But he did not say this.

Both the rogues begged him to be so good as to come nearer, and asked if he did not approve of the colors and the pattern. Then they pointed to the empty loom, and the poor old Minister went on opening his eyes; but he could see nothing, for there was nothing to see.

"Mercy!" thought he, "can I indeed be so stupid? I never thought that, and not a soul must know it. Am I not fit for my office? No, it will never do for me to tell that I could not see the stuff."

"Don't you say anything to it?" asked one, as he went on weaving.

"O, it is charming—quite enchanting!" answered the old Minister, as he peered through his spectacles. "What a fine pattern, and what colors! Yes, I shall tell the Emperor that I am very much pleased with it."

"Well, we are glad of that," said both the weavers; and then they named the colors, and explained the strange pattern. The old Minister listened attentively, that he might be able to repeat it when the Emperor came. And he did so.

Now the rogues asked for more money, and silk and gold, which they declared they wanted for weaving. They put all into their own pockets, and not a thread was put upon the loom; they continued to work at the empty frames as before.

The Emperor soon sent again, dispatching another honest officer of the court, to see how the weaving was going on, and if the stuff would soon be ready. He fared just like the first: he looked and looked, but, as there was nothing to be seen but the empty looms, he could see nothing.

"Is not that a pretty piece of stuff?" asked the two

rogues; and they displayed and explained the handsome pattern which was not there at all.

"I am not stupid!" thought the man: "it must be my good office, for which I am not fit. It is funny enough, but I must not let it be noticed." And so he praised the stuff which he did not see, and expressed his pleasure at the beautiful colors and charming pattern. "Yes, it is enchanting," he told the Emperor.

All the people in the town were talking of the gorgeous stuff. The Emperor wished to see it himself while it was still upon the loom. With a whole crowd of chosen men, among whom were also the two honest statesmen who had already been there, he went to the two cunning rogues, who were now weaving with might and main without fibre or thread.

"Is not that splendid?" said the two statesmen, who had already been there once. "Does not your Majesty remark the pattern and the colors?" And they pointed to the empty loom, for they thought that the others could see the stuff.

"What's this?" thought the Emperor. "I can see nothing at all! That is terrible. Am I stupid? Am I not fit to be Emperor? That would be the most dreadful thing that could happen to me. O, it is *very* pretty!" he said aloud. "It has our highest approbation." And he nodded in a contented way, and gazed at the empty loom, for he would not say that he saw nothing. The whole suite whom he had with him looked and looked, and saw nothing, any more than the rest; but, like the Emperor, they said, "That *is* pretty!" and counseled him to wear the splendid new clothes for the first time at the great procession that was presently to take place. "It is splendid, excellent!" went from mouth to mouth. On all sides there seemed to be general rejoicing, and the Emperor gave the rogues the title of Imperial Court Weavers.

The whole night before the morning on which the procession was to take place, the rogues were up, and kept more than sixteen candles burning. The people could see that they were hard at work, completing the Emperor's new clothes. They pretended to take the stuff down from the loom; they made cuts in the air with great scissors; they sewed with needles without thread; and at last they said, "Now the clothes are ready!"

The Emperor came himself with his noblest cavaliers; and the two rogues lifted up one arm as if they were holding something, and said, "See, here are the trousers! here is the coat! here is the cloak!" and so on. "It is as light as a spider's web: one would think one had nothing on; but that is just the beauty of it."

"Yes," said all the cavaliers; but they could not see anything, for nothing was there.

"Will your Imperial Majesty please to condescend to take off your clothes?" said the rogues; "then we will put on you the new clothes here in front of the great mirror."

The Emperor took off his clothes, and the rogues pretended to put on him each new garment as it was ready; and the Emperor turned round and round before the mirror.

"O, how well they look! how capitally they fit!" said all. "What a pattern! what colors! That *is* a splendid dress!"

"They are standing outside with the canopy, which is to be borne above your Majesty in the procession!" announced the head Master of the Ceremonies.

"Well, I am ready," replied the Emperor. "Does it not suit me well?" And then he turned again to the mirror, for he wanted it to appear as if he contemplated his adornment with great interest.

The two chamberlains, who were to carry the train, stooped down with their hands toward the floor, just as if they were picking up the mantle; then they pretended to be holding something in the air. They did not dare to let it be noticed that they saw nothing.

So the Emperor went in procession under the rich canopy, and every one in the streets said, "How incomparable are the Emperor's new clothes! what a train he has to his mantle! how it fits him!" No one would let it be perceived that he could see nothing, for that would have shown that he was not fit for his office, or was very stupid. No clothes of the Emperor's had ever had such a success as these.

"But he has nothing on!" a little child cried out at last.

"Just hear what that innocent says!" said the father: and one whispered to another what the child had said.

"But he has nothing on!" said the whole people at length. That touched the Emperor, for it seemed to him that they were right; but he thought within himself, "I must go through with the procession." And so he held himself a little higher, and the chamberlains held on tighter than ever, and carried the train which did not exist at all.

THE LITTLE SEA-MAID

FAR out in the sea the water is as blue as the petals of the most beautiful corn-flower, and as clear as the purest glass. But it is very deep, deeper than any cable will sound; many steeples must be placed one above the other to reach from the ground to the surface of the water. And down there live the sea-people.

Now, you must not believe there is nothing down there but the naked sand; no,—the strangest trees and plants grow there, so pliable in their stalks and leaves that at the least motion of the water they move just as if they had life. All fishes, great and small, glide among the twigs, just as here the birds do in the trees. In the deepest spot of all lies the Sea-king's castle: the walls are of coral, and the tall, Gothic windows of the clearest amber; shells form the roof, and they open and shut according as the water flows. It looks lovely, for in each shell lie gleaming pearls, a single one of which would have great value in a queen's diadem.

The Sea-king below there had been a widower for many years, while his old mother kept house for him. She was a clever woman, but proud of her rank, so she wore twelve oysters on her tail, while the other great people were only allowed to wear six. Beyond this she was deserving of great praise, especially because she was very fond of her grand-daughters, the little Sea-princesses. These were six pretty children; but the youngest was the most beautiful of all. Her skin was as clear and as fine as a rose leaf;

her eyes were as blue as the deepest sea; but, like all the rest, she had no feet, for her body ended in a fish-tail.

All day long they could play in the castle, down in the halls, where living flowers grew out of the walls. The great amber windows were opened, and then the fishes swam in to them, just as the swallows fly in to us when we open our windows; but the fishes swam straight up to the Princesses, ate out of their hands, and let themselves be stroked.

Outside the castle was a great garden with bright red and dark blue flowers; the fruit glowed like gold, and the flowers like flames of fire; and they continually kept moving their stalks and leaves. The earth itself was the finest sand, but blue as the flame of brimstone. A peculiar blue radiance lay upon everything down there: one would have thought oneself high in the air, with the canopy of heaven above and around, rather than at the bottom of the deep sea. During a calm the sun could be seen; it appeared like a purple flower, from which all light streamed out.

Each of the little Princesses had her own little place in the garden, where she might dig and plant at her good pleasure. One gave her flower-bed the form of a whale; another thought it better to make hers like a little sea-woman: but the youngest made hers quite round, like the sun and had flowers which gleamed red as the sun itself. She was a strange child, quiet and thoughtful, and when the other sisters made a display of the beautiful things they had received out of wrecked ships, she would have nothing beyond the red flowers which resembled the sun, except a pretty marble statue. This was a figure of a charming boy, hewn out of white clear stone, which had sunk down to the bottom of the sea from a wreck. She planted a pink weeping willow beside this statue; the tree grew famously, and hung its fresh branches over the statue towards the blue sandy ground, where the shadow showed violet, and moved like the branches themselves; it seemed as if the ends of the branches and the roots were playing together and wished to kiss each other.

There was no greater pleasure for her than to hear of the world of men above them. The old grandmother had to tell all she knew of ships and towns, of men and animals. It seemed particularly beautiful to her that up on the earth the flowers shed fragrance, for they had none down at the bottom of the sea, and that the trees were green, and that the fishes which one saw there among the trees could sing so loud and clear that it was a pleasure to hear them. What the grandmother called fishes were the little birds; the Princess could not understand them in any other way, for she had never seen a bird.

"When you have reached your fifteenth year," said the grandmother, " you shall have leave to rise up out of the sea, to sit on the rocks in the moonlight, and to see the great ships as they sail by. Then you will see forests and towns!"

In the next year one of the sisters was fifteen years of age, but each of the others was one year younger than the next; so that the youngest had full five years to wait before she could come up from the bottom of the sea, and find how our world looked. But one promised to tell the others what she had seen and what she had thought the most beautiful on the first day of her visit; for their grandmother could not tell them enough—there was so much about which they wanted information.

No one was more anxious about these things than the youngest—just that one who had the longest time to wait, and who was always quiet and thoughtful. Many a night she stood by the open window, and looked up through the dark blue water at the fishes splashing with their fins and tails. Moon and stars she could see; they certainly shone quite faintly, but through the water they looked much larger than they appear in our eyes. When something like a black cloud passed among them, she knew that it was either a whale swimming over her head, or a ship with many people: they certainly did not think that a pretty little sea-maid was standing down below stretching up her white hands towards the keel of their ship.

Now the eldest Princess was fifteen years old, and might mount up to the surface of the sea.

When she came back, she had a hundred things to tell,— but the finest thing, she said, was to lie in the moonshine on a sand-bank in the quiet sea, and to look at the neigh-

boring coast, with the large town, where the lights twinkled
like a hundred stars, and to hear the music and the noise
and clamor of carriages and men, to see the many church
steeples, and to hear the sound of the bells. Just because
she could not get up to these, she longed for them more than
for anything.

O how the youngest sister listened! and afterwards when
she stood at the open window and looked up through the
dark-blue water, she thought of the great city with all its
bustle and noise; and then she thought she could hear the
church bells ringing, even down to the depth where she was.

In the following year, the second sister received permission to mount upward through the water and to swim
whither she pleased. She rose up just as the sun was setting, and this spectacle, she said, was the most beautiful.
The whole sky looked like gold, and as to the clouds, she
could not properly describe their beauty. They sailed away
over her head, purple and violet-colored, but far quicker
than the clouds there flew a flight of wild swans, like a long
white veil, over the water towards where the sun stood.
She swam towards them; but the sun sank, and the roseate
hue faded on the sea and in the clouds.

In the following year the next sister went up. She was
the boldest of them all, and therefore she swam up a
broad stream that poured its waters into the sea. She saw
glorious green hills clothed with vines; palaces and castles
shone forth from amid splendid woods; she heard how all
the birds sang; and the sun shone so warm that she was
often obliged to dive under the water to cool her glowing
face. In a little bay she found a whole swarm of little
mortals. They were quite naked, and splashed about in
the water; she wanted to play with them, but they fled in
affright and a little black animal came,—it was a dog, but
she had never seen a dog,—and it barked at her so terribly
that she became frightened, and tried to gain the open sea.
But she could never forget the glorious woods, the green
hills, and the pretty children, who could swim in the water,
though they had not fish-tails.

The fourth sister was not so bold: she remained out in
the midst of the wild sea, and declared that just there it was

most beautiful. One could see for many miles around, and the sky above looked like a bell of glass. She had seen ships, but only in the far distance—they looked like sea-gulls; and the funny dolphins had thrown somersaults, and the great whales spouted out water from their nostrils, so that it looked like hundreds of fountains all around.

Now came the turn of the fifth sister. Her birthday came in the winter, and so she saw what the others had not seen the first time. The sea looked quite green, and great icebergs were floating about; each one separated like a pearl, she said, and yet was much taller than the church steeples built by men. They showed themselves in the strangest forms, and shone like diamonds. She had seated herself upon one of the greatest of all, and let the wind play with her long hair; and all the sailing ships tacked about in a very rapid way beyond where she sat: but toward evening the sky became covered with clouds, it thundered and lightened, and the black waves lifted the great ice-blocks high up, and let them glow in the red glare. On all the ships the sails were reefed, and there was fear and anguish. But she sat quietly upon her floating iceberg, and saw the forked blue flashes dart into the sea.

Each of the sisters, as she came up for the first time to the surface of the water, was delighted with the new and beautiful sights she saw; but as they now had permission, as grown-up girls, to go whenever they liked, it became in-different to them. They wished themselves back again, and after a month had elapsed they said it was best of all down below, for there one felt so comfortably at home.

Many an evening hour the five sisters took one another by the arm and rose up in a row over the water. They had splendid voices, more charming than any mortal could have; and when a storm was approaching, so that they could apprehend that ships would go down, they swam on before the ships and sang lovely songs, which told how beautiful it was at the bottom of the sea, and exhorted the sailors not to be afraid to come down. But these could not under-stand the words, and thought it was the storm sighing; and they did not see the splendors below, for if the ships sank they were drowned, and came as corpses to the Sea-king's palace.

When the sisters thus rose up, arm in arm, in the evening time, through the water, the little sister stood all alone looking after them; and she felt as if she must weep; but the sea-maid has no tears and for this reason she suffers far more acutely.

"O if I were only fifteen years old!" said she. "I know I shall love the world up there very much, and the people who live and dwell there."

At last she was really fifteen years old.

"Now, you see, you are grown up," said the grandmother, the old dowager. "Come, let me adorn you like your sisters."

And she put a wreath of white lilies in the little maid's hair, but each flower was half a pearl; and the old lady let eight great oysters attach themselves to the Princess's tail, in token of her high rank.

"But that hurts so!" said the little Sea-maid.

"Yes, pride must suffer pain," replied the old lady.

O how glad she would have been to shake off all the tokens of rank and lay aside the heavy wreath! Her red flowers in the garden suited her better; but she could not help it. "Farewell!" she said, and then she rose, light and clear as a water-bubble, up through the sea.

The sun had just set when she lifted her head above the sea, but all the clouds still shone like roses and gold, and in the pale red sky the evening-stars gleamed bright and beautiful. The air was mild and fresh, and the sea quite calm. There lay a great ship with three masts; one single sail only was set, for not a breeze stirred, and around in the shrouds and on the yards sat the sailors. There was music and singing, and as the evening closed in, hundreds of colored lanterns were lighted up, and looked as if the flags of every nation were waving in the air. The little Sea-maid swam straight to the cabin window, and each time the sea lifted her up, she could look through the panes, which were clear as crystal, and see many people standing within dressed in their best. But the handsomest of all was the young Prince with the great black eyes: he was certainly not much more than sixteen years old; it was his birthday, and that was the cause of all this feasting. The sailors were dancing upon deck; and when the young Prince came out, more than a hundred rockets rose into the air; they shone like day, so that the little Sea-maid was quite startled, and dived under the water; but soon she put out her head again, and then it seemed just as if all the stars of heaven were falling down upon her. She had never seen such fire-works. Great suns spurted fire all around, glorious fiery fishes flew up into the blue air, and everything was mirrored in the clear blue sea. The ship itself was so brightly lit up that every separate rope could be seen, and the people therefore appeared the more plainly. O how handsome the young Prince was! And he pressed the people's hands and smiled, while the music rang out in the glorious night.

It became late; but the little Sea-maid could not turn her eyes from the ship and from the beautiful Prince. The colored lanterns were extinguished, rockets ceased to fly into the air, and no more cannons were fired; but there was a murmuring and a buzzing deep down in the sea; and she sat on the water, swaying up and down, so that she could look into the cabin. But as the ship got more way, one sail after another was spread. And now the waves rose higher, great clouds came up, and in the distance there was lightning. O! it was going to be fearful weather, therefore the sailors furled the sails. The great ship flew in swift career over the wild sea: the waters rose up like great black mountains, which wanted to roll over the masts; but like a swan the ship dived into the valleys between these high waves, and then let itself be lifted on high again. To the little Sea-maid this seemed merry sport, but to the sailors it appeared very differently. The ship groaned and creaked; the thick planks were bent by the heavy blows; the sea broke into the ship; the mainmast snapped in two like a thin reed, and the ship lay over on her side, while the water rushed into the hold. Now the little Sea-maid saw that the people were in peril; she herself was obliged to take care to avoid the beams and fragments of the ship which were floating about on the waters. One moment it was so pitch dark that not a single object could be descried, but when it lightened it became so bright that she could distinguish every one on board. She looked particularly for the young Prince, and when the ship parted she saw him sink into the sea. Then she was very glad, for now he would come down to her. But then she remembered that people could not live in the water, and that when he got down to her father's palace he would certainly be dead. No, he must not die: so she swam about among the beams and planks that strewed the surface, quite forgetting that one of them might have crushed her. Diving down deep under the water, she again rose high up among the waves, and in this way she at last came to the Prince, who could scarcely swim longer in that stormy sea. His arms and legs began to fail him, his beautiful eyes closed, and he would have died had the little Sea-maid not come. She held his head up over the water, and then allowed the waves to carry her and him whither they listed.

When the morning came the storm had passed by. Of the ship not a fragment was to be seen. The sun came up red and shining out of the water; it was as if its beams brought back the hue of life to the cheeks of the Prince, but his eyes remained closed. The Sea-maid kissed his high, fair forehead and put back his wet hair, and he seemed to her to be like the marble statue in her little garden: she kissed him again and hoped that he might live.

Now she saw in front of her the dry land—high blue mountains, on whose summits the white snow gleamed as if swans were lying there. Down on the coast were glorious green forests, and a building—she could not tell whether it was a church or a convent—stood there. In its garden grew orange and citron-trees, and high palms waved in front of the gate. The sea formed a little bay there; it was quite calm, but very deep. Straight toward the rock where the fine white sand had been cast up, she swam with the handsome Prince, and laid him upon the sand, taking especial care that his head was raised in the warm sunshine.

Now all the bells rang in the great white building, and many young girls came walking through the garden. Then the little Sea-maid swam farther out between some high stones that stood up out of the water, laid some sea-foam

upon her hair and neck, so that no one could see her little
countenance, and then she watched to see who would come
to the poor Prince.

In a short time a young girl went that way. She seemed
to be much startled, but only for a moment; then she brought
more people, and the Sea-maid perceived that the Prince
came back to life, and that he smiled at all around him.
But he did not cast a smile at her: he did not know that
she had saved him. And she felt very sorrowful; and when
he was led away into the great building, she dived mournfully under the water and returned to her father's palace.

She had always been gentle and melancholy, but now she
became much more so. Her sisters asked her what she had
seen the first time she rose up to the surface, but she would
tell them nothing.

Many an evening and many a morning she went up to the
place where she had left the Prince. She saw how the
fruits of the garden grew ripe and were gathered; she saw
how the snow melted on the high mountain; but she did not
see the Prince, and so she always returned home more
sorrowful still. Then her only comfort was to sit in her
little garden, and to wind her arm round the beautiful
marble statue that resembled the Prince; but she did not tend
her flowers; they grew as if in a wilderness over the paths,
and trailed their long leaves and stalks up into the branches
of trees, so that it became quite dark there.

At last she could endure it no longer, and told all to one
of her sisters, and then the others heard of it too; but nobody knew of it beyond these and a few other sea-maids,
who told the secret to their intimate friends. One of
these knew who the Prince was; she too had seen the festival
on board the ship; and she announced whence he came and
where his kingdom lay.

"Come, little sister," said the other Princesses; and
linking their arms together, they rose up in a long row out
of the sea, at the place where they knew the Prince's
palace lay.

This palace was built of a kind of bright yellow stone,
with great marble staircases, one of which led directly down
into the sea. Over the roof rose splendid gilt cupolas,

and between the pillars which surrounded the whole dwelling, stood marble statues which looked as if they were alive. Through the clear glass in the high windows one looked into the glorious halls, where costly silk hangings and tapestries were hung up, and all the walls were decked with splendid pictures, so that it was a perfect delight to see them. In the midst of the greatest of these halls a great fountain plashed; its jets shot high up toward the glass dome in the ceiling, through which the sun shone down upon the water and upon the lovely plants growing in the great basin.

Now she knew where he lived, and many an evening and many a night she spent there on the water. She swam far closer to the land than any of the others would have dared to venture; indeed, she went quite up the narrow channel under the splendid marble balcony, which threw a broad shadow upon the water. Here she sat and watched the young Prince, who thought himself quite alone in the bright moonlight.

Many an evening she saw him sailing, amid the sounds of music, in his costly boat with the waving flags; she peeped up through the green reeds, and when the wind caught her silver-white veil and any one saw it he thought it was a white swan spreading out its wings.

Many a night when the fishermen were on the sea with their torches, she heard much good told of the young Prince; and she rejoiced that she had saved his life when he was driven about, half dead, on the wild billows: she thought how quietly his head had reclined on her bosom, and how heartily she had kissed him; but he knew nothing of it, and could not even dream of her.

More and more she began to love mankind, and more and more she wished to be able to wander about among those whose world seemed far larger than her own. For they could fly over the sea in ships, and mount up the high hills far above the clouds, and the lands they possessed stretched out in woods and fields farther than her eyes could reach. There was much she wished to know, but her sisters could not answer all her questions; therefore she applied to the old grandmother; and the old lady knew the upper world, which she rightly called "the countries above the sea," very well.

"If people are not drowned," asked the little Sea-maid, "can they live forever? Do they not die as we die down here in the sea?"

"Yes," replied the old lady. "They too must die, and their life is even shorter than ours. We can live to be three hundred years old, but when we cease to exist here, we are turned into foam on the surface of the water, and have not even a grave down here among those we love. We have not an immortal soul; we never receive another life; we are like the green sea-weed, which, when once cut through, can never bloom again. Men, on the contrary, have a soul which lives forever, which lives on after the body has become dust; it mounts up through the clear air, up to all the shining stars! As we rise up out of the waters and behold all the lands of the earth, so they rise up to unknown glorious places which we can never see."

"Why did we not receive an immortal soul?" asked the little Sea-maid, sorrowfully. "I would gladly give all the hundreds of years I have to live to be a human being only for one day, and to have a hope of partaking the heavenly kingdom."

"You must not think of that," replied the old lady. "We feel ourselves far more happy and far better than mankind yonder."

"Then I am to die and be cast as foam upon the sea, not hearing the music of the waves, nor seeing the pretty flowers and the red sun? Can I not do anything to win an immortal soul?"

"No!" answered the grandmother. "Only if a man were to love you so that you should be more to him than father or mother; if he should cling to you with his every thought and with all his love, and let the priest lay his right hand in yours with a promise of faithfulness here and in all eternity, then his soul would be imparted to your body, and you would receive a share of the happiness of mankind. He would give a soul to you and yet retain his own. But that can never come to pass. What is considered beautiful here in the sea—the fish-tail—they would consider ugly on

the earth: they don't understand it; there one must have
the clumsy supports which they call legs, to be called beautiful."

Then the little Sea-maid sighed and looked mournfully
upon her fish-tail.

"Let us be glad!" said the old lady. "Let us dance and
leap in the three hundred years we have to live. That is
certainly long enough; after that we can rest ourselves all
the better. This evening we shall have a court ball."

It was a splendid sight, such as is never seen on earth.
The walls and the ceiling of the great dancing-saloon were
of thick but transparent glass. Several hundreds of huge
shells, pink and grass-green, stood on each side in rows,
filled with a blue fire which lit up the whole hall and shone
through the walls, so that the sea without was quite lit up;
one could see all the innumerable fishes, great and small,
swimming toward the glass walls; of some the scales
gleamed with purple, while in others they shone like silver
and gold. Through the midst of the hall flowed a broad
stream, and on this the sea-men and sea-women danced to
their own charming songs. Such beautiful voices the
people of the earth have not. The little Sea-maid sang
the most sweetly of all, and the whole court applauded
with hands and tails, and for a moment she felt gay in her
heart, for she knew she had the loveliest voice of all in the
sea or on the earth. But soon she thought again of the
world above her; she could not forget the charming Prince,
or her sorrow at not having an immortal soul like his.
Therefore she crept out of her father's palace, and while
everything within was joy and gladness, she sat melancholy
in her little garden. Then she heard the bugle horn sounding through the waters, and thought, "Now he is certainly
sailing above, he on whom my wishes hang, and in whose
hand I should like to lay my life's happiness. I will dare
everything to win him and an immortal soul. While my
sisters dance yonder in my father's palace, I will go to
the sea-witch of whom I have always been so much afraid:
perhaps she can counsel and help me."

Now the little Sea-maid went out of her garden to the
foaming whirlpools behind which the sorceress dwelt. She

had never travelled that way before. No flowers grew there, no sea grass; only the naked gray sand stretched out toward the whirlpools, where the water rushed round like roaring mill-wheels and tore down everything it seized into the deep. Through the midst of these rushing whirlpools she was obliged to pass to get in to the domain of the witch; and for a long way there was no other road but one over warm gushing mud: this the witch called her turf-moor. Behind it lay her house in the midst of a singular forest, in which all the trees and bushes were polyps—half animals, half plants. They looked like hundred-headed snakes growing up out of the earth. All the branches were long, slimy arms, with fingers like supple worms, and they moved limb by limb from the root to the farthest point; all that they could seize on in the water they held fast and did not let it go. The little Sea-maid stopped in front of them quite frightened; her heart beat with fear, and she was near turning back; but then she thought of the Prince and the human soul, and her courage came back again. She bound her long flying hair closely around her head, so that the polyps might not seize it. She put her hands together on her breast and then shot forward, as a fish shoots through the water, among the ugly polyps, which stretched out their supple arms and fingers after her. She saw that each of them held something it had seized with hundreds of little arms, like strong iron bands. People who had perished at sea, and had sunk deep down, looked forth as white skeletons from among the polyps' arms; ships' oars and chests they also held fast, and skeletons of land animals, and a little sea-woman whom they had caught and strangled; and this seemed the most terrible of all to our little Princess.

Now she came to a great marshy place in the wood, where fat water-snakes rolled about, showing their ugly cream-colored bodies. In the midst of this marsh was a house built of white bones of shipwrecked men; there sat the Sea-witch, feeding a toad out of her mouth, just as a person might feed a little canary-bird with sugar. She called the ugly fat water-snakes her little chickens, and allowed them to crawl upward and all about her.

"I know what you want," said the Sea-witch. "It is

stupid of you, but you shall have your way, for it will bring you to grief, my pretty Princess. You want to get rid of your fish-tail, and to have two supports instead of it, like those the people of the earth walk with, so that the young Prince may fall in love with you, and you may get an immortal soul." And with this the Witch laughed loudly and disagreeably, so that the toad and the water-snakes tumbled down to the ground, where they crawled about. "You come just in time," said the Witch: "after to-morrow at sunrise I could not help you until another year had gone by. I will prepare a draught for you, with which you must swim to land to-morrow before the sun rises, and seat yourself there and drink it; then your tail will shrivel up and become what the people of the earth call legs; but it will hurt you— it will seem as if you were cut with a sharp sword. All who see you will declare you to be the prettiest human being they ever beheld. You will keep your graceful walk; no dancer will be able to move so lightly as you; but every step you take will be as if you trod upon sharp knives, and as if your blood must flow. If you will bear all this, I can help you."

"Yes!" said the little Sea-maid, with a trembling voice; and she thought of the Prince and the immortal soul.

"But remember," said the Witch, "when you have once received a human form, you can never be a sea-maid again; you can never return through the water to your sisters, or to your father's palace; and if you do not win the Prince's love, so that he forgets father and mother for your sake, is attached to you heart and soul, and tells the priest to join your hands, you will not receive an immortal soul. On the first morning after he has married another your heart will break, and you will become foam on the water."

"I will do it," said the little Sea-maid: but she became as pale as death.

"But you must pay me, too," said the Witch; "and it is not a trifle that I ask. You have the finest voice of all here at the bottom of the water; with that you think to enchant him; but this voice you must give to me. The best thing you possess I will have for my costly draught! I must give you my own blood in it, so that the draught may be as sharp as a two-edged sword."

"But if you take away my voice," said the little Sea-maid, "what will remain to me?"

"Your beautiful form," replied the Witch, "your graceful walk, and your speaking eyes: with those you can take captive a human heart. Well, have you lost your courage? Put out your little tongue, and then I will cut it off for my payment, and then you shall have the strong draught."

"It shall be so," said the little Sea-maid.

And the Witch put on her pot to brew the draught.

"Cleanliness is a good thing," said she; and she cleaned out the pot with the snakes, which she tied up in a big knot; then she scratched herself, and let her black blood drop into it. The stream rose up in the strangest forms, enough to frighten the beholder. Every moment the Witch threw something else into the pot; and when it boiled thoroughly, there was a sound like the weeping of a crocodile. At last the draught was ready. It looked like the purest water.

"There you have it," said the Witch.

And she cut off the little Sea-maid's tongue, so that now the Princess was dumb, and could neither sing nor speak.

She could see her father's palace. The torches were extinguished in the great hall, and they were certainly sleeping within, but she did not dare to go to them, now that she was dumb and was about to quit them forever. She felt as if her heart would burst with sorrow. She crept into the garden, took a flower from each bed of her sisters, blew a thousand kisses toward the palace, and rose up through the dark blue sea.

The sun had not yet risen when she beheld the Prince's castle, and mounted the splendid marble staircase. The moon shone beautifully clear. The little Sea-maid drank the burning sharp draught, and it seemed as if a two-edged sword went through her delicate body. She fell down in a swoon, and lay as if she were dead. When the sun shone out over the sea she awoke, and felt a sharp pain; but just before her stood the handsome young Prince. He fixed his coal-black eyes upon her, so that she cast down her own, and then she perceived that her fish-tail was gone, and that she had the prettiest pair of white feet a little girl could have. But she had no clothes, so she shrouded herself in her long hair. The Prince asked how she came there! and she looked at him mildly, but very mournfully, with her dark-blue eyes, for she could not speak. Then he took her by the hand, and led her into the castle. Each step she took was, as the Witch had told her, as if she had been treading on pointed needles and knives, but she bore it gladly. At the Prince's right hand she moved on, light as a soap-bubble, and he, like all the rest, was astonished at her graceful, swaying movements.

She now received splendid clothes of silk and muslin. In the castle she was the most beautiful creature to be seen; but she was dumb, and could neither sing nor speak. Lovely slaves, dressed in silk and gold, stepped forward, and sang before the Prince and his royal parents; one sang more charmingly than all the rest, and the Prince smiled at her and clapped his hands. Then the little Sea-maid became sad; she knew that she herself had sung far more sweetly, and thought,—

"O! that he only knew I had given away my voice forever to be with him!"

Now the slaves danced pretty waving dances to the loveliest music; then the little Sea-maid lifted her beautiful white arms, stood on the tips of her toes, and glided dancing over the floor as no one had yet danced. At each movement her beauty became more apparent, and her eyes spoke more directly to the heart than the song of the slaves.

All were delighted, and especially the Prince, who called her his little foundling; and she danced again and again, although every time she touched the earth it seemed as if she were treading upon sharp knives. The Prince said that she should always remain with him, and she received permission to sleep on a velvet cushion before his door.

He had a page's dress made for her, that she might accompany him on horseback. They rode through the blooming woods, where the green boughs swept their shoulders, and the little birds sang in the fresh leaves. She climbed with the Prince up the high mountains, and although her delicate feet bled so that even the others could see it, she laughed at it herself, and followed him until they saw the clouds sailing beneath them, like a flock of birds travelling to distant lands.

At home in the Prince's castle, when the others slept at night, she went out on to the broad marble steps. It cooled her burning feet to stand in the cold sea-water, and then she thought of the dear ones in the deep.

Once, in the night-time, her sisters came, arm in arm. Sadly they sang as they floated above the water; and she beckoned to them, and they recognized her, and told her how she had grieved them all. Then she visited them every night; and once she saw in the distance her old grandmother, who had not been above the surface for many years, and the Sea-king with his crown upon his head. They stretched out their hands toward her, but did not venture so near the land as her sisters.

Day by day the Prince grew more fond of her. He loved her as one loves a dear, good child, but it never came into his head to make her his wife; and yet she must become his wife, or she would not receive an immortal soul, and would have to become foam on the sea on his marriage morning.

"Do you not love me best of them all?" the eyes of the little Sea-maid seemed to say, when he took her in his arms and kissed her fair forehead.

"Yes, you are the dearest to me!" said the Prince, "for you have the best heart of them all. You are the most devoted to me, and are like a young girl whom I once saw, but whom I certainly shall not find again. I was on board a ship which was wrecked. The waves threw me ashore near a holy temple where several young girls performed the service. The youngest of them found me by the shore and saved my life. I only saw her twice: she was the only one in the world I could love, but you chase her picture out of my mind, you are so like her. She belongs to the holy temple, and therefore my good fortune has sent you to me. We will never part!"

"Ah! he does not know that I saved his life," thought the little Sea-maid. "I carried him over the sea to the wood where the temple stands. I sat there under the foam and looked to see if any one would come. I saw the beautiful girl whom he loves better than me." And the Sea-maid sighed deeply—she could not weep. "The maiden belongs to the holy temple," she said, "and will never come out into the world—they will meet no more. I am with him and see him every day; I will cherish him, love him, give up my life for him."

But now they said that the Prince was to marry, and that the beautiful daughter of a neighboring King was to be his wife, and that was why such a beautiful ship was being prepared. The story was, that the Prince travelled to visit the land of the neighboring King, but it was done that he might see the King's daughter. A great company was to go with him. The little Sea-maid shook her head and smiled; she knew the Prince's thoughts far better than any of the others.

"I must travel," he had said to her; "I must see the beautiful Princess: my parents desire it, but they do not wish to compel me to bring her home as my bride. I cannot love her. She is not like the beautiful maiden in the temple whom you resemble. If I were to choose a bride, I would rather choose you, my dear dumb foundling with the speaking eyes."

And he kissed her red lips and played with her long hair, so that she dreamed of happiness and of an immortal soul.

"You are not afraid of the sea, my dumb child?" said he, when they stood on the superb ship which was to carry him to the country of the neighboring King; and he told her of storm and calm, of strange fishes in the deep, and of what the divers had seen there. And she smiled at his tales, for she knew better than any one what happened at the bottom of the sea.

In the moonlight night, when all were asleep, except the steersman who stood by the helm, she sat on the side of the ship gazing down through the clear water. She fancied she saw her father's palace. High on the battlements stood her old grandmother, with the silver crown on her head, and looking through the rushing tide up to the vessel's keel. Then her sisters came forth over the water, and looked mournfully at her and wrung their white hands. She beckoned to them and smiled, and wished to tell them that she was well and happy; but the cabin-boy approached her and her sisters dived down, so that he thought the white objects he had seen were foam on the surface of the water.

The next morning the ship sailed into the harbor of the neighboring King's splendid city. All the church bells sounded, and from the high towers the trumpets were blown, while the soldiers stood there with flying colors and flashing bayonets. Each day brought some festivity with it; balls and entertainments followed one another; but the Princess was not yet there. People said she was being educated in a holy temple far away, where she was learning every royal virtue. At last she arrived.

The little Sea-maid was anxious to see the beauty of the Princess, and was obliged to acknowledge it. A more lovely apparition she had never beheld. The Princess's skin was pure and clear, and behind the long dark eyelashes there smiled a pair of faithful, dark-blue eyes.

" You are the lady who saved me when I lay like a corpse upon the shore ! " said the Prince; and he folded his blushing bride to his heart. " O, I am too, too happy ! " he cried to the little Sea-maid. " The best hope I could have is fulfilled. You will rejoice at my happiness, for you are the most devoted to me of them all ! "

And the little Sea-maid kissed his hand; and it seemed already to her as if her heart was broken, for his wedding morning was to bring death to her, and change her into foam on the sea.

All the church bells were ringing, and heralds rode about the streets announcing the betrothal. On every altar fragrant oil was burning in gorgeous lamps of silver. The priests swung their censers, and bride and bridegroom laid hand in hand, and received the bishop's blessing. The little Sea-maid was dressed in cloth of gold, and held up the bride's train; but her ears heard nothing of the festive music, her eye marked not the holy ceremony; she thought of the night of her death, and of all that she had lost in this world.

On the same evening the bride and bridegroom went on board the ship. The cannon roared, all the flags waved; in the midst of the ship a costly tent of gold and purple, with the most beautiful cushions, had been set up, and there the married pair were to sleep in the cool, still night.

The sails swelled in the wind, and the ship glided smoothly and lightly over the clear sea. When it grew dark, colored lamps were lighted and the sailors danced merry dances on deck. The little Sea-maid thought of the first time when she had risen up out of the sea, and beheld a similar scene of splendor and joy; and she joined in the whirling dance, and flitted on as the swallow flits away when he is pursued; and all shouted and admired her, for she had danced so prettily. Her delicate feet were cut as if with knives, but she did not feel it, for her heart was wounded far more painfully. She knew this was the last evening on which she should see him for whom she had left her friends and her home, and had given up her beautiful voice, and had suffered unheard-of pains every day, while he was utterly unconscious of all. It was the last evening she should breathe the same air with him, and behold the starry sky and the deep sea; and everlasting night without thought or dream awaited her, for she had no soul, and could win none. And everything was merriment and gladness on the ship till past midnight, and she laughed and danced with thoughts of death in her heart. The Prince kissed his beautiful bride, and she played with his raven hair, and hand in hand they went to rest in the splendid tent. It became quiet on the ship; only the helmsman stood by the helm, and the little Sea-maid leaned her white arms upon the bulwark and gazed out toward the east for the morning dawn—the first ray, she knew, would kill her. Then she saw her sisters rising out of the flood; they were pale, like herself; their long, beautiful hair no longer waved in the wind; it had been cut off.

"We have given it to the witch, that we might bring you help, so that you may not die to-night. She has given us a knife; here it is—look! how sharp! Before the sun rises you must thrust it into the heart of the Prince, and when the warm blood falls upon your feet they will grow together again into a fish-tail, and you will become a sea-maid again, and come back to us, and live your three hundred years before you become dead salt sea-foam. Make haste! He or you must die before the sun rises! Our old grandmother mourns so that her white hair has fallen off, as ours did under the witch's scissors. Kill the Prince and come back! Make haste! Do you see that red streak in the sky? In a few minutes the sun will rise, and you must die!"

And they gave a very mournful sigh, and vanished beneath the waves. The little Sea-maid drew back the curtain from the tent, and saw the beautiful bride lying with her head on the Prince's breast; and she bent down and kissed his brow, and gazed up at the sky where the morning red was gleaming brighter and brighter; then she looked at the sharp knife, and again fixed her eyes upon the Prince, who in his sleep murmured his bride's name. She only was in his thoughts, and the knife trembled in the Sea-maid's hand. But then she flung it far away into the waves—they gleamed red where it fell, and it seemed as if drops of blood spurted up out of the water. Once more she looked with half-extinguished eyes upon the Prince; then she threw herself from the ship into the sea, and felt her frame dissolving into foam.

Now the sun rose up out of the sea. The rays fell mild and warm upon the cold sea-foam, and the little Sea-maid felt nothing of death. She saw the bright sun, and over her head sailed hundreds of glorious ethereal beings—she could see them through the white sails of the ship and the red clouds of the sky; their speech was melody, but of such a spiritual kind that no human ear could hear it, just as no human eye could see them; without wings they floated through the air. The little Sea-maid found that she had a frame like these, and was rising more and more out of the foam.

"Whither am I going?" she asked; and her voice sounded like that of other beings, so spiritual, that no earthly music could be compared to it.

"To the daughters of the air!" replied the others. "A sea-maid has no immortal soul, and can never gain one, except she win the love of a mortal. Her eternal existence depends upon the power of another. The daughters of the air have likewise no immortal soul, but they can make themselves one through good deeds. We fly to the hot countries, where the close, pestilent air kills men, and there we bring coolness. We disperse the fragrance of the flowers through the air, and spread refreshment and health. After we have striven for three hundred years to accomplish all the good we can bring about, we receive an immortal soul, and take part in the eternal happiness of men. You, poor little Sea-maid, have striven with your whole heart after the goal we pursue; you have suffered and endured; you have by good works raised yourself to the world of spirits, and can gain an immortal soul after three hundred years."

And the little Sea-maid lifted her glorified eyes toward God's sun, and for the first time she felt them fill with tears. On the ship there was again life and noise. She saw the Prince and his bride searching for her; then they looked mournfully at the pearly foam, as if they knew that she had thrown herself into the waves. Invisible, she kissed the forehead of the bride, fanned the Prince, and mounted with the other children of the air on the rosy cloud which floated through the ether. After three hundred years we shall thus float into Paradise!

"And we may even get there sooner," whispered a daughter of the air. "Invisibly we float into the houses of men where children are, and for every day on which we find a good child that brings joy to its parents and deserves their love, our time of probation is shortened. The child does not know when we fly through the room; and when we smile with joy at the child's conduct, a year is counted off from the three hundred; but when we see a naughty or a wicked child, we shed tears of grief, and for every tear a day is added to our time of trial."

THE ELFIN MOUND

SEVERAL large lizards were running quickly into the cleft of an old tree; they could understand each other perfectly, for they all spoke the lizard language.

"What a noise there is in the old Elfin mound!" said one of the Lizards. "What a rumbling and uproar! For two nights I have not been able to close my eyes, and might just as well have had a toothache, for then I certainly should not have slept."

"There is a something going on there," said the other Lizard. "They let the mound stand on four red poles till the crowing of the cock, to have it thoroughly aired; and the Elfin damsels have learnt new dances, in which there is some stamping. A something is going on, I'm sure."

"Yes; I have spoken to an earth-worm of my acquaintance," said the third Lizard. "The Earth-worm came direct from the mound, where day and night he had been rummaging about in the ground. He had heard a good deal; for he can see nothing, poor wretch, but eavesdropping and listening he understands to perfection. Visitors are expected at the Elfin mound; visitors of rank, but who they were, the Earth-worm either would not or could not say. All the Jacks-o'-the-lantern have been ordered to prepare a procession by torch-light; and all the silver and gold, of which there is plenty in the Elfin mound, will be polished and laid in the moonshine."

"But who can the strangers be?" said all the Lizards. "What can be going on? Listen! what a humming and buzzing!"

At the same instant the Elfin mound opened, and an elderly Elfin damsel, without a back, but for the rest very respectably dressed, came tripping forth. It was the old Elfin King's housekeeper; she was distantly related to him, and wore an amber heart on her forehead. Her feet were so nimble—trip—trap—trip—trap!—how she skipped along, right away to the moor to the Night-raven.

"You will be invited to the Elfin mound, and that tonight," said she. "But would you not do us a great favor, and take charge of the invitations? As you do not give parties yourself, you must do us this service. Strangers of high rank are coming to us; magicians of no small importance, let me tell you; and so the old Elfin King wants to show himself off to advantage."

"Who is to be invited?" asked the Night-raven.

"Why, to the grand ball everybody may come; men even, if they do but speak in their sleep, or are able to do something in our way. But the principal banquet is to be very select; those of the first rank only are to be invited. I have had a long discussion with the Elfin King; for, according to my notions, we cannot even ask ghosts. The Sea-god and his daughters must be invited first; 'tis true, they don't much like coming on dry land, but they will have probably a wet stone to sit upon, or maybe something better still; and then, I think, they will not refuse for this once. We must have the old Mountain Dwarfs of the first class, with tails; the Elf of the Brook, and the Brownie, and then, I think, we must not omit the Swart Elf, and the Skeleton Horse: they belong, it is true, to the clergy, who are not of our sort; however, 'tis their office, and they are, moreover, nearly related to us, and are continually paying us visits."

"Caw!" said the Night-raven, and flew away to invite the company.

The Elfin maidens were already dancing on the Elfin mound: they danced with long shawls, woven of haze and moonshine; and to all who like this sort of dancing, it seems pretty. In the centre of the Elfin mound was the great hall, splendidly ornamented; the floor was washed with moonshine, and the walls were rubbed with witches' fat, so that they shone in the light like tulip-leaves. In the kitchen there was a great quantity of frogs among the dishes; adders' skins, with little children's fingers inside; salad of mushroom-seed; wet mice's snouts and hemlock; beer, from the brewery of the old Witch of the Moor; sparkling saltpetre wine from a grave-cellar,—all very substantial eating: rusty nails and church-window glass were among the delicacies and kickshaws.

The old Elfin King had his golden crown polished with powdered slate-pencil. It was the pencil of the head-scholar; and to obtain this one is very difficult for the Elfin King.

They hung up the curtains in the bed-chamber, and fastened them with adder spittle. There was, indeed, a humming and a buzzing in the Elfin mound!

"Now we must perfume the place with singed hair and pigs' bristles; and then I think I shall have done my share of the business," said the little Elfin damsel.

"Dear papa," said the least of the daughters, "shall I now know who the high visitors are?"

"Well then," said he, "I suppose I must tell you. Two of

my daughters are to show themselves off, in order to get married. Two will certainly be married. The aged Mountain Elf of Norway, who lives in the old Dovre-field, and possesses many craggy castles, and a gold-mine too,—which is a better thing than one imagines,—is coming here with his two sons; and they are to choose themselves wives. The hoary Elf is an honest old Norwegian, merry and straightforward. I have known him since many a long day, when we drank together to better acquaintance and good fellowship. He came here to fetch his wife,—she is dead now,—who was the daughter of the Rock-king. O, how I long to see the old northern Elf! His sons, people say, are coarse, blustering fellows; but maybe one wrongs them, and when older, they will improve."

"And when will they come?" asked his daughter.

"That depends on wind and weather," said the Elfin King. "They travel economically; they will come here by water. I wish they would go through Sweden; but the old gentleman has no inclination that way. He does not keep pace with the time, and that I can't bear."

At the same moment two Jacks-o'-the-lantern came hopping in, one faster than the other, and for that reason one was first.

"They're coming! they're coming!" cried they.

"Give me my crown; and let me stand in the moonshine," said the Elfin King.

The daughters held up their long shawls and bowed to the earth.

There stood the hoary Mountain Elf, with a crown of hardened icicles and polished fir-cones on his head, and wrapped up in a mantle of fur and boots of the same. His sons, on the contrary, went with open throats, for they disdained the cold.

"Is that a mound?" asked the lesser of the youths, pointing to Elfin-home. "In Norway we call such a thing a hole."

"Boy," said the father, "a mound rises upward, and a hole goes inward. Have you no eyes in your head?"

Now they went into the Elfin mound, where there was very choice company, certainly; and had come together with such speed, one might have thought they had been borne thither on the breeze; however, the arrangements for every one were neat and pretty. The sea-folk sat at table in large water-butts; and they said they felt just as if they were at home. All observed good manners at the table, except the two little Norwegian Mountain Elves, who put their feet on the board, for they thought that all they did was becoming.

"Take your feet away from the plates," said the old Elf; and then they obeyed, although not immediately. They tickled the ladies next them with fir-cones; then they pulled off their boots, to be more at ease, and gave them to the ladies to hold for them; but their father was very different. He told about the proud Norwegian rocks, and of the waterfalls, which, covered with foam, dashed downwards, raging and roaring like thunder; he told about the salmon, that leaps up against the falling waters, when the Spirit of the flood plays on her golden harp. He related about the clear winter nights, when the bells on the sledges jingle, and the youths run with flaming torches over the smooth ice, which is so transparent that they could see how affrighted the fishes were beneath their feet. He, indeed, could recount so that one saw and heard the things he described; when, huzza! all of a sudden, the old Elf gave one of the Elfin damsels a smacking kiss; and yet they were not even distantly related.

The Elfin maidens were now to dance, simple as well as stamping dances; and then came the most difficult one of all, the so-called "Dance out of the dance." Confound it! their legs grew so long, one did not know which was the beginning nor which was the end: one could not distinguish legs from arms; all was twirling about in the air like sawdust; and they went whizzing round to such a degree that the Skeleton Horse grew quite sick, and was obliged to leave the table.

"Brrrrr!" said the gray-headed Elf; "that's a regular Highland fling, as it's called. But what can they do besides spinning about like a whirlwind?"

"That you shall see," said the King, calling the youngest of his daughters. She was as delicate and fair as moonlight, and was the daintiest of all the sisters. She put a white wand in her mouth, and vanished. That was her art.

But the old Mountain Elf said, "This was an art he should

not at all like in his wife, nor did he think his sons would either."

The other could walk beside her own self, as though she had a shadow, which is a thing Elves never have.

The third one's talent was of a very different kind; she had learned in the brewery of the Witch of the Moor, and she knew how to lard alder-wood with glow-worms.

"She would make a good housewife," said the Mountain Elf, blinking, for he did not at all like drinking so much.

Then came the fourth Elfin maiden; she had a large golden harp, and when she touched the first string, everybody lifted up the left foot, for the Elves are all left-sided; and when she touched the next, everybody was forced to do whatever she pleased.

"That is a dangerous damsel," said the Mountain Elf; but both his sons went out of the Elfin mound, for they were tired of it.

"What can the next daughter do?" asked the old Elf.

"I have learned to love the Norwegians," said she; "and I will not marry unless I can go to Norway."

But the youngest of the sisters whispered into the old Elf's ear, "She only says that, because she has heard in an old Norwegian rhyme, that when even the world is at an end, the rocks of Norway will stand firm; and that's the reason she wants to go there, for she is greatly afraid of death."

"Ho, ho!" said the old Elf; "that's the way the wind blows, is it? But what can the seventh and last do?"

"The sixth comes before the seventh," said the Elfin King, for he knew how to count; but the sixth at first would not come forward.

"I can do nothing except tell people the truth," said she. "No one troubles about me, and I have enough to do to get my shroud ready."

Now came the seventh and last. And what could she do? She could tell as many fairy-tales as she chose.

"Here are my five fingers," said the old Mountain Elf. "For each one tell me a story."

And the Elfin maiden took hold of him by the wrist, and he laughed till he was almost choked; and when she came to the finger that wore a golden ring, just as if it knew that matrimony was going on, the old Elf said, " Hold fast what you have! The hand is yours! I will take you myself to wife!"

And the Elfin maiden said that the fairy-tale to the ring-finger and to the little finger were wanting.

"O, we'll hear them in winter," said the old Elf; "and about the fir-tree too, and about the birch, and the gifts of the wood-nymphs, and about the crackling frost. You shall have opportunities enough of telling stories, for no one under-stands that yonder. And there we will sit in our rocky dwelling, where the pine-torch is burning, and where we drink mead out of the golden horns of the old Norwegian kings; I got some as a present from the Water-spirit. And when we are sitting so together, Garbo will come to pay us a visit, and he will sing to you all the songs of the mountain maidens. How merry we shall be! The salmon will leap in the waterfall, and dash against the walls of rock; but he will not be able to come in to us, after all! Yes, yes; one leads a happy, comfortable life in dear old Norway! But where are the boys?"

Where were they? Why, they were running about the fields, blowing out the wills-o'-the-wisp that were coming quite orderly to have a procession with torches.

"What's all this harum-scarum about?" said the old Elf. "I have taken a step-mother for you; methinks now you may choose a wife too."

But they said they liked speechifying and boon companion-ship better, and had no taste for matrimony; and so they made speeches, tossed off their glasses, and turned them topsy-turvy, to show that they were quite empty. They then pulled off their coats, and lay down on the table to sleep. But the old Elf danced round the room with his young bride, and exchanged boots with her; for that is much more genteel than exchanging rings.

"The cock is crowing!" said the elderly damsel who at-tended to the housekeeping. "We must now bolt the shut-ters, lest the sun should spoil our complexions."

And then the mound closed. The Lizards ran about and up and down the cleft tree and one said to the other, "How much I like the old Mountain Elf!"

"I like the merry boys better," said the Earth-worm; but then he could not see, poor wretch!

THE WILD SWANS

FAR away, where the swallows fly when our winter comes on, lived a King who had eleven sons, and one daughter named Eliza. The eleven brothers were Princes, and each went to school with a star on his breast and his sword by his side. They wrote with pencils of diamond upon slates of gold, and learned by heart just as well as they read; one could see directly that they were Princes. Their sister Eliza sat upon a little stool of plate-glass, and had a picture-book which had been bought for the value of half a kingdom.

O, the children were particularly well off; but it was not always to remain so.

Their father, who was king of the whole country, married a bad Queen who did not love the poor children at all. On the very first day they could notice this. In the whole palace there was great feasting, and the children were playing there. Then guests came; but instead of the children receiving, as they had been accustomed to do, all the spare cake and all the roasted apples, they only had some sand given them in a tea-cup, and were told that they might make believe that was something good.

The next week the Queen took the little sister Eliza into the country, to a peasant and his wife; and but a short time had elapsed before she told the King so many falsehoods about the poor Princes, that he did not trouble himself any more about them.

"Fly out into the world and get your own living," said the wicked Queen. "Fly like great birds without a voice."

But she could not make it so bad for them as she had intended, for they became eleven magnificent wild swans. With a strange cry they flew out of the palace windows, far over the park and into the wood.

It was yet quite early morning when they came by the place where their sister Eliza lay asleep in the peasant's room. Here they hovered over the roof, turned their long

necks, and flapped their wings; but no one heard or saw it.
They were obliged to fly on, high up toward the clouds, far
away into the wide world; there they flew into a great dark
wood, which stretched away to the sea-shore.

Poor little Eliza stood in the peasant's room and played
with a green leaf, for she had no other playthings. And she
pricked a hole in the leaf, and looked through it up at the
sun, and it seemed to her that she saw her brothers' clear
eyes; each time the warm sun shone upon her cheeks she
thought of all the kisses they had given her.

Each day passed just like the rest. When the wind swept
through the great rose-hedges outside the house, it seemed to
whisper to them, "What can be more beautiful than you?"
But the roses shook their heads, and answered, "Eliza!"
And when the old woman sat in front of her door on Sunday
and read in her hymn-book, the wind turned the leaves and
said to the book, "Who can be more pious than you?" and
the hymn-book said, "Eliza!" And what the rose-bushes
and the hymn-book said was the simple truth.

When she was fifteen years old she was to go home. And
when the Queen saw how beautiful she was, she became
spiteful, and filled with hatred toward her. She would have
been glad to change her into a wild swan, like her brothers,
but she did not dare to do so at once, because the King
wished to see his daughter.

Early in the morning the Queen went into the bath, which
was built of white marble, and decked with soft cushions
and the most splendid tapestry; and she took three toads and
kissed them, and said to the first,—

"Sit upon Eliza's head when she comes into the bath, that
she may become as stupid as you. Seat yourself upon her
forehead," she said to the second, "that she may become as
ugly as you, and her father may not know her. Rest on her
heart," she whispered to the third, "that she may receive an
evil mind and suffer pain from it."

Then she put the toads into the clear water, which at once
assumed a green color; and calling Eliza, caused her to
undress and step into the water. And while Eliza dived, one
of the toads sat upon her hair, and the second on her forehead, and the third on her heart; but she did not seem to

notice it; and as soon as she rose, three red poppies were floating on the water. If the creatures had not been poisonous, and if the witch had not kissed them, they would have been changed into red roses. But at any rate they became flowers, because they had rested on the girl's head, and forehead, and heart. She was too good and innocent for sorcery to have power over her.

When the wicked Queen saw that, she rubbed Eliza with walnut juice, so that the girl became dark brown, and smeared a hurtful ointment on her face, and let her beautiful hair hang in confusion. It was quite impossible to recognize the pretty Eliza.

When her father saw her he was much shocked, and declared this was not his daughter. No one but the yard dog and the swallows would recognize her; but they were poor animals who had nothing to say in the matter.

Then poor Eliza wept, and thought of her eleven brothers who were all away. Sorrowfully she crept out of the castle, and walked all day over field and moor till she came into the great wood. She did not know whither she wished to go, only she felt very downcast, and longed for her brothers: they had certainly been, like herself, thrust forth into the world, and she would seek for them and find them.

She had been only a short time in the wood when the night fell; she quite lost the path, therefore she lay down upon the soft moss, prayed her evening prayer, and leaned her head against the stump of a tree. Deep silence reigned around, the air was mild, and in the grass and in the moss gleamed like a green fire hundreds of glow-worms; when she lightly touched one of the twigs with her hand, the shining insects fell down upon her like shooting stars.

The whole night long she dreamed of her brothers. They were children again playing together, writing with their diamond pencils upon their golden slates, and looking at the beautiful picture-book which had cost half a kingdom. But on the slates they were not writing, as they had been accustomed to do, lines and letters, but the brave deeds they had done, and all they had seen and experienced; and in the picture-book everything was alive—the birds sang, and the people went out of the book and spoke with Eliza and her brothers. But when the leaf was turned, they jumped back again directly, so that there should be no confusion.

When she awoke the sun was already standing high. She could certainly not see it, for the lofty trees spread their branches far and wide above her. But the rays played there above like a gauzy veil, there was a fragrance from the fresh verdure, and the birds almost perched upon her shoulders. She heard the plashing of water: it was from a number of springs all flowing into a lake which had the most delightful sandy bottom. It was surrounded by thick growing bushes, but at one part the stags had made a large opening, and here Eliza went down to the water. The lake was so clear, that if the wind had not stirred the branches and the bushes, so that they moved, one would have thought they were painted upon the depths of the lake, so clearly was every leaf mirrored, whether the sun shone upon it or whether it lay in shadow.

When Eliza saw her own face she was terrified—so brown and ugly was she; but when she wetted her little hand and rubbed her eyes and her forehead, the white skin gleamed forth again. Then she undressed and went down into the fresh water: a more beautiful king's daughter than she was could not be found in the world. And when she had dressed herself again and plaited her long hair, she went to the bubbling spring, drank out of the hollow of her hand, and then wandered into the wood, not knowing whither she went. She thought of her dear brothers, and knew that Heaven would certainly not forsake her. It is God who lets the wild apples grow, to satisfy the hungry. He showed her a wild apple-tree, with the boughs bending under the weight of the fruit. Here she took her midday meal, placing props under the boughs, and then went into the darkest part of the forest. There it was so still that she could hear her own footsteps, as well as the rustling of every dry leaf which bent under her feet. Not one bird was to be seen, not one ray of sunlight could find its way through the great dark boughs of the trees; the lofty trunks stood so close together that when she looked before her it appeared as though she were surrounded by sets of palings one behind the other. O, here was a solitude such as she had never before known!

The night came on quite dark. Not a single glow-worm now gleamed in the grass. Sorrowfully she lay down to sleep. Then it seemed to her as if the branches of the trees parted above her head, and mild eyes of angels looked down upon her from on high.

When the morning came, she did not know if it had really been so or if she had dreamed it.

She went a few steps forward, and then she met an old woman with berries in her basket, and the old woman gave her a few of them. Eliza asked the dame if she had not seen eleven Princes riding through the wood.

" No," replied the old woman, " but yesterday I saw eleven swans swimming in the river close by, with golden crowns on their heads."

And she led Eliza a short distance farther, to a declivity, and at the foot of the slope a little river wound its way. The trees on its margin stretched their long leafy branches across toward each other, and where their natural growth would not allow them to come together the roots had been torn out of the ground, and hung, intermingled with the branches, over the water.

Eliza said farewell to the old woman, and went beside the river to the place where the stream flowed out to the great open ocean.

The whole glorious sea lay before the young girl's eyes, but not one sail appeared upon its surface, and not a boat was to be seen. How was she to proceed? She looked at the innumerable little pebbles on the shore; the water had worn them all round. Glass, iron-stones, everything that was there, had received its shape from the water, which was much softer than even her delicate hand.

" It rolls on unweariedly, and thus what is hard becomes smooth. I will be just as unwearied. Thanks for your lesson, you clear rolling waves; my heart tells me that one day you will lead me to my dear brothers."

On the foam-covered sea-grass lay eleven white swan feathers, which she collected into a bunch. Drops of water were upon them—whether they were dew-drops or tears nobody could tell. Solitary it was there on the strand, but she did not feel it, for the sea showed continual changes—

more in a few hours than the lovely lakes can produce in a whole year. Then a great black cloud came. It seemed as if the sea would say, "I can look angry too;" and then the wind blew and the waves turned their white side outward. But when the clouds gleamed red and the winds slept, the sea looked like a rose leaf; sometimes it became green, sometimes white. But however quietly it might rest, there was still a slight motion on the shore; the water rose gently like the breast of a sleeping child.

When the sun was just about to set, Eliza saw eleven wild swans, with crowns on their heads, flying toward the land: they swept along one after the other, so that they looked like a long white band. Then Eliza descended the slope and hid herself behind a bush. The swans alighted near her and flapped their great white wings.

As soon as the sun had disappeared beneath the water, the swans' feathers fell off, and eleven handsome Princes, Eliza's brothers, stood there. She uttered a loud cry, for although they were greatly altered, she knew and felt that it must be they. And she sprang into their arms and called them by their names; and the Princes felt supremely happy when they saw their little sister again; and they knew her, though she was now tall and beautiful. They smiled and wept; and soon they understood how cruel their step-mother had been to them all.

"We brothers," said the eldest, "fly about as wild swans as long as the sun is in the sky, but directly it sinks down we receive our human form again. Therefore we must always take care that we have a resting-place for our feet when the sun sets, for if at that moment we were flying up toward the clouds, we should sink down into the deep as men. We do not dwell here; there lies a land just as fair as this beyond the sea. But the way thither is long; we must cross the great sea, and on our path there is no island where we could pass the night, only a little rock stands forth in the midst of the waves; it is but just large enough for us to rest upon it close to each other. If the sea is rough, the foam spurts far over us, but we thank God for the rock. There we pass the night in our human form; but for this rock we could never visit our beloved native land, for we require two of the longest days in the year for our journey. Only once in each year is it granted to us to visit our home. For eleven days we may stay here and fly over the great wood, from whence we can see the palace in which we were born, and in which our father lives, and the high church tower, beneath whose shade our mother lies buried. Here it seems to us as though the bushes and trees were our relatives; here the wild horses career across the steppe, as we have seen them do in our childhood; here the charcoal-burner sings the old songs to which we danced as children; here is our father-land; hither we feel ourselves drawn, and here we have found you, our dear little sister. Two days more we may stay here; then we must away across the sea to a glorious land, but which is not our native land. How can we bear you away? for we have neither ship nor boat."

"In what way can I release you?" asked the sister; and they conversed nearly the whole night, only slumbering for a few hours.

She was awakened by the rustling of the swans' wings above her head. Her brothers were again enchanted, and they flew in wide circles and at last far away; but one of them, the youngest, remained behind, and the swan laid his head in her lap, and she stroked his wings; and the whole day they remained together. Towards evening the others came back and when the sun had gone down they stood there in their own shapes.

"To-morrow we fly far away from here, and cannot come back until a whole year has gone by. But we cannot leave you thus! Have you courage to come with us? My arm is strong enough to carry you in the wood; and should not all our wings be strong enough to fly with you over the sea?"

"Yes, take me with you," said Eliza.

The whole night they were occupied in weaving a net of the pliable willow bark and tough reeds; and it was great and strong. On this net Eliza lay down; and when the sun rose, and her brothers were changed into wild swans, they seized the net with their beaks, and flew with their beloved sister, who was still asleep, high up towards the clouds. The sunbeams fell exactly upon her face, so one of the swans flew over her head, that his broad wings might overshadow her.

They were far away from the shore when Eliza awoke: she was still dreaming, so strange did it appear to her to be carried high through the air and over the sea. By her side lay a branch with beautiful ripe berries, and a bundle of sweet-tasting roots. The youngest of the brothers had collected them and placed them there for her. She smiled at him thankfully, for she recognized him; he it was who flew over her and shaded her with his wings.

They were so high that the greatest ship they descried beneath them seemed like a white sea-gull lying upon the waters. A great cloud stood behind them—it was a perfect mountain; and upon it Eliza saw her own shadow and those of the eleven swans; there they flew on, gigantic in size. Here was a picture, a more splendid one than she had ever yet seen. But as the sun rose higher and the cloud was left farther behind them, the floating, shadowy images vanished away.

The whole day they flew onward through the air, like a whirring arrow, but their flight was slower that it was wont to be, for they had their sister to carry. Bad weather came on; the evening drew near; Eliza looked anxiously at the setting sun, for the lonely rock in the ocean could not be seen. It seemed to her as if the swans beat the air more strongly with their wings. Alas! she was the cause that they did not advance fast enough. When the sun went down, they must become men and fall into the sea and drown. Then she prayed a prayer from the depths of her heart; but still she could descry no rock. The dark clouds came nearer in a great, black, threatening body, rolling forward like a mass of lead, and the lightning burst forth, flash upon flash.

Now the sun just touched the margin of the sea. Eliza's heart trembled. Then the swans darted downward so swiftly that she thought they were falling, but they paused again. The sun was half hidden below the water. And now for the first time she saw the little rock beneath her, and it looked no larger than a seal might look, thrusting his head forth from the water. The sun sank very fast; at last it appeared only like a star; and then her foot touched the firm land. The sun was extinguished like the last spark in a piece of burned paper; her brothers were standing around her, arm in arm,

but there was not more than just enough room for her and
for them. The sea beat against the rock and went over her
like small rain; the sky glowed in continual fire, and peal on
peal the thunder rolled; but sister and brothers held each
other by the hand and sang psalms, from which they gained
comfort and courage.

In the morning twilight the air was pure and calm. As
soon as the sun rose the swans flew away with Eliza from the
island. The sea still ran high, and when they soared up aloft
the white foam looked like millions of white swans swimming
upon the water.

When the sun mounted higher, Eliza saw before her, half
floating in the air, a mountainous country with shining
masses of ice on its water, and in the midst of it rose a castle,
apparently a mile long, with row above row of elegant col-
umns, while beneath waved the palm woods and bright
flowers as large as mill-wheels. She asked if this was the
country to which they were bound, but the swans shook their
heads, for what she beheld was the gorgeous, ever-changing
palace of Fata Morgana, and into this they might bring no
human being. As Eliza gazed at it, mountains, woods, and
castle fell down, and twenty proud churches, all nearly alike,
with high towers and pointed windows, stood before them.
She fancied she heard the organs sounding, but it was the
sea she heard. When she was quite near the churches they
changed to a fleet sailing beneath her, but when she looked
down it was only a sea-mist gliding over the ocean. Thus
she had a continual change before her eyes, till at last she
saw the real land to which they were bound. There arose
the most glorious blue mountains, with cedar forests, cities,
and palaces. Long before the sun went down she sat on the
rock, in front of a great cave overgrown with delicate green
trailing plants looking like embroidered carpets.

" Now we shall see what you will dream of here to-night,"
said the youngest brother; and he showed her to her bed-
chamber.

" Heaven grant that I may dream of a way to release you,"
she replied.

And this thought possessed her mightily, and she prayed
ardently for help; yes, even in her sleep she continued to

pray. Then it seemed to her as if she were flying high in the air to the cloudy palace of Fata Morgana; and the fairy came out to meet her, beautiful and radiant; and yet the fairy was quite like the old woman who had given her the berries in the wood, and had told her of the swans with golden crowns on their heads.

"Your brothers can be released," said she. "But have you courage and perseverance? Certainly, water is softer than your delicate hands, and yet it changes the shape of stones; but it feels not the pain that your fingers will feel; it has no heart, and cannot suffer the agony and torment you will have to endure. Do you see the stinging-nettle which I hold in my hand. Many of the same kind grow around the cave in which you sleep: those only, and those that grow upon church-yard graves, are serviceable,—remember that. Those you must pluck, though they will burn your hands into blisters. Break these nettles to pieces with your feet, and you will have flax; of this you must plait and weave eleven shirts of mail with long sleeves: throw these over the eleven swans, and the charm will be broken. But recollect well, from the moment you begin this work until it is finished, even though it should take years to accomplish, you must not speak. The first word you utter will pierce your brothers' hearts like a deadly dagger. Their lives hang on your tongue. Remember all this!"

And she touched her hand with the nettle; it was like a burning fire, and Eliza woke with the smart. It was broad daylight; and close by the spot where she had slept lay a nettle like the one she had seen in her dream. She fell upon her knees and prayed gratefully, and went forth from the cave to begin her work.

With her delicate hands she groped among the ugly nettles. These stung like fire, burning great blisters on her arms and hands; but she thought she would bear it gladly if she could only release her dear brothers. Then she bruised every nettle with her bare feet and plaited the green flax.

When the sun had set her brothers came, and they were frightened when they found her dumb. They thought it was some new sorcery of their wicked stepmother's; but when they saw her hands, they understood what she was doing for their sake, and the youngest brother wept. And where his tears dropped she felt no more pains, and the burning blisters vanished.

She passed the night at her work, for she could not sleep till she had delivered her dear brothers. The whole of the following day, while the swans were away, she sat in soli• tude, but never had time flown so quickly with her as now. One shirt of mail was already finished, and now she began the second.

Then a hunting-horn sounded among the hills, and she was struck with fear. The noise came nearer and nearer; she heard the barking dogs, and timidly she fled into the cave, bound into a bundle the nettles she had collected and prepared, and sat upon the bundle.

Immediately a great dog came bounding out of the ravine, and then another, and another; they barked loudly, ran back, and then came again. Only a few minutes had passed before all the huntsmen stood before the cave, and the handsomest of them was the King of the country. He came forward to Eliza, for he had never seen a more beautiful maiden.

"How did you come hither, you delightful child?" he asked.

Eliza shook her head, for she might not speak—it would cost her brothers their deliverance and their lives. And she hid her hands under her apron, so that the King might not see what she was suffering.

"Come with me," said he. "You cannot stop here. If you are as good as you are beautiful, I will dress you in velvet and silk, and place the golden crown on your head, and you shall dwell in my richest castle, and rule."

And then he lifted her on his horse. She wept and wrung her hands; but the King said:—

"I only wish for your happiness; one day you will thank me for this."

And then he galloped away among the mountains with her on his horse, and the hunters galloped at their heels.

When the sun went down, the fair, regal city lay before them, with its churches and cupolas; and the King led her into the castle, where great fountains plashed in the lofty marble halls, and where walls and ceilings were covered with glorious pictures. But she had no eyes for all this—she only wept and mourned. Passively she let the woman put royal robes upon her, and weave pearls in her hair, and draw dainty gloves over her blistered fingers.

When she stood there in full array, she was dazzlingly beautiful, so that the court bowed deeper than ever. And the King chose her for his bride, although the Archbishop shook his head and whispered that the beauteous, fresh maid was certainly a witch, who blinded the eyes and led astray the heart of the King.

But the King gave no ear to this, but ordered that the music should sound, and the costliest dishes should be served, and the most beauteous maidens should dance before them. And she was led through fragrant gardens into gorgeous halls; but never a smile came upon her lips or shone in her eyes: there she stood, a picture of grief. Then the King opened a little chamber close by, where she was to sleep. This chamber was decked with splendid green tapestry, and completely resembled the cave in which she had been. On the floor lay the bundle of flax which she had prepared from the nettles, and under the ceiling hung the shirt of mail she had completed. All these things one of the huntsmen had brought with him as curiosities.

"Here you may dream yourself back in your former home," said the King. "Here is the work which occupied you there, and now, in the midst of all your splendor, it will amuse you to think of that time."

When Eliza saw this that lay so near her heart, a smile played round her mouth and the crimson blood came back into her cheeks. She thought of her brothers' deliverance, and kissed the King's hand; and he pressed her to his heart, and caused the marriage feast to be announced by all the church bells. The beautiful dumb girl out of the wood was to become the Queen of the country.

Then the Archbishop whispered evil words into the King's ear, but they did not sink into the King's heart. The marriage would take place; the Archbishop himself was obliged to place the crown on her head, and with wicked spite he pressed the narrow circlet so tightly upon her brow that it pained her. But a heavier ring lay close around her heart—

sorrow for her brothers; she did not feel the bodily pain. Her mouth was dumb, for a single word would cost her brothers their lives, but her eyes glowed with love for the kind, handsome King, who did everything to rejoice her. She loved him with her whole heart, more and more every day. O that she had been able to confide in him and to tell him of her grief! But she was compelled to be dumb, and to finish her work in silence. Therefore at night she crept away from his side, and went quietly into the little chamber which was decorated like the cave, and wove one shirt of mail after another. But when she began the seventh she had no flax left.

She knew that in the church-yard nettles were growing that she could use; but she must pick them herself, and how was she to go out there?

"O, what is the pain in my fingers to the torment my heart endures?" thought she. "I must venture it, and help will not be denied me!"

With a trembling heart, as though the deed she purposed doing had been evil, she crept into the garden in the moonlight night, and went through the lanes and through the deserted streets to the church-yard. There, on one of the broadest tombstones, she saw sitting a circle of lamias. These hideous wretches took off their ragged garments, as if they were going to bathe; then with their skinny fingers they clawed open the fresh graves, and with fiendish greed they snatched up the corpses and ate the flesh. Eliza was obliged to pass close by them, and they fastened their evil glances upon her; but she prayed silently, and collected the burning nettles, and carried them into the castle.

Only one person had seen her, and that was the Archbishop. He was awake while others slept. Now he felt sure his opinion was correct, that all was not as it should be with the Queen; she was a witch, and thus she had bewitched the King and the whole people.

In secret he told the King what he had seen and what he feared; and when the hard words came from his tongue, the pictures of saints in the cathedral shook their heads, as though they could have said, "It is not so! Eliza is innocent!" But the Archbishop interpreted this differently—he thought they were bearing witness against her, and shaking their heads at her sinfulness. Then two heavy tears rolled down the King's cheeks; he went home with doubt in his heart, and at night pretended to be asleep; but no quiet sleep came upon his eyes, for he noticed Eliza got up. Every night she did this, and each time he followed her silently, and saw how she disappeared from her chamber.

From day to day his face became darker. Eliza saw it, but did not understand the reason; but it frightened her— and what did she not suffer in her heart for her brothers? Her hot tears flowed upon the royal velvet and purple; they lay there like sparkling diamonds, and all who saw the splendor wished they were queens. In the mean time she had almost finished her work. Only one shirt of mail was still to be completed, but she had no flax left, and not a single nettle. Once more, for the last time, therefore, she must go to the church-yard, only to pluck a few handfuls. She thought with terror of this solitary wandering and of the horrible lamias, but her will was firm as her trust in Providence.

Eliza went on, but the King and the Archbishop followed her. They saw her vanish into the church-yard through the wicket-gate; and when they drew near, the lamias were sitting upon the tomb-stone as Eliza had seen them; and the King turned aside, for he fancied her among them, whose head had rested against his breast that very evening.

"The people must condemn her," said he.

And the people condemned her to suffer death by fire.

Out of the gorgeous regal halls she was led into a dark, damp cell, where the wind whistled through the grated window; instead of velvet and silk they gave her the bundle of nettles which she had collected; on this she could lay her head; and the hard, burning coats of mail which she had woven were to be her coverlet. But nothing could have been given her that she liked better. She resumed her work and prayed. Without, the street boys were singing jeering songs about her, and not a soul comforted her with a kind word.

But toward evening there came the whirring of a swan's wings close by the grating—it was the youngest of her brothers. He had found his sister, and she sobbed aloud with joy, though she knew that the approaching night would probably be the last she had to live. But now the work was almost finished, and her brothers were here.

Now came the Archbishop, to stay with her in her last hour, for he had promised the King to do so. And she shook her head, and with looks and gestures she begged him to depart, for in this night she must finish her work, or else all would be in vain, all her tears, her pain, and her sleepless nights. The Archbishop withdrew, uttering evil words against her; but poor Eliza knew she was innocent, and continued her work.

It was still twilight; not till an hour afterward would the sun rise. And the eleven brothers stood at the castle gate, and demanded to be brought before the King. That could not be, they were told, for it was still almost night; the King was asleep, and might not be disturbed. They begged, they threatened, and the sentries came, yes, even the King himself came out, and asked what was the meaning of this. At that moment the sun rose, and no more were the brothers to be seen, but eleven wild swans flew away over the castle.

All the people came flocking out at the town gate, for they wanted to see the witch burned. An old horse drew the cart on which she sat. They had put upon her a garment of coarse sackcloth. Her lovely hair hung loose about her beautiful head; her cheeks were as pale as death; and her lips moved silently, while her fingers were engaged with the green flax. Even on the way to death she did not interrupt the work she had begun; the ten shirts of mail lay at her feet, and she wrought at the eleventh. The mob derided her.

" Look at the red witch, how she mutters! She has no hymn-book in her hand; no, there she sits with her ugly sorcery—tear it in a thousand pieces! "

And they all pressed upon her, and wanted to tear up the shirts of mail. Then eleven wild swans came flying up, and sat round about her on the cart, and beat with their wings; and the mob gave way before them, terrified.

" That is a sign from Heaven! She is certainly innocent! " whispered many. But they did not dare to say it aloud.

Now the executioner seized her by the hand; then she

hastily threw the eleven shirts over the swans, and immediately eleven handsome Princes stood there. But the youngest had a swan's wing instead of an arm, for a sleeve was wanting to his shirt—she had not quite finished it.

"Now I may speak!" she said. "I am innocent!"

And the people who saw what happened bowed before her as before a saint; but she sank lifeless into her brothers' arms, such an effect had suspense, anguish, and pain had upon her.

"Yes, she is innocent," said the eldest brother.

And now he told everything that had taken place; and while he spoke a fragrance arose as of a million of roses, for every piece of fagot in the pile had taken root and was sending forth shoots; and a fragrant hedge stood there, tall and great, covered with red roses, and at the top a flower, white and shining, gleaming like a star. This flower the King plucked and placed in Eliza's bosom; and she arose with peace and happiness in her heart.

And all the church bells rang of themselves, and the birds came in great flocks. And back to the castle went such a marriage-procession as no King had ever seen.

THE GARDEN OF PARADISE

ONCE there was a King's son. No one had so many and so beautiful books as he; everything that had happened in this world he could read there, and could see pictures of it all in lovely copper-plates. Of every people, and of every land he could get intelligence; but there was not a word to tell where the Garden of Paradise could be found, and it was just that of which he thought most.

His grandmother had told him, when he was quite little, but was to begin to go to school, that every flower in this Paradise Garden was a delicate cake, and the pistils contained the choicest wine; on one of the flowers history was written, and on another geography or tables, so that one had only to eat cake, and one knew a lesson; and the more one ate, the more history, geography, or tables did one learn.

At that time he believed this. But when he became a

bigger boy, and learned more and became wiser, he understood well that the splendor in the Garden of Paradise must be of quite a different kind.

"O, why did Eve pluck from the Tree of Knowledge? Why did Adam eat the forbidden fruit? If I had been he, it would never have happened—then sin would never have come into the world."

That he said then, and he still said it when he was seventeen years old. The Garden of Paradise filled all his thoughts.

One day he walked in the wood. He was walking quite alone, for that was his greatest pleasure. The evening came, and the clouds gathered together; rain streamed down as if the sky were one single river from which the water was pouring; it was dark as it usually is at night in the deepest well. Often he slipped on the smooth grass, often he fell over the smooth stones which peered up out of the wet, rocky ground. Everything was soaked with water, and there was not a dry thread on the poor Prince. He was obliged to climb over great blocks of stone, where the water spurted from the thick moss. He was nearly fainting. Then he heard a strange rushing, and saw before him a great illuminated cave. In the midst of it burned a fire so large that a stag might have been roasted at it. And this was in fact being done. A glorious deer had been stuck, horns and all, upon a spit, and was turning slowly between two felled pine trunks. An elderly woman, large and strongly built, looking like a disguised man, sat by the fire, into which she threw one piece of wood after another.

"Come nearer!" said she. "Sit down by the fire and dry your clothes."

"There's a great draught here!" said the Prince; and he sat down on the ground.

"That will be worse when my sons come home," replied the Woman. "You are here in the Cavern of the Winds, and my sons are the four Winds of the world; can you understand that?"

"Where are your sons?" asked the Prince.

"It is difficult to answer when stupid questions are asked," said the Woman. "My sons do business on their own ac-

count. They play at shuttlecock with the clouds up yonder
in the King's hall."

And she pointed upwards.

"O, indeed!" said the Prince. "But you speak rather
gruffly, by the way, and are not so mild as the women I
generally see about me."

"Yes, they have most likely nothing else to do! I must be
hard, if I want to keep my sons in order; but I can do it,
though they are obstinate fellows. Do you see the four
sacks hanging there by the wall? They are just as frightened of those as you used to be of the rod stuck behind
the glass. I can bend the lads together, I tell you, and then
I pop them into the bag; we don't make any ceremony.
There they sit, and may not wander about again until I
think fit to allow them. But here comes one of them."

It was the North Wind, who rushed in with piercing cold;
great hailstones skipped about on the floor, and snow-flakes
fluttered about. He was dressed in a jacket and trousers
of bear-skin; a cap of seal-skin was drawn down over his
ears; long icicles hung on his beard, and one hailstone after
another rolled from the collar of his jacket.

"Do not go so near the fire directly," said the Prince;
"you might get your hands and face frost-bitten."

"Frost-bitten?" repeated the North Wind, and he laughed
aloud. "Cold is exactly what rejoices me most! But what
kind of little tailor art thou? How did you find your way
into the Cavern of the Winds?"

"He is my guest," interposed the old Woman, "and if
you're not satisfied with this explanation you may go into
the sack; do you understand me?"

You see that was the right way; and now the North Wind
told whence he came, and where he had been for almost a
month.

"I came from the Polar Sea," said he; "I have been in the
bear's icy land with the walrus hunters. I sat and slept on
the helm when they went away from the North Cape, and
when I awoke, now and then, the storm-bird flew round my
legs. That's a comical bird! He gives a sharp clap with
his wings, and then holds them quite still and shoots along
in full career."

"Don't be too long-winded," said the Mother of the Winds. "And so you came to the Bear's Island?"

"It is very beautiful there. There's a floor for dancing on as flat as a plate. Half-thawed snow, with a little moss, sharp stones, and skeletons of walruses and polar bears lay around, and likewise gigantic arms and legs of a rusty green color. One would have thought the sun had never shone there. I blew a little upon the mist, so that one could see the hut; it was a house built of wreck-wood and covered with walrus-skins—the fleshy side turned outwards. It was full of green and red, and on the roof sat a live polar bear who was growling. I went to the shore to look after birds'-nests, and saw the unfledged nestlings screaming and opening their beaks; then I blew down into their thousand throats, and taught them to shut their mouths. Farther on the huge walruses were splashing like great maggots with pigs' heads, and teeth an ell long!"

"You tell your story well, my son," said the old Lady. "My mouth waters when I hear you!"

"Then the hunting began! The harpoon was hurled into the walrus's breast, so that a smoking stream of blood spurted like a fountain over the ice. When I thought of my sport, I blew, and let my sailing ships, the big icebergs, crush the boats between them. O, how the people whistled and how they cried! but I whistled louder than they. They were obliged to throw the dead walruses and their chests and tackle out upon the ice. I shook the snow-flakes over them, and let them drive south in their crushed boats with their booty to taste salt-water. They'll never come to Bear's Island again!"

"Then you have done a wicked thing!" said the Mother of the Winds.

"What good I have done others may tell," replied he. "But here comes a brother from the west. I like him best of all: he tastes of the sea and brings a delicious coolness with him."

"Is that little Zephyr?" asked the Prince.

"Yes, certainly, that is little Zephyr," replied the old Woman. "But he is not little. Years ago he was a pretty boy, but that's past now."

He looked like a wild man, but he had a broad-brimmed hat on, to save his face. In his hand he held a club of mahogany, hewn in the American mahogany forests. It was no trifle.

"Where do you come from?" said his mother.

"Out of the forest wilderness," said he, "where the water-snake lies in the wet grass, and the people don't seem to be wanted."

"What were you doing there?"

"I looked into the deepest river, and watched how it rushed down from the rocks, and turned to spray, and shot up toward the clouds to carry the rainbow. I saw the wild buffalo swimming in the stream, but the stream carried him away. He drifted with the flock of wild ducks that flew up where the water fell down in a cataract. The buffalo had to go down it! That pleased me, and I blew a storm, so that ancient trees were split up into splinters!"

"And have you done nothing else?" asked the old Dame.

"I have thrown somersaults in the Savannahs: I have stroked the wild horses and shaken the cocoa-nut palms. Yes, yes, I have stories to tell! But one must not tell all one knows. You know that, old Lady."

And he kissed his mother so roughly that she almost tumbled over. He was a terribly wild young fellow!

Now came the South Wind, with a turban on and flying Bedouin's cloak.

"It's terribly cold out here!" cried he, and threw some more wood on the fire. "One can feel that the North Wind came first."

"It's so hot that one could roast a Polar bear here," said the North Wind.

"You're a Polar bear yourself," retorted the South Wind.

"Do you want to be put in the sack?" asked the old Dame. "Sit upon the stone yonder and tell me where you have been."

"In Africa, mother," he answered. "I was out hunting the lion with the Hottentots in the land of the Kaffirs. Grass grows there in the plains, green as an olive. There the ostrich ran races with me, but I am swifter than he. I came into the desert where the yellow sand lies: it looks there like the bottom of the sea. I met a caravan. The people were killing their last camel to get water to drink, but it was very little they got. The sun burned above and the sand below. The outspread deserts had no bounds. Then I rolled in the fine loose sand, and whirled it up in great pillars. That was a dance! You should have seen how the dromedary stood there terrified, and the merchant drew the caftan over his head. He threw himself down before me, as before Allah, his God. Now they are buried—a pyramid of sand covers them all. When I some day blow that away, the sun will bleach the white bones; then travellers may see that men have been there before them. Otherwise, one would not believe that, in the desert!"

"So you have done nothing but evil!" exclaimed the Mother. "March into the sack!"

And before he was aware, she had seized the South Wind round the body, and popped him into the bag. He rolled about on the floor; but she sat on the sack, and then he had to keep quiet.

"Those are lively boys of yours," said the Prince.

"Yes," she replied, "and I know how to punish them! Here comes the fourth!"

That was the East Wind, who came dressed like a Chinaman.

"O! do you come from that region?" said the mother. "I thought you had been in the Garden of Paradise."

"I don't fly there till to-morrow," said the East Wind. "It will be a hundred years to-morrow since I was there. I come from China now, where I danced around the porcelain tower till all the bells jingled again! In the streets the officials were being thrashed: the bamboos were broken upon their shoulders, yet they were high people, from the first to the ninth grade. They cried, 'Many thanks, my paternal benefactor!' but it did not come from their hearts. And I rang the bells and sang 'Tsing, Tsang, tsu!'"

"You are foolish," said the old Dame. "It is a good thing that you are going into the Garden of Paradise to-morrow, that always helps on your education. Drink bravely out of the spring of wisdom, and bring home a little bottleful for me."

"That I will do," said the East Wind. "But why have you clapped my brother South in the bag? Out with him! He shall tell me about the Phœnix bird, for about that bird the Princess in the Garden of Paradise always wants to hear, when I pay my visit every hundredth year. Open the sack, then you shall be my sweetest of mothers, and I will give you two pocketsful of tea, green and fresh as I plucked it at the place where it grew!"

"Well, for the sake of the tea, and because you are my darling boy, I will open the sack."

She did so, and the South Wind crept out, but he looked quite downcast, because the strange Prince had seen his disgrace.

"There you have a palm-leaf for the Princess," said the South Wind. "This palm-leaf was given me by the Phœnix bird, the only one who is in the world. With his beak he has scratched upon it a description of all the hundred years he has lived. Now she may read herself how the Phœnix bird set fire to her nest, and sat upon it, and was burned to death like a Hindoo's widow. How the dry branches crackled! What a smoke and a steam there was! At last everything burst into a flame, and the old Phœnix turned to ashes, but her egg lay red-hot in the fire; it burst with a great bang, and the young one flew out. Now this young one is ruler over all the birds, and the only Phœnix in the world. It has bitten a hole in the palm-leaf I have given you. That is a greeting to the Princess."

"Let us have something to eat," said the Mother of the Winds.

And now they all sat down to eat of the roasted deer. The Prince sat beside the East Wind, and they soon became good friends.

"Just tell me," said the Prince, "what Princess is that about whom there is so much talk here? and where does the Garden of Paradise lie?"

"Ho, ho!" said the East Wind, "do you want to go there? Well, then, fly to-morrow with me! But I must tell you, however, that no man has been there since the time of Adam and Eve. You have read of them in your Bible histories?"

"Yes," said the Prince.

"When they were driven away, the Garden of Paradise sank into the earth; but it kept warm its sunshine, its mild air, and all its splendor. The Queen of the Fairies lives there, and there lies the Island of Happiness, where death never comes, and where it is beautiful. Sit upon my back to-morrow, and I will take you with me; I think it can very well be done. But now leave off talking, for I want to sleep."

And then they all went to rest.

In the early morning the Prince awoke, and was not a little astonished to find himself high above the clouds. He was sitting on the back of the East Wind, who was faithfully holding him; they were so high in the air that the woods and fields, rivers and lakes, looked as if they were painted on a map below them.

"Good morning!" said the East Wind. "You might very well sleep a little longer, for there is not much to be seen on the flat country under us, unless you care to count the churches. They stand like dots of chalk on the green carpet."

What he called green carpet was field and meadow.

"It was rude of me not to say good-by to your mother and your brothers," said the Prince.

"When one is asleep, one must be excused," replied the East Wind.

And then they flew on faster than ever. One could hear them in the tops of the trees, for when they passed over them the leaves and twigs rustled; one could hear them on the sea and on the lakes, for when they flew by the water rose higher, and the great ships bowed themselves toward the water like swimming swans.

Toward evening, when it became dark, the great towns looked charming, for lights were burning below, here and there; it was just as when one has lighted a piece of paper, and sees all the little sparks which vanish one after another. And the Prince clapped his hands; but the East Wind begged him to let that be, and rather to hold fast, otherwise he might easily fall down and get caught on a church spire.

The eagle in the dark woods flew lightly, but the East Wind flew more lightly still. The Cossack on his little horse skimmed swiftly over the surface of the earth, but the Prince skimmed more swiftly still.

"Now you can see the Himalayas," said the East Wind. "That is the highest mountain range in Asia. Now we shall soon get to the Garden of Paradise."

Then they turned more to the south, and soon the air was fragrant with flowers and spices; figs and pomegranates grew wild, and the wild vine bore clusters of red and purple grapes. Here both alighted, and stretched themselves on the soft grass, where the flowers nodded to the wind, as though they would have said, "Welcome!"

"Are we now in the Garden of Paradise?" asked the Prince.

"Not at all," replied the East Wind. "But we shall soon get there. Do you see the rocky wall yonder, and the great cave, where the vines cluster like a broad green curtain? Through that we shall pass. Wrap yourself in your cloak. Here the sun scorches you, but a step farther it will be icy cold. The bird which hovers past the cave has one wing in the region of summer and the other in the wintry cold."

"So this is the way to the Garden of Paradise?" observed the Prince.

They went into the cave. Ugh! but it was icy cold there, but this did not last long. The East Wind spread out his wings, and they gleamed like the brightest fire. What a cave was that! Great blocks of stone, from which the water dripped down, hung over them in the strangest shapes; sometimes it was so narrow that they had to creep on their hands and knees, sometimes as lofty and broad as in the open air. The place looked like a number of mortuary chapels, with dumb organ pipes, the organs themselves being petrified.

"We are going through the way of death to the Garden of Paradise, are we not?" inquired the Prince.

The East Wind answered not a syllable, but he pointed forward to where a lovely blue light gleamed upon them. The stone blocks over their heads became more and more like a mist, and at last looked like a white cloud in the moonlight. Now they were in a deliciously mild air, fresh as on the hills, fragrant as among the roses of the valley. There ran a river clear as the air itself, and the fishes were like silver and gold: purple eels, flashing out blue sparks at every moment, played in the water below; and the broad water-plant leaves shone in the colors of the rainbow; the flower itself was an orange-colored burning flame, to which the water gave nourishment, as the oil to the burning lamp; a bridge of marble, strong, indeed, but so lightly built that it looked as if made of lace and glass beads, led them across the water to the Island of Happiness, where the Garden of Paradise bloomed.

Were they palm-trees that grew here, or gigantic water-plants? Such verdant, mighty trees the Prince had never beheld; the most wonderful climbing plants hung there in long festoons, as one only sees them illuminated in gold and colors on the margins of gold missal-books, or twined among the initial letters. Here were the strangest group-ings of birds, flowers, and twining lines. Close by, in the grass, stood a flock of peacocks, with their shining starry trains outspread.

Yes, it was really so! But when the Prince touched these, he found they were not birds, but plants; they were great burdocks, which shone like the peacock's gorgeous train. The lion and the tiger sprang to and fro like agile cats among the green bushes, which were fragrant as the blossom of the olive-tree; and the lion and the tiger were tame. The wild wood-pigeon shone like the most beautiful pearl, and beat her wings against the lion's mane; and the antelope, usually so timid, stood by, nodding its head, as if it wished to play too.

Now came the Fairy of Paradise. Her garb shone like the sun, and her countenance was cheerful like that of a happy mother when she is well pleased with her child. She was young and beautiful, and was followed by a number of pretty maidens, each with a gleaming star in her hair. The East Wind gave her the written leaf from the Phœnix bird, and her eyes shone with pleasure.

She took the Prince by the hand and led him into her

palace, where the walls had the color of a splendid tulip-leaf when it is held up in the sunlight. The ceiling was a great sparkling flower, and the more one looked up at it, the deeper did its cup appear. The Prince stepped to the window and looked through one of the panes. Here he saw the Tree of Knowledge, with the serpent, and Adam and Eve were standing close by.

"Were they not driven out?" he asked.

And the Fairy smiled, and explained to him that Time had burned in the picture upon that pane, but not as people are accustomed to see pictures. No; there was life in it; the leaves of the trees moved, men came and went as in a dissolving view. And he looked through another pane, and there was Jacob's dream, with the ladder reaching up into heaven, and the angels with great wings were ascending and descending. Yes, everything that had happened in the world lived and moved in the glass panes; such cunning pictures only Time could burn in.

The Fairy smiled, and led him into a great lofty hall, whose walls appeared transparent. Here were portraits, and each face looked fairer than the last. There were to be seen millions of happy ones who smiled and sang, so that it flowed together into a melody; the uppermost were so small that they looked like the smallest rose-bud when it is drawn as a point upon paper. And in the midst of the hall stood a great tree with rich, pendent boughs; golden apples, great and small, hung like oranges among the leaves. That was the Tree of Knowledge, of whose fruit Adam and Eve had eaten. From each leaf fell a shining red dew-drop; it was as though the tree wept tears of blood.

"Let us now get into the boat," said the Fairy; "then we will enjoy some refreshment on the heaving waters. The boat rocks, yet does not quit its station; but all the lands of the earth will glide past in our sight."

And it was wonderful to behold how the whole coast moved. There came the lofty snow-covered Alps, with clouds and black pine-trees; the horn sounded with its melancholy note, and the shepherd trolled his merry song in the valley. Then the banana-trees bent their long, hanging branches over the boat; coal-black swans swam on the water, and the

strangest animals and flowers showed themselves upon the
shore. That was New Holland, the fifth great division of the
world, which glided past with a background of blue hills.
They heard the song of the priests, and saw the savages
dancing to the sound of drums and of bone trumpets. Egypt's
pyramids, towering aloft to the clouds; overturned pillars and
sphinxes half buried in the sand sailed past likewise. The
northern lights shone over the extinct volcanoes of the Pole
—it was a fire-work that no one could imitate. The Prince
was quite happy, and he saw a hundred times more than we
can relate here.

" And can I always stay here? " asked he.

"That depends upon yourself," answered the Fairy. "If
you do not, like Adam, yield to the temptation to do what is
forbidden, you may always remain here."

"I shall not touch the apples on the Tree of Knowledge!"
said the Prince. "Here are thousands of fruits just as
beautiful as those."

"Search your own heart, and if you are not strong enough,
go away with the East Wind that brought you hither. He is
going to fly back, and will not show himself here again for a
hundred years: the time will pass for you in this place as if it
were a hundred hours, but it is a long time for the temptation
of sin. Every evening, when I leave you, I shall have to call
to you, 'Come with me!' and I shall have to beckon to you
with my hand; but stay where you are: do not go with me,
or your longing will become greater with every step. You
will then come into the hall where the Tree of Knowledge
grows; I sleep under its fragrant, pendent boughs; you will
bend over me, and I must smile; but if you press a kiss upon
my mouth, the Paradise will sink deep into the earth and be
lost to you. The keen wind of the desert will rush around
you, the cold rain drop upon your head, and sorrow and woe
will be your portion."

"I shall stay here!" said the Prince.

And the East Wind kissed him on the forehead, and
said,—

"Be strong, and we shall meet here again in a hundred
years. Farewell! farewell!"

And the East Wind spread out his broad wings, and they

flashed like sheet lightning in harvest-time, or like the northern light in the cold winter.

"Farewell! farewell!" sounded from among the flowers and the trees. Storks and pelicans flew away in rows like fluttering ribbons, and bore him company to the boundary of the garden.

"Now we will begin our dances!" cried the Fairy. "At the end, when I dance with you, when the sun goes down, you will see me beckon to you; you will hear me call to you, 'Come with me;' but do not obey. For a hundred years I must repeat this every evening; every time, when the trial is past, you will gain more strength; at last you will not think of it at all. This evening is the first time. Now I have warned you."

And the Fairy led him into a great hall of white transparent lilies: the yellow stamens in each flower formed a little golden harp, which sounded like stringed instrument and flute. The most beautiful maidens, floating and slender, clad in gauzy mist, glided by in the dance, and sang of the happiness of living, and declared that they would never die, and that the Garden of Paradise would bloom forever.

And the sun went down. The whole sky shone like gold, which gave to the lilies the hue of the most glorious roses; and the Prince drank of the foaming wine which the maidens poured out for him, and felt a happiness he had never before known. He saw how the background of the hall opened, and the Tree of Knowledge stood in a glory which blinded his eyes; the singing there was soft and lovely as the voice of his dear mother, and it was as though she sang, "My child! my beloved child!"

Then the Fairy beckoned to him, and called out persuasively,—

"Come with me! come with me!"

And he rushed toward her, forgetting his promise,—forgetting it the very first evening; and still she beckoned and smiled. The fragrance, the delicious fragrance around became stronger, the harps sounded far more lovely, and it seemed as though the millions of smiling heads in the hall, where the Tree grew, nodded and sang, "One must know everything—man is the lord of the earth." And they were no longer drops of blood that the Tree of Knowledge wept; they were red, shining stars which he seemed to see.

"Come! come!" the quivering voice still cried, and at every step the Prince's cheeks burned more hotly and his blood flowed more rapidly.

"I must!" said he. "It is no sin; it cannot be one. Why not follow beauty and joy? I only want to see her asleep; there will be nothing lost if I only refrain from kissing her: and I will not kiss her; I am strong and have a resolute will!"

And the Fairy threw off her shining cloak and bent back the branches, and in another moment she was hidden among them.

"I have not yet sinned," said the Prince, "and I will not."

And he pushed the boughs aside. There she slept already, beautiful as only a fairy in the Garden of Paradise can be. She smiled in her dreams, and he bent over her, and saw tears quivering beneath her eyelids!

"Do you weep for me?" he whispered. "Weep not, thou glorious woman! Now only I understand the bliss of Paradise! It streams through my blood, through my thoughts; the power of the angel and of increasing life I feel in my mortal body! Let what will happen to me now; one moment like this is wealth enough!"

And he kissed the tears from her eyes—his mouth touched hers.

Then there resounded a clap of thunder so loud and dreadful that no one had ever heard the like, and everything fell down; and the beautiful Fairy and the charming Paradise sank down, deeper and deeper. The Prince saw it vanish into the black night; like a little bright star it gleamed out of the far distance. A deadly chill ran through his frame, and he closed his eyes, and lay for a long time as one dead.

The cold rain fell upon his face, the keen wind roared round his head, and then his senses returned to him.

"What have I done?" he sighed. "I have sinned like Adam—sinned so that Paradise has sunk deep down!"

And he opened his eyes, and the star in the distance—the star that gleamed like the Paradise that had sunk down—was the morning-star in the sky.

He stood up, and found himself in the great forest, close

by the Cave of the Winds, and the Mother of the Winds sat by his side: she looked angry, and raised her arm in the air.

"The very first evening!" said she. "I thought it would be so! Yes, if you were my son, you would have to go into the sack!"

"Yes, he shall go in there!" said Death. He was a strong old man, with a scythe in his hand, and with great black wings. "Yes, he shall be laid in his coffin, but not yet: I only register him, and let him wander awhile in the world to expiate his sins and to grow better. But one day I shall come. When he least expects it, I shall clap him in the black coffin, put him on my head, and fly up toward the star. There, too, blooms the Garden of Paradise; and if he is good and pious he will go in there; but if his thoughts are evil, and his heart still full of sin, he will sink with his coffin deeper than Paradise has sunk, and only every thousandth year I shall fetch him, that he may sink deeper, or that he may attain to the star—the shining star up yonder!"

THE CONSTANT TIN SOLDIER

THERE were once five-and-twenty tin soldiers; they were all brothers, for they had all been born of one old tin spoon. They shouldered their muskets and looked straight before them; their uniform was red and blue, and very splendid. The first thing they had heard in the world, when the lid was taken off their box, had been the words "Tin soldiers!" These words were uttered by a little boy, clapping his hands; the soldiers had been given to him, for it was his birthday; and now he put them upon the table. Each soldier was exactly like the rest; but one of them had been cast last of all, and there had not been enough tin to finish him; but he stood as firmly upon one leg as the others on their two; and it was just this soldier who became remarkable.

On the table on which they had been placed stood many other playthings, but the toy that attracted most attention was a neat castle of card-board. Through the little windows one could see straight into the hall. Before the castle some little trees were placed round a little looking-glass, which was to represent a clear lake. Waxen swans swam on this lake, and were mirrored in it. This was all very pretty; but the prettiest of all was a little lady, who stood at the open door of the castle; she was also cut out in paper, but she had a dress of the clearest gauze, and a little narrow blue ribbon over her shoulders, that looked like a scarf; and in the middle of this ribbon was a shining tinsel rose, as big as her whole face. The little Lady stretched out both her arms, for she was a dancer, and then she lifted one leg so high that the Tin Soldier could not see it at all, and thought that, like himself, she had but one leg.

" That would be the wife for me," thought he; "but she is very grand. She lives in a castle, and I have only a box, and there are five-and-twenty of us in that. It is no place for her. But I must try to make acquaintance with her."

And then he lay down at full length behind a snuff-box which was on the table; there he could easily watch the little dainty lady, who continued to stand on one leg without losing her balance.

When the evening came, all the other tin soldiers were put into their box, and the people in the house went to bed. Now the toys began to play at " visiting," and at " war," and " giving balls." The tin soldiers rattled in their box, for they wanted to join, but could not lift the lid. The Nut-cracker threw somersaults, and the Pencil amused itself on the table; there was so much noise that the Canary woke up, and began to speak too, and even in verse. The only two who did not stir from their places were the Tin Soldier and the Dancing Lady; she stood straight up on the point of one of her toes, and stretched out both her arms: and he was just as enduring on his one leg; and he never turned his eyes away from her.

Now the clock struck twelve—and, bounce!—the lid flew off the snuff-box; but there was not snuff in it, but a little black goblin; you see, it was a trick.

" Tin Soldier," said the Goblin, " don't stare at things that don't concern you."

But the Tin Soldier pretended not to hear him.

" Just you wait till to-morrow ! " said the Goblin.

But when the morning came, and the children got up, the Tin Soldier was placed in the window; and whether it was the Goblin or the draught that did it, all at once the window flew open, and the Soldier fell, head over heels, out of the third story.

That was a terrible passage! He put his leg straight up, and struck with his helmet downward, and his bayonet between the paving-stones.

The servant-maid and the little boy came down directly to look for him, but though they almost trod upon him they could not see him. If the soldier had cried out, "Here I am!" they would have found him; but he did not think it fitting to call out loudly, because he was in uniform.

Now it began to rain; the drops soon fell thicker, and at last it came down in a complete stream. When the rain was past, two street boys came by.

"Just look!" said one of them, "there lies a tin soldier. He must come out and ride in the boat."

And they made a boat out of a newspaper, and put the Tin Soldier in the middle of it; and so he sailed down the gutter, and the two boys ran beside him and clapped their hands. Goodness preserve us! how the waves rose in that gutter, and how fast the stream ran! But then it had been a heavy rain. The paper boat rocked up and down, and sometimes turned round so rapidly that the Tin Soldier trembled; but he re-mained firm, and never changed countenance, and looked straight before him, and shouldered his musket.

All at once the boat went into a long drain, and it became as dark as if he had been in his box.

"Where am I going now?" he thought. "Yes, yes, that's the Goblin's fault. Ah! if the little Lady only sat here with me in the boat, it might be twice as dark for what I should care."

Suddenly there came a great water-rat, which lived under the drain.

"Have you a passport?" said the Rat. "Give me your passport."

But the Tin Soldier kept silence, and only held his musket tighter than ever.

The boat went on, but the Rat came after it. Hu! how he gnashed his teeth, and called out to the bits of straw and wood,—

"Hold him! hold him! he hasn't paid toll—he hasn't shown his passport!"

But the stream became stronger and stronger. The Tin Soldier could see the bright daylight where the arch ended; but he heard a roaring noise, which might well frighten a bolder man. Only think—just where the tunnel ended, the drain ran into a great canal; and for him that would have been as dangerous as for us to be carried down a great waterfall.

Now he was already so near it that he could not stop. The boat was carried out, the poor Tin Soldier stiffening himself as much as he could, and no one could say that he moved an eyelid. The boat whirled round three or four times, and was full of water to the very edge—it must sink. The Tin Soldier stood up to his neck in water, and the boat sank deeper and deeper, and the paper was loosened more and more; and now the water closed over the Soldier's head. Then he thought of the pretty little Dancer, and how he should never see her again; and it sounded in the Soldier's ears:—

> "Farewell, farewell, thou warrior brave,
> Die shalt thou this day."

And now the paper parted, and the Tin Soldier fell out; but at that moment he was snapped up by a great fish.

O, how dark it was in that fish's body! It was darker yet than in the drain tunnel; and then it was very narrow, too. But the Tin Soldier remained unmoved, and lay at full length, shouldering his musket.

The fish swam to and fro; he made the most wonderful movements, and then became quite still. At last something flashed through him like lightning. The daylight shone quite clear, and a voice said aloud, "The Tin Soldier!" The fish had been caught, carried to market, bought, and taken into the kitchen, where the cook cut him open with a large knife. She seized the Soldier round the body with both her hands, and carried him into the room, where all were anxious to see the remarkable man who had travelled about in the inside of a fish; but the Tin Soldier was not at all proud. They placed him on the table, and there—no! What curious things may happen in the world! The Tin Soldier was in the very room in which he had been before! he saw the same children, and the same toys stood upon the table; and there was the pretty castle with the graceful little Dancer. She was still balancing herself on one leg, and held the other extended in the air. She was faithful too. That moved the Tin Soldier: he was very near weeping tin tears, but that would not have been proper. He looked at her, but they said nothing to each other.

Then one of the little boys took the Tin Soldier and flung him into the stove. He gave no reason for doing this. It must have been the fault of the Goblin in the snuff-box.

The Tin Soldier stood there quite illuminated, and felt a heat that was terrible; but whether this heat proceeded from the real fire or from love he did not know. The colors had quite gone off from him; but whether that had happened on the journey, or had been caused by grief, no one could say. He looked at the little Lady, she looked at him, and he felt that he was melting; but he stood firm, shouldering his musket. Then suddenly the door flew open, and the draught of air caught the Dancer, and she flew like a sylph just into the stove to the Tin Soldier, and flashed up in a flame, and then was gone! Then the Tin soldier melted down into a lump, and when the servant-maid took the ashes out next day, she found him in the shape of a little tin heart. But of the Dancer nothing remained but the tinsel rose, and that was burned as black as a coal.

THE DAISY

Now you shall hear!

Out in the country, close by the road-side, there was a country-house: you yourself have certainly once seen it. Before it is a little garden with flowers, and a paling which is painted. Close by it, by the ditch, in the midst of the most beautiful green grass, grew a little Daisy. The sun shone as warmly and as brightly upon it as on the great splendid garden flowers, and so it grew from hour to hour. One morning it stood in full bloom, with its little shining white leaves spreading like rays round the little yellow sun in the centre.

It never thought that no man would notice it down in the grass, and that it was a poor despised floweret; no, it was very merry, and turned to the warm sun, looked up at it, and listened to the Lark caroling high in the air.

The little Daisy was as happy as if it were a great holiday, and yet it was only a Monday. All the children were at school; and while they sat on their benches learning, it sat on its little green stalk, and learned also from the warm sun, and from all around, how good God is. And the Daisy was very glad that everything that it silently felt was sung so loudly and charmingly by the Lark. And the Daisy looked up with a kind of respect to the happy bird who could sing and fly; but it was not at all sorrowful because it could not fly and sing also.

"I can see and hear," it thought: "the sun shines on me, and the forest kisses me. O, how richly have I been gifted!"

Within the palings stood many stiff, aristocratic flowers— the less scent they had the more they flaunted. The peonies blew themselves out to be greater than the roses, but size will not do it; the tulips had the most splendid colors, and they knew that, and held themselves bolt upright, that they might be seen more plainly. They did not notice the little Daisy outside there, but the Daisy looked at them the more, and thought, "How rich and beautiful they are! Yes, the pretty bird flies across to them and visits them. I am glad that I stand so near them, for at any rate I can enjoy the sight of their splendor!" And just as she thought that—"keevit!" —down came flying the Lark, but not down to the peonies and tulips—no, down into the grass to the lowly Daisy, which started so with joy that it did not know what to think.

The little bird danced round about it, and sang,—

"O, how soft the grass is! and see what a lovely little flower, with gold in its heart and silver on its dress!"

For the yellow point in the Daisy looked like gold, and the little leaves around it shone silvery white.

How happy was the little Daisy—no one can conceive how happy! The bird kissed it with his beak, sang to it, and then flew up again into the blue air. A quarter of an hour passed, at least, before the Daisy could recover itself. Half

ashamed, yet inwardly rejoiced, it looked at the other flowers
in the garden, for they had seen the honor and happiness it
had gained, and must understand what a joy it was. But the
tulips stood up twice as stiff as before, and they looked quite
peaky in the face and quite red, for they had been vexed.
The peonies were quite wrong-headed: it was well they could
not speak, or the Daisy would have received a good scolding.
The poor little flower could see very well that they were not
in a good humor, and that hurt it sensibly. At this moment
there came into the garden a girl with a great sharp, shining
knife; she went straight up to the tulips, and cut off one after
another of them.

"O!" sighed the little Daisy, "that is dreadful! Now it
is all over with them."

Then the girl went away with the tulips. The Daisy was
glad to stand out in the grass, and to be only a poor little
flower; it felt very grateful; and when the sun went down it
folded its leaves and went to sleep, and dreamed all night
long about the sun and the pretty little bird.

The next morning, when the flower again happily stretched
out all its white leaves, like little arms, toward the air and
the light, it recognized the voice of the bird, but the song he
was singing sounded mournfully. Yes, the poor Lark had
good reason to be sad: he was caught, and now sat in a cage
close by the open window. He sang of free and happy roaming, sang of the young green corn in the fields, and of the
glorious journey he might make on his wings high through
the air. The poor Lark was not in good spirits, for there
he sat a prisoner in a cage.

The little Daisy wished very much to help him. But what
was it to do? Yes, that was difficult to make out. It quite
forgot how everything was so beautiful around, how warm
the sun shone, and how splendidly white its own leaves were.
Ah! it could think only of the imprisoned bird, and how it
was powerless to do anything for him.

Just then two little boys came out of the garden. One of
them carried in his hand the knife which the girl had used
to cut off the tulips. They went straight up to the little Daisy,
which could not at all make out what they wanted.

"Here we may cut a capital piece of turf for the Lark,"

said one of the boys; and he began to cut off a square patch round about the Daisy, so that the flower remained standing in its piece of grass.

"Tear off the flower!" said the other boy.

And the Daisy trembled with fear, for to be torn off would be to lose its life; and now it wanted particularly to live, as it was to be given with the piece of turf to the captive Lark.

"No, let it stay," said the other boy; "it makes such a nice ornament."

And so it remained, and was put into the Lark's cage. But the poor bird complained aloud of his lost liberty, and beat his wings against the wires of his prison; and the little Daisy could not speak—could say no consoling word to him, gladly as it would have done so. And thus the whole morning passed.

"Here is no water," said the captive Lark. "They are all gone out, and have forgotten to give me anything to drink. My throat is dry and burning. It is like fire and ice within me, and the air is so close. O, I must die! I must leave the warm sunshine, the fresh green, and all the splendor that God has created!"

And then he thrust his beak into the cool turf to refresh himself a little with it. Then the bird's eye fell upon the Daisy, and he nodded to it, and kissed it with his beak, and said,—

"You also must wither in here, poor little flower. They have given you to me with the little patch of green grass on which you grow, instead of the whole world which was mine out there! Every little blade of grass shall be a great tree for me, and every one of your fragrant leaves a great flower. Ah, you only tell me how much I have lost!"

"If I could only comfort him!" thought the Daisy.

It could not stir a leaf; but the scent which streamed forth from its delicate leaves was far stronger than is generally found in these flowers; the bird also noticed that, and though he was fainting with thirst, and in his pain plucked up the green blades of grass, he did not touch the flower.

The evening came on, and yet nobody appeared to bring the poor bird a drop of water. Then he stretched out his pretty wings and beat the air frantically with them; his song changed to a mournful piping, his little head sank down toward the flower, and the bird's heart broke with want and yearning. Then the flower could not fold its leaves, as it had done on the previous evening, and sleep; it drooped, sorrowful and sick, toward the earth.

Not till the next morn did the boys come; and when they found the bird dead they wept—wept many tears—and dug him a neat grave, which they adorned with leaves of flowers. The bird's corpse was put into a pretty red box, for he was to be royally buried—the poor bird! While he was alive and sang they forgot him, and let him sit in his cage and suffer want; but now that he was dead he had adornment and many tears.

But the patch of turf with the Daisy on it was thrown out into the high road: no one thought of the flower that had felt the most for the little bird, and would have been so glad to console him.

THE NIGHTINGALE

IN China, you must know, the Emperor is a Chinaman, and all whom he has about him are Chinamen too. It happened a good many years ago, but that's just why it's worth while to hear the story, before it is forgotten. The Emperor's palace was the most splendid in the world; it was made entirely of porcelain, very costly, but so delicate and brittle that one had to take care how one touched it. In the garden were to be seen the most wonderful flowers, and to the costliest of them silver bells were tied, which sounded, so that nobody should pass by without noticing the flowers. Yes, everything in the Emperor's garden was admirably arranged. And it extended so far, that the gardener himself did not know where the end was. If a man went on and on, he came into a glorious forest with high trees and deep lakes. The wood extended straight down to the sea, which was blue and deep; great ships could sail to and fro beneath the branches of the trees; and in the trees lived a nightingale, which sang so splendidly that even the poor Fisherman, who had many other things to do, stopped still and listened, when he had gone out at night to throw out his nets, and heard the Nightingale.

"How beautiful that is!" he said; but he was obliged to attend to his property, and thus forgot the bird. But when in the next night the bird sang again, and the Fisherman heard it, he exclaimed again, "How beautiful that is!"

From all the countries of the world travellers came to the city of the Emperor and admired it, and the palace, and the garden, but when they heard the Nightingale, they said, "That is the best of all!"

And the travellers told of it when they came home; and the learned men wrote many books about the town, the palace, and the garden. But they did not forget the Nightingale; that was placed highest of all; and those who were poets wrote most magnificent poems about the Nightingale in the wood by the deep lake.

The books went through all the world, and a few of them once came to the Emperor. He sat in his golden chair, and read, and read: every moment he nodded his head, for it pleased him to peruse the masterly descriptions of the city, the palace, and the garden. "But the Nightingale is the best of all!"—it stood written there.

"What's that?" exclaimed the Emperor. "I don't know the Nightingale at all! Is there such a bird in my empire, and even in my garden? I've never heard of that. To think that I should have to learn such a thing for the first time from books!"

And hereupon he called his Cavalier. This Cavalier was so grand that if any one lower in rank than himself dared to speak to him, or to ask him any question, he answered nothing but "P!"—and that meant nothing.

"There is said to be a wonderful bird here called a Nightingale!" said the Emperor. "They say it is the best thing in all my great empire. Why have I never heard anything about it?"

"I have never heard him named," replied the Cavalier. "He has never been introduced at court."

"I command that he shall appear this evening, and sing before me," said the Emperor. "All the world knows what I possess, and I do not know it myself!"

"I have never heard him mentioned," said the Cavalier, "I will seek for him. I will find him."

But where was he to be found? The Cavalier ran up and down all the staircases, through halls and passages, but no one among all those whom he met had heard talk of the Nightingale. And the Cavalier ran back to the Emperor, and said that it must be a fable invented by the writers of books.

"Your Imperial Majesty cannot believe how much is written that is fiction, besides something that they call the black art."

"But the book in which I read this," said the Emperor, "was sent to me by the high and mighty Emperor of Japan, and therefore it cannot be a falsehood. I will hear the Nightingale! It must be here this evening! It has my imperial favor; and if it does not come, all the court shall be trampled upon after the court has supped!"

"Tsing-pe!" said the Cavalier; and again he ran up and down all the staircases, and through all the halls and corridors; and half the court ran with him, for the courtiers did not like being trampled upon.

Then there was a great inquiry after the wonderful Nightingale, which all the world knew excepting the people at court.

At last they met with a poor little girl in the kitchen, who said,—

"The Nightingale? I know it well; yes, it can sing gloriously. Every evening I get leave to carry my poor sick mother the scraps from the table. She lives down by the strand, and when I get back and am tired, and rest in the wood, then I hear the Nightingale sing. And then the water comes into my eyes, and it is just as if my mother kissed me!"

"Little Kitchen Girl," said the Cavalier, "I will get you a place in the kitchen, with permission to see the Emperor dine, if you will lead us to the Nightingale, for it is announced for this evening."

So they all went out into the wood where the Nightingale was accustomed to sing; half the court went forth. When they were in the midst of their journey a cow began to low.

"O!" cried the court page, "now we have it! That shows a wonderful power in so small a creature! I have certainly heard it before."

"No, those are cows lowing!" said the little Kitchen Girl. "We are a long way from the place yet!"

Now the frogs began to croak in the marsh.

"Glorious!" said the Chinese Court Preacher. "Now I hear it—it sounds just like little church bells."

"No, those are frogs!" said the little Kitchen-maid. "But now I think we shall soon hear it."

And then the Nightingale began to sing.

"That is it!" exclaimed the little Girl. "Listen, listen! and yonder it sits."

And she pointed to a little gray bird up in the boughs.

"Is it possible?" cried the Cavalier. "I should never have thought it looked like that! How simple it looks! It must certainly have lost its color at seeing such grand people around."

"Little Nightingale!" called the Kitchen-maid, quite loudly, "our gracious Emperor wishes you to sing before him."

"With the greatest pleasure!" replied the Nightingale, and began to sing most delightfully.

"It sounds just like glass bells!" said the Cavalier. "And look at its little throat, how it's working! It's wonderful that we should never have heard it before. That bird will be a great success at court."

"Shall I sing once more before the Emperor?" asked the Nightingale, for it thought the Emperor was present.

"My excellent little Nightingale," said the Cavalier, "I have great pleasure in inviting you to a court festival this evening, when you shall charm his Imperial Majesty with your beautiful singing."

"My song sounds best in the greenwood!" replied the Nightingale; still it came willingly when it heard what the Emperor wished.

The palace was festively adorned. The walls and the flooring, which were of porcelain, gleamed in the rays of thousands of golden lamps. The most glorious flowers, which could ring clearly, had been placed in the passages. There was a running to and fro, and a thorough draught, and all the bells rang so loudly that one could not hear one's self speak.

In the midst of the great hall, where the Emperor sat, a golden perch had been placed, on which the Nightingale was to sit. The whole court was there, and the little Cook-maid had got leave to stand behind the door, as she had now received the title of a real court cook. All were in full dress, and all looked at the little gray bird, to which the Emperor nodded.

And the Nightingale sang so gloriously that the tears came into the Emperor's eyes, and the tears ran down over his cheeks; and then the Nightingale sang still more sweetly, that went straight to the heart. The Emperor was so much pleased that he said the Nightingale should have his golden slipper to wear round its neck. But the Nightingale declined this with thanks, saying it had already received a sufficient reward.

"I have seen tears in the Emperor's eyes—that is the real treasure to me. An emperor's tears have a peculiar power. I am rewarded enough!" And then it sang again with a sweet, glorious voice.

"That's the most amiable coquetry I ever saw!" said the ladies who stood round about, and then they took water in their mouths to gurgle when any one spoke to them. They thought they should be nightingales too. And the lackeys and chambermaids reported that they were satisfied too; and that was saying a good deal, for they are the most difficult to please. In short, the Nightingale achieved a real success.

It was now to remain at court, to have its own cage, with liberty to go out twice every day and once at night. Twelve servants were appointed when the Nightingale went out, each of whom had a silken string fastened to the bird's leg, which they held very tight. There was really no pleasure in an excursion of that kind.

The whole city spoke of the wonderful bird, and when two people met, one said nothing but "Nightin," and the other said "gale;" and then they sighed, and understood one another. Eleven peddlers' children were named after the bird, but not one of them could sing a note.

One day the Emperor received a large parcel, on which was written "The Nightingale."

"There we have a new book about this celebrated bird," said the Emperor.

But it was not a book, but a little work of art, contained in a box, an artificial nightingale, which was to sing like a natural one, and was brilliantly ornamented with diamonds, rubies, and sapphires. So soon as the artificial bird was wound up, he could sing one of the pieces that he really sang, and then his tail moved up and down, and shone with silver and gold. Round his neck hung a little ribbon, and on that was written, "The Emperor of China's Nightingale is poor compared to that of the Emperor of Japan."

"That is capital!" said they all, and he who had brought the artificial bird immediately received the title, Imperial Head-Nightingale-Bringer.

"Now they must sing together; what a duet that will be!"

And so they had to sing together; but it did not sound very well, for the real Nightingale sang in its own way, and the artificial bird sang waltzes.

"That's not his fault," said the Play-master; "he's quite perfect, and very much in my style."

Now the artificial bird was to sing alone. He had just as much success as the real one, and then it was much handsomer to look at—it shone like bracelets and breastpins.

Three-and-thirty times over did it sing the same piece, and yet was not tired. The people would gladly have heard it again, but the Emperor said that the living Nightingale ought to sing something now. But where was it? No one had noticed that it had flown away out of the open window, back to the greenwood.

"But what is become of that?" said the Emperor.

And all the courtiers abused the Nightingale, and declared that it was a very ungrateful creature.

"We have the best bird, after all," said they.

And so the artificial bird had to sing again, and that was the thirty-fourth time that they listened to the same piece. For all that they did not know it quite by heart, for it was so very difficult. And the Play-master praised the bird particularly; yes, he declared that it was better than a nightingale, not only with regard to its plumage and the many beautiful diamonds, but inside as well.

"For you see, ladies and gentlemen, and above all, your Imperial Majesty, with a real nightingale one can never calculate what is coming, but in this artificial bird everything is settled. One can explain it; one can open it, and make people understand where the waltzes come from, how they go, and how one follows up another."

"Those are quite our own ideas," they all said.

And the speaker received permission to show the bird to the people on the next Sunday. The people were to hear it sing too, the Emperor commanded; and they did hear it, and were as much pleased as if they had all got tipsy upon tea, for that's quite the Chinese fashion; and they all said, "O!" and held up their forefingers and nodded. But the poor Fisherman, who had heard the real Nightingale, said,—

"It sounds pretty enough, and the melodies resemble each other, but there's something wanting, though I know not what!"

The real Nightingale was banished from the country and empire. The artificial bird had its place on a silken cushion close to the Emperor's bed; all the presents it had received, gold and precious stones, were ranged about it; in title it had advanced to be the High Imperial After-Dinner-Singer, and in rank, to number one on the left hand; for the Emperor considered that side the most important in which the heart is placed, and even in an emperor the heart is on the left side; and the Play-master wrote a work of five-and-twenty volumes about the artificial bird; it was very learned and very long, full of the most difficult Chinese words; but yet all the people declared that they had read it, and understood it, for fear of being considered stupid, and having their bodies trampled on.

So a whole year went by. The Emperor, the court, and all the other Chinese knew every little twitter in the artificial bird's song by heart. But just for that reason it pleased them best—they could sing with it themselves, and they did so. The street boys sang, "Tsi-tsi-tsi-glug-glug!" and the Emperor himself sang it too. Yes, that was certainly famous.

But one evening, when the artificial bird was singing its best, and the Emperor lay in bed listening to it, something inside the bird said, "Whizz!" Something cracked.

"Whir-r-r!" All the wheels ran round, and then the music stopped.

The Emperor immediately sprang out of bed, and caused his body physician to be called; but what could *he* do? Then they sent for a watchmaker, and after a good deal of talking and investigation, the bird was put into something like order; but the Watchmaker said that the bird must be carefully treated, for the barrels were worn, and it would be impossible to put new ones in in such a manner that the music would go. There was great lamentation; only once in a year was it permitted to let the bird sing, and that was almost too much. But then the Play-master made a little speech, full of heavy words, and said this was just as good as before—and so of course it was as good as before.

Now five years had gone by, and a real grief came upon the whole nation. The Chinese were really fond of their Emperor, and now he was ill, and could not, it was said, live much longer. Already a new Emperor had been chosen, and the people stood out in the street and asked the Cavalier how their old Emperor did.

"P!" said he, and shook his head.

Cold and pale lay the Emperor in his great gorgeous bed; the whole court thought him dead, and each one ran to pay homage to the new ruler. The chamberlains ran out to talk it over, and the ladies'-maids had a great coffee party. All about, in all the halls and passages, cloth had been laid down so that no footstep could be heard, and therefore it was quiet there, quite quiet. But the Emperor was not dead yet: stiff and pale he lay on the gorgeous bed with the long velvet curtains and the heavy gold tassels; high up, a window stood open, and the moon shone in upon the Emperor and the artificial bird.

The poor Emperor could scarcely breathe; it was just as if something lay upon his chest: he opened his eyes, and then he saw that it was Death who sat upon his chest, and had put on his golden crown, and held in one hand the Emperor's sword and in the other his beautiful banner. And all around, from among the folds of the splendid velvet curtains, strange heads peered forth; a few very ugly, the rest quite lovely and mild. These were all the Emperor's bad and good deeds, that stood before him now that Death sat upon his heart.

"Do you remember this?" whispered one to the other. "Do you remember that?" and then they told him so much that the perspiration ran from his forehead.

"I did not know that!" said the Emperor. "Music! music! the great Chinese drum!" he cried, "so that I need not hear all they say!" And they continued speaking, and Death nodded like a Chinaman to all they said.

"Music! music!" cried the Emperor. "You little precious golden bird, sing, sing! I have given you gold and costly presents; I have even hung my golden slipper around your neck—sing now, sing!"

But the bird stood still; no one was there to wind him up, and he could not sing without that; but Death continued to stare at the Emperor with his great hollow eyes, and it was quiet, fearfully quiet.

Then there sounded from the window, suddenly, the most lovely song. It was the little live Nightingale, that sat outside on a spray. It had heard of the Emperor's sad plight, and had come to sing to him of comfort and hope. And as it sang the spectres grew paler and paler; the blood ran quicker and more quickly through the Emperor's weak limbs; and even Death listened, and said,—

"Go on, little Nightingale, go on!"

"But will you give me that splendid golden sword? Will you give me that rich banner? Will you give me the Emperor's crown?"

And Death gave up each of these treasures for a song. And the Nightingale sang on and on; and it sang of the quiet church-yard, where the white roses grow, where the elder-blossom smells sweet, and where the fresh grass is moistened by the tears of survivors. Then Death felt a longing to see his garden, and floated out at the window in the form of a cold, white mist.

"Thanks! thanks!" said the Emperor. "You heavenly little bird! I know you well. I banished you from my country and empire, and yet you have charmed away the evil faces from my couch, and banished Death from my heart! How can I reward you?"

"You have rewarded me!" replied the Nightingale. "I drawn tears from your eyes, when I sang the first time—

I shall never forget that. Those are the jewels that rejoice a singer's heart. But now sleep and grow fresh and strong again. I will sing you something."

And it sang, and the Emperor fell into a sweet slumber. Ah! how mild and refreshing that sleep was! The sun shone upon him through the windows, when he awoke refreshed and restored; not one of his servants had yet returned, for they all thought he was dead; only the Nightingale still sat beside him and sang.

"You must always stay with me," said the Emperor. "You shall sing as you please; and I'll break the artificial bird into a thousand pieces."

"Not so," replied the Nightingale. "It did well as long as it could; keep it as you have done till now. I cannot build my nest in the palace to dwell in; but let me come when I feel the wish; then I will sit in the evening on the spray yonder by the window, and sing you something, so that you may be glad and thoughtful at once. I will sing of those who are happy and of those who suffer. I will sing of good and of evil that remain hidden round about you. The little singing bird flies far around, to the poor fisherman, to the peasant's roof, to every one who dwells far away from you and from your court. I love your heart more than your crown, and yet the crown has an air of sanctity about it. I will come and sing to you—but one thing you must promise me."

"Everything!" said the Emperor; and he stood there in his imperial robes, which he had put on himself, and pressed the sword which was heavy with gold to his heart.

"One thing I beg of you: tell no one that you have a little bird who tells you everything. Then it will go all the better."

And the Nightingale flew away.

The servants came in to look to their dead Emperor, and— yes, there he stood, and the Emperor said "Good morning!"

THE STORKS

On the last house in a little village stood a stork's nest. The Mother Stork sat in it with her four young ones, who stretched out their heads with the pointed black beaks, for

their beaks had not yet turned red. A little way off stood the
Father Stork, all alone on the ridge of the roof, quite upright
and stiff; he had drawn up one of his legs, so as not to be
quite idle while he stood sentry. One would have thought
he had been carved out of wood, so still did he stand. He
thought, "It must look very grand, that my wife has a sentry
standing by her nest. They can't tell that it is her husband.
They certainly think I have been commanded to stand here.
That looks so aristocratic!" And he went on standing on
one leg.

Below in the street a whole crowd of children were playing; and when they caught sight of the Storks, one of the
boldest of the boys, and afterwards all of them, sang the
old verse about the Storks. But they only sang it just as he
could remember it:—

> "Stork, stork, long-legged stork;
> Off to thy home I prithee walk.
> Thy dear wife is in the nest,
> Where she rocks her young to rest.
>
> "The first he will be hanged,
> The second will be hit,
> The third he will be shot,
> And the fourth put on the spit."

"Just hear what those boys are saying!" said the little
Stork children. "They say we're to be hanged and killed."

"You're not to care for that!" said the Mother Stork.
"Don't listen to it, and then it won't matter."

But the boys went on singing, and pointed at the Storks
mockingly with their fingers; only one boy, whose name was
Peter, declared that it was a sin to make a jest of animals,
and he would not join in it at all.

The Mother Stork comforted her children. "Don't you
mind it at all," she said; "see how quiet your father stands,
though it's only on one leg."

"We are very much afraid," said the young Storks; and
they drew their heads far back into the nest.

Now to-day, when the children came out again to play, and
saw the Storks, they sang their song,—

> "The first he will be hanged,
> The second will be hit."

"Shall we be hanged and beaten?" asked the young Storks.

"No, certainly not," replied the mother. "You shall learn to fly; I'll exercise you; then we shall fly into the meadows and pay a visit to the frogs; they will bow before us in the water, and sing 'Co-ax! co-ax!' and then we shall eat them up. That will be a real pleasure."

"And what then?" asked the young Storks.

"Then all the Storks will assemble, all that are here in the whole country, and the autumn exercises begin: then one must fly well, for that is highly important, for whoever cannot fly properly will be thrust dead by the general's beak; so take care and learn well when the exercising begins."

"But then we shall be killed, as the boys say—and only listen, now they're singing again."

"Listen to me, and not to them," said the Mother Stork. "After the great review we shall fly away to the warm countries, far away from here, over mountains and forests. We shall fly to Egypt, where there are three covered houses of stone, which curl in a point and tower above the clouds; they are called pyramids, and are older than a stork can imagine. There is a river in that country which runs out of its bed, and then all the land is turned to mud. One walks about in the mud, and eats frogs."

"O!" cried all the young ones.

"Yes! It is glorious there! One does nothing all day long but eat; and while we are so comfortable over there, here there is not a green leaf on the trees; here it is so cold that the clouds freeze to pieces, and fall down in little white rags!"

It was the snow that she meant, but she could not explain it in any other way.

"And do the naughty boys freeze to pieces?" asked the young Storks.

"No, they don't freeze to pieces; but they are not far from it, and must sit in the dark room and cower. You, on the other hand, can fly about in foreign lands, where there are flowers, and the sun shines warm."

Now some time had elapsed, and the nestlings had grown so large that they could stand upright in the nest and look far around; and the Father Stork came every day with delicious frogs, little snakes, and all kinds of stork-dainties as he found them. O! it looked funny when he performed feats before them. He laid his head quite back upon his tail, and clapped with his beak as if he had been a little clapper; and then he told them stories, all about the marshes.

"Listen! now you must learn to fly," said the Mother Stork one day; and all the four young ones had to go out on the ridge of the roof. O, how they tottered! how they balanced themselves with their wings, and yet they were nearly falling down.

"Only look at me," said the mother. "Thus you must hold your heads! Thus you must pitch your feet! One, two! one, two! That's what will help you on in the world."

Then she flew a little way, and the young ones made a little clumsy leap. Bump!—there they lay, for their bodies were too heavy.

"I will not fly!" said one of the young Storks, and crept back into the nest. "I don't care about getting to the warm countries."

"Do you want to freeze to death here, when the winter comes? Are the boys to come and hang you, and singe you, and roast you? Now I'll call them."

"O no!" cried the young Stork, and hopped out on to the roof again like the rest.

On the third day they could actually fly a little, and then they thought they could also soar and hover in the air. They tried it, but—bump!—down they tumbled, and they had to shoot their wings again quickly enough. Now the boys came into the street again and sang their song,—

"Stork, stork, long-legged stork!"

"Shall we fly down and pick their eyes out?" asked the young Storks.

"No," replied the mother, "let them alone. Only listen to me; that's far more important. One, two, three!—now we fly round to the right. One, two, three!—now to the left round the chimney! See, that was very good! the last kick with the feet was so neat and correct that you shall have permission to-morrow to fly with me to the marsh! Several nice

Stork families go there with their young: show them that mine are the nicest, and that you can start proudly; that looks well, and will get you consideration."

" But are we not to take revenge on the rude boys?" asked the young Storks.

"Let them scream as much as they like. You will fly up to the clouds, and get to the land of the pyramids, when they will have to shiver, and not have a green leaf or a sweet apple."

"Yes, we will revenge ourselves!" they whispered to one another; and then the exercising went on.

Among all the boys down in the street, the one most bent upon singing the teasing song was he who had begun it, and he was quite a little boy. He could hardly be more than six years old. The young Storks certainly thought he was a hundred, for he was much bigger than their mother and father; and how should they know how old children and grown-up people can be! Their revenge was to come upon this boy, for it was he who had begun, and he always kept on. The young Storks were very angry; and as they grew bigger they were less inclined to bear it: at last their mother had to promise them that they should be revenged, but not till the last day of their stay.

" We must first see how you behave at the grand review. If you get through badly, so that the general stabs you through the chest with his beak, the boys will be right, at least in one way. Let us see."

"Yes, you shall see!" cried the young Storks; and then they took all imaginable pains. They practiced every day, and flew so neatly and so lightly that it was a pleasure to see them.

Now the autumn came on; all the Storks began to assemble, to fly away to the warm countries while it is winter here. That *was* a review. They had to fly over forests and villages, to show how well they could soar, for it was a long journey they had before them. The young Storks did their parts so well that they got as a mark, " Remarkably well, with frogs and snakes." That was the highest mark; and they might eat the frogs and snakes; and that is what they did.

" Now we will be revenged!" they said.

"Yes, certainly!" said the Mother Stork. "What I have thought of will be the best. I know the pond in which all the little mortals lie till the stork comes and brings them to their parents. The pretty little babies lie there and dream so sweetly as they never dream afterwards. All parents are glad to have such a child, and all children want to have a sister or a brother. Now we will fly to the pond, and bring one for each of the children who have not sung the naughty song and laughed at the Storks."

"But he who began to sing,—that naughty, ugly boy!" screamed the young Storks; "what shall we do with him?"

"There is a little dead child in the pond, one that has dreamed itself to death; we will bring that for him. Then he will cry because we have brought him a little dead brother. But that good boy—you have not forgotten him, the one who said, 'It is wrong to laugh at animals!'—for him we will bring a brother and a sister too. And as his name is Peter, all of you shall be called Peter too."

And it was done as she said; all the storks were named Peter, and so they are all called even now.

THE DARNING-NEEDLE

THERE was once a darning-needle, who thought herself so fine, she imagined she was an embroidering-needle.

"Take care, and mind you hold me tight!" she said to the Fingers that took her out. "Don't let me fall! If I fall on the ground I shall certainly never be found again, for I am so fine!"

"That's as it may be," said the Fingers; and they grasped her round the body.

"See, I'm coming with a train!" said the Darning-needle, and she drew a long thread after her, but there was no knot in the thread.

The Fingers pointed the needle just at the cook's slipper, in which the upper leather had burst, and was to be sewn together.

"That's vulgar work," said the Darning-needle. "I shall never get through. I'm breaking! I'm breaking!" And she really broke. "Did I not say so?" said the Darning-needle; "I'm too fine!"

"Now it's quite useless," said the Fingers; but they were obliged to hold her fast, all the same; for the cook dropped some sealing-wax upon the needle, and pinned her handkerchief together with it in front.

"So, now I'm a breast-pin!" said the Darning-needle. "I knew very well that I should come to honor: when one is something, one comes to something!"

And she laughed quietly to herself—and one can never see when a darning-needle laughs. There she sat, as proud as if she was in a state coach, and looked all about her.

"May I be permitted to ask if you are of gold?" she inquired of the pin, her neighbor. "You have a very pretty appearance, and a peculiar head, but it is only little. You must take pains to grow, for it's not every one that has sealing-wax dropped upon him."

And the Darning-needle drew herself up so proudly that she fell out of the handkerchief right into the sink, which the cook was rinsing out.

"Now we're going on a journey," said the Darning-needle. "If I only don't get lost!"

But she really was lost.

"I'm too fine for this world," she observed, as she lay in the gutter. "But I know who I am, and there's always something in that!"

So the Darning-needle kept her proud behavior, and did not lose her good humor. And things of many kinds swam over her, chips and straws and pieces of old newspapers.

"Only look how they sail!" said the Darning-needle. "They don't know what is under them! I'm here, I remain firmly here. See, there goes a chip thinking of nothing in the world but of himself—of a chip! There's a straw going by now. How he turns! how he twirls about! Don't think only of yourself, you might easily run up against a stone. There swims a bit of newspaper. What's written upon it has long been forgotten, and yet it gives itself airs. I sit quietly and patiently here. I know who I am, and I shall remain what I am."

One day something lay close beside her that glittered

splendidly; then the Darning-needle believed that it was a diamond; but it was a bit of broken bottle; and because it shone, the Darning-needle spoke to it, introducing herself as a breast-pin.

"I suppose you are a diamond?" she observed.

"Why, yes, something of that kind."

And then each believed the other to be a very valuable thing; and they began speaking about the world, and how very conceited it was.

"I have been in a lady's box," said the Darning-needle, "and this lady was a cook. She had five fingers on each hand, and I never saw anything so conceited as those five fingers. And yet they were only there that they might take me out of the box and put me back into it."

"Were they of good birth?" asked the Bit of Bottle.

"No, indeed," replied the Darning-needle; "but very haughty. There were five brothers, all of the finger family. They kept very proudly together, though they were of different lengths: the outermost, the thumbling, was short and fat; he walked out in front of the ranks, and only had one joint in his back, and could only make a single bow; but he said that if he were hacked off a man, that man was useless for service in war. Daintymouth, the second finger, thrust himself into sweet and sour, pointed to sun and moon, and gave the impression when they wrote. Longman, the third looked at all the others over his shoulder. Goldborder, the fourth, went about with a golden belt round his waist; and little Playman did nothing at all, and was proud of it. There was nothing but bragging among them, and therefore I went away."

"And now we sit here and glitter!" said the Bit of Bottle.

At that moment more water came into the gutter, so that it overflowed, and the Bit of Bottle was carried away.

"So he is disposed of," observed the Darning-needle. "I remain here, I am too fine. But that's my pride, and my pride is honorable." And proudly she sat there, and had many great thoughts. "I could almost believe I had been born of a sunbeam, I'm so fine! It really appears as if the sunbeams were always seeking for me under the water. Ah! I'm so fine that my mother cannot find me. If I had my old eye, which broke off, I think I should cry; but, no, I should not do that: it's not genteel to cry."

One day a couple of street boys lay grubbing in the gutter, where they sometimes found old nails, farthings, and similar treasures. It was dirty work, but they took great delight in it.

"O!" cried one, who had pricked himself with the Darning-needle, "there's a fellow for you!"

"I'm not a fellow; I'm a young lady!" said the Darning-needle.

But nobody listened to her. The sealing-wax had come off, and she had turned black; but black makes one look slender, and she thought herself finer even than before.

"Here comes an egg-shell sailing along!" said the boys; and they stuck the Darning-needle fast in the egg-shell.

"White walls, and black myself! that looks well," remarked the Darning-needle. "Now one can see me. I only hope I shall not be seasick!" But she was not seasick at all. "It is good against seasickness, if one has a steel stomach, and does not forget that one is a little more than an ordinary person! Now my seasickness is over. The finer one is, the more one can bear."

"Crack!" went the egg-shell, for a wagon went over her.

"Good heavens, how it crushes one!" said the Darning-needle. "I'm getting seasick now,—I'm quite sick."

But she was not really sick, though the wagon went over her; she lay there at full length, and there she may lie.

THE SHADOW

IT is in the hot lands that the sun burns, sure enough! there the people become quite mahogany brown, aye, and in *the hottest* lands they are burnt to negroes. But now it was only to the *hot* lands that a learned man had come from the cold; there he thought that he could run about just as when at home, but he soon found out his mistake.

He, and all sensible folks, were obliged to stay within doors; the window-shutters and doors were closed the whole day; it looked as if the whole house slept, or there was no one at home.

The narrow street, with the high houses, was built so that the sunshine must fall there from morning till evening,—it was really not to be borne.

The learned man from the cold lands—he was a young man, and seemed to be a clever man—sat in a glowing oven; it took effect on him, he became quite meagre—even his shadow shrunk in, for the sun had also an effect on it. It was first toward evening, when the sun was down, that they began to freshen up again.

In the warm lands every window has a balcony, and the people came out on all the balconies in the street—for one must have air, even if one be accustomed to be mahogany! It was lively both up and down the street. Tailors, and shoemakers, and all the folks, moved out into the street; chairs and tables were brought forth; and candles burnt— yes, above a thousand lights were burning; and the one talked and the other sung, and people walked and church- bells rang, and asses went along with a dingle-dingle-dong! for they too had bells on. The street boys were scream- ing and hooting, and shouting and shooting, with devils and detonating balls: and there came corpse bearers and hood wearers,—for there were funerals with psalm and hymn; and then the din of carriages driving and company arriving, —yes, it was, in truth, lively enough down in the street. Only in that single house, which stood opposite that in which the learned foreigner lived, it was quite still; and yet some one lived there, for there stood flowers in the balcony—they grew so well in the sun's heat!—and that they could not do unless they were watered; and some one must water them—there must be somebody there. The door opposite was also opened late in the evening, but it was dark within, at least in the front room; further in there was heard the sound of music. The learned foreigner thought it quite mar- velous, but now—it might be that he only imagined it, for he found everything marvelous out there in the warm lands, if there had only been no sun. The stranger's landlord said that he didn't know who had taken the house opposite, one saw no person about, and as to the music, it appeared to him to be extremely tiresome. " It is as if some one sat there and practiced a piece that he could not master—al-

ways the same piece. 'I shall master it!' says he; but yet
he cannot master it, however long he plays."

One night the stranger awoke—he slept with the doors
of the balcony open—the curtain before it was raised by the
wind, and he thought that a strange lustre came from the
opposite neighbor's house; all the flowers shone like flames,
in the most beautiful colors, and in the midst of the flowers
stood a slender, graceful maiden,—it was as if she also
shone; the light really hurt his eyes. He now opened them
quite wide—yes, he was quite awake; with one spring he
was on the floor; he crept gently behind the curtain, but the
maiden was gone; the flowers shone no longer, but there they
stood, fresh and blooming as ever: the door was ajar, and,
far within, the music sounded so soft and delightful, one
could really melt away in sweet thoughts from it. Yet it
was like a piece of enchantment. And who lived there?
Where was the actual entrance? The whole of the ground-
floor was a row of shops, and there people could not always
be running through.

One evening, the stranger sat out on the balcony. The
light burnt in the room behind him; and thus it was quite
natural that his shadow should fall on his opposite neighbor's wall. Yes, there it sat, directly opposite, between the
flowers on the balcony; and when the stranger moved, the
shadow also moved: for that it always does.

"I think my shadow is the only living thing one sees over
there," said the Learned Man. "See! how nicely it sits
between the flowers. The door stands half-open: now the
shadow should be cunning, and go into the room, look about,
and then come and tell me what it had seen. Come, now!
be useful, and do me a service," said he, in jest. "Have the
kindness to step in. Now! art thou going?" and then he
nodded to the Shadow, and the Shadow nodded again.
"Well, then, go! but don't stay away."

The stranger rose, and his Shadow on their opposite neighbor's balcony rose also; the stranger turned round, and the
Shadow also turned round. Yes! if any one had paid particular attention to it, they would have seen, quite distinctly
that the Shadow went in through the half-open balcony-
door of their opposite neighbor, just as the stranger went

into his own room, and let the long curtain fall down after him.

Next morning, the Learned Man went out to drink coffee and read the newspapers.

"What is that?" said he, as he came out into the sunshine. "I have no shadow! So, then, it has actually gone last night, and not come again. It is really tiresome!"

This annoyed him: not so much because the shadow was gone, but because he knew there was a story about a man without a shadow. It was known to everybody at home, in the cold lands; and if the Learned Man now came there and told his story, they would say that he was imitating it, and that he had no need to do. He would, therefore, not talk about it at all; and that was wisely thought.

In the evening, he went out again on the balcony. He had placed the light directly behind him, for he knew that the shadow would always have its master for a screen, but he could not entice it. He made himself little; he made himself great; but no shadow came again. He said, "Hem! hem!" but it was of no use.

It was vexatious; but in the warm lands everything grows so quickly; and after the lapse of eight days he observed, to his great joy, that a new shadow came in the sunshine. In the course of three weeks he had a very fair shadow, which, when he set out for his home in the northern lands, grew more and more in the journey, so that at last it was so long and so large that it was more than sufficient.

The Learned Man then came home, and he wrote books about what was true in the world, and about what was good, and what was beautiful; and there passed days and years,— yes! many years passed away.

One evening, as he was sitting in his room, there was a gentle knocking at the door.

"Come in!" said he; but no one came in; so he opened the door, and there stood before him such an extremely lean man, that he felt quite strange. As to the rest, the man was very finely dressed,—he must be a gentleman.

"Whom have I the honor of speaking to?" asked the Learned Man.

"Yes! I thought as much," said the fine man. "I thought

you would not know me. I have got so much body. I have even got flesh and clothes. You certainly never thought of seeing me so well off. Do you not know your old Shadow? You certainly thought I should never more return. Things have gone on well with me since I was last with you. I have, in all respects, become very well off. Shall I purchase my freedom from service? If so, I can do it;" and then he rattled a whole bunch of valuable seals that hung to his watch, and he stuck his hand in the thick gold chain he wore around his neck;—nay! how all his fingers glittered with diamond rings; and then all were pure gems.

"Nay, I cannot recover from my surprise!" said the Learned Man: "what is the meaning of all this?"

"Something common it is not," said the Shadow: "but you yourself do not belong to the common order; and I, as you know well, have from a child followed in your footsteps. As soon as you found I was capable to go out alone in the world, I went my own way. I am in the most brilliant circumstances, but there came a sort of desire over me to see you once more before you die;—you will die, I suppose? I also wished to see this land again,—for you know we always love our native land. I know you have got another Shadow again; have I anything to pay to it or you? If so, you will oblige me by saying what it is."

"Nay, is it really thou?" said the Learned Man: "it is most remarkable. I never imagined that one's old shadow could come again as a man."

"Tell me what I have to pay," said the Shadow; "for I don't like to be in any sort of debt."

"How canst thou talk so?" said the Learned Man; "what debt is there to talk about? Make thyself as free as any one else. I am extremely glad to hear of thy good fortune: sit down, old friend, and tell me a little how it has gone with thee, and what thou hast seen at our opposite neighbor's there—in the warm lands."

"Yes, I will tell you all about it," said the Shadow, and sat down: "but then you must also promise me, that, wherever you may meet me, you will never say to any one here in the town that I have been your shadow. I intend to get betrothed, for I can provide for more than one family."

"Be quite at thy ease about that," said the Learned Man; "I shall not say to any one who thou actually art; there is my hand—I promise it, and a man's bond is his word."

"A word is a shadow," said the Shadow, "and as such it must speak."

It was really quite astonishing how much of a man it was. It was dressed entirely in black, and of the very finest cloth; it had patent leather boots, and a hat that could be folded together, so that it was bare crown and brim; not to speak of what we already know it had—seals, gold neck-chain, and diamond rings; yes, the Shadow was well-dressed, and it was just that which made it quite a man.

"Now I shall tell you my adventures," said the Shadow; and then he sat, with the polished boots on, as heavily as he could on the arm of the Learned Man's new shadow, which lay like a poodle-dog at his feet. Now this was perhaps from arrogance; and the shadow on the ground kept itself so still and quiet, that it might hear all that passed: it wished to know how it could get free, and work its way up, so as to become its own master.

"Do you know who lived in our opposite neighbor's house?" said the Shadow; "it was the most charming of all beings, it was Poetry! I was there for three weeks, and that has as much effect as if one had lived three thousand years, and read all that was composed and written; that is what I say, and it is right. I have seen everything, and I know everything!"

"Poetry!" cried the Learned Man; "yes, yes, she is often an anchoret in the large towns! Poetry! yes, I have seen her,—a single, short moment, but sleep came into my eyes! She stood on the balcony and shone as the aurora borealis shines. Go on, go on!—thou wert on the balcony, and went through the door-way, and then—"

"Then I was in the antechamber," said the Shadow. "You always sat and looked over to the antechamber. There was no light; there was a sort of twilight, but the one door stood open directly opposite the other through a long row of rooms and saloons, and there it was lighted up. I should have been completely killed if I had gone over to the maiden, but I was circumspect, I took time to think, and that one must always do."

"And what didst thou then see?" asked the Learned Man.

"I saw everything, and I shall tell all to you; but,—it is no pride on my part,—as a free man, and with the knowledge I have, not to speak of my position in life, my excellent circumstances,—I certainly wish that you would say *you* to me!"

"I beg your pardon," said the Learned Man; "it is an old habit with me. *You* are perfectly right, and I shall remember it; but now *you* must tell me all that *you* saw!"

"Everything!" said the Shadow, "for I saw everything, and I know everything!"

"How did it look in the furthest saloon?" asked the Learned Man. "Was it there as in the fresh woods? Was it there as in a holy church? Were the saloons like the starlit firmament when we stand on the high mountains?"

"Everything was there!" said the Shadow. "I did not go quite in; I remained in the foremost room, in the twilight, but I stood there quite well; I saw everything, and I know everything! I have been in the antechamber at the court of Poetry."

"But *what did* you see? Did all the gods of the olden times pass through the large saloons? Did the old heroes combat there? Did sweet children play there, and relate their dreams?"

"I tell you I was there, and you can conceive that I saw everything there was to be seen. Had you come over there, you would not have been a man; but I became so! And besides, I learned to know my inward nature, my innate qualities, the relationship I had with Poetry. At the time I was with you, I thought not of that, but always—you know it well —when the sun rose, and when the sun went down, I became so strangely great; in the moonlight I was very near being more distinct than yourself; at that time I did not understand my nature; it was revealed to me in the antechamber! I became a man! I came out matured; but you were no longer in the warm lands: as a man I was ashamed to go as I did. I was in want of boots, of clothes, of the whole human varnish that makes a man perceptible. I took my way—I tell it to you, but you will not put it in any book—I took my way to the cake woman—I hid myself behind her; the woman didn't think how much she concealed. I went out first in the evening; I ran about the streets in the moonlight; I made myself long up the walls—it tickles the back so delightfully! I ran up, and I ran down, peeped into the highest windows, into the saloons, and on the roofs. I peeped in where no one could peep, and I saw what no one else saw, what no one should see! This is, in fact, a base world! I would not be a man if it were not now once accepted and regarded as something to be so! I saw the most unimaginable things with the women, with the men, with parents, and with the sweet, matchless children; I saw," said the Shadow, "what no human being must know, but what they would all so willingly know—what is bad in their neighbor. Had I written a newspaper, it would have been read! but I wrote direct to the persons themselves, and there was consternation in all the towns where I came. They were so afraid of me, and yet they were so excessively fond of me. The professors made a professor of me; the tailors gave me new clothes—I am well furnished; the master of the mint struck new coin for me, and the women said I was so handsome! and so I became the man I am. And I now bid you farewell;—here is my card—I live on the sunny side of the street, and am always at home in rainy weather!" And so away went the Shadow.

"That was most extraordinary!" said the Learned Man.

Years and days passed away, then the Shadow came again.

"How goes it?" said the Shadow.

"Alas!" said the Learned Man, "I write about the true, and the good, and the beautiful, but no one cares to hear such things! I am quite desperate, for I take it so much to heart!"

"But I don't!" said the Shadow; "I become fat, and it is that one wants to become! You do not understand the world. You will become ill by it. You must travel! I shall make a tour this summer; will you go with me? I should like to have a travelling companion! will you go with me, as shadow? It will be a great pleasure for me to have you with me,—I shall pay the travelling expenses!"

"Nay, this is too much!" said the Learned Man.

"It is just as one takes it," said the Shadow. "It will do you much good to travel!—will you be my shadow?—you shall have everything free on the journey!"

"Nay, that is too bad!" said the Learned Man.

"But it is just so with the world!" said the Shadow, "and so it will be!" and away it went again.

The Learned Man was not at all in the most enviable state; grief and torment followed him, and what he said about the true, and the good, and the beautiful was, to most persons, like roses for a cow!—he was quite ill at last.

"You really look like a shadow!" said his friends to him; and the Learned Man trembled, for he thought of it.

"You must go to a watering-place!" said the Shadow, who came and visited him; "there is nothing else for it! I will take you with me for old acquaintance sake; I will pay the travelling expenses, and you write the descriptions—and you may make them amusing if you please. I will go to a watering-place,—my beard does not grow out as it ought—that is also a sickness, and one must have a beard. Now you be wise and accept the offer; we shall travel as comrades!"

And so they travelled; the Shadow was master, and the master was the Shadow; they drove with each other, they rode and walked together, side by side, before and behind, just as the sun was; the Shadow always took care to keep itself in the master's place. Now the Learned Man didn't think much about that; he was a very kind-hearted man, and particularly mild and friendly, and so he said one day to the Shadow: "As we have now become companions, and in this way have grown up together from childhood, shall we not drink *'thou'* together? it is more familiar."

"You are right!" said the Shadow, who was now the proper master. "It is said in a very straightforward and well-meant manner. You, as a learned man, certainly know how strange nature is. Some persons cannot bear to touch gray paper, or they become ill; others shiver in every limb if one rub a pane of glass with a nail: I have just such a feeling on hearing you say *thou* to me; I feel myself as if pressed to the earth in my first situation with you. You see that it is a feeling; that it is not pride. I cannot allow you to say *thou* to me, but I will willingly say *thou* to you, so it is half done!"

So the Shadow said *thou* to its former master.

"This is rather too bad," thought he, "that I must say *you* and he say *thou*," but he was now obliged to put up with it.

So they came to a watering-place where there were many strangers, and amongst them was a princess who was troubled with seeing too well; and that was so alarming!

She directly observed that the stranger who had just come was quite a different sort of person to all the others: "He has come here in order to get his beard to grow, they say; but I see the real cause, he cannot cast a shadow."

She had become inquisitive; and so she entered into conversation directly with the strange gentleman, on their promenades. As the daughter of a king, she needed not to stand upon trifles, so she said, "Your complaint is, that you cannot cast a shadow?"

"Your royal highness must be improving considerably," said the Shadow. "I know your complaint is, that you see too clearly; but it has decreased, you are cured. I just happen to have a very unusual shadow! Do you not see that person who always goes with me? Other persons have a common shadow, but I do not like what is common to all. We give our servants finer cloth for their livery than we ourselves use, and so I had my shadow trimmed up into a man: yes, you see I have even given him a shadow. It is somewhat expensive, but I like to have something for myself!"

"What!" thought the Princess, "should I really be cured! These baths are the first in the world! In our time water has wonderful powers. But I shall not leave the place, for it now begins to be amusing here. I am extremely fond of that stranger. Would that his beard should not grow, for in that case he will leave us."

In the evening the Princess and the Shadow danced together in the large ball-room. She was light, but he was still lighter; she had never had such a partner in the dance. She told him from what land she came, and he knew that land; he had been there, but then she was not at home; he had peeped in at the window above and below—he had seen both the one and the other, so he could answer the Princess, and make insinuations, so that she was quite astonished; he must be the wisest man in the whole world! she felt such respect for what he knew! So that when they again danced together, she fell in love with him; and that the Shadow could remark, for she almost pierced him through with her eyes. So they danced once more together; and she was about to declare herself, but she was discreet; she thought of her country and kingdom, and of the many persons she would have to reign over.

"He is a wise man," said she to herself—"it is well; and he dances delightfully—that is also good; but has he solid knowledge?—that is just as important!—he must be examined."

So she began, by degrees, to question him about the most difficult things she could think of, and which she herself could not have answered; so that the Shadow made a strange face.

"You cannot answer these questions?" said the Princess.

"They belong to my childhood's learning," said the Shadow. "I really believe my shadow, by the door there, can answer them!"

"Your shadow!" said the Princess; "that would indeed be marvelous!"

"I will not say for a certainty that he can," said the Shadow, "but I think so; he has now followed me for so many years, and listened to my conversation—I should think it possible. But your royal highness will permit me to observe, that he is so proud of passing himself off for a man, that when he is to be in a proper humor—and he must be so to answer well—he must be treated quite like a man."

"O! I like that!" said the Princess.

So she went to the Learned Man by the door, and she spoke with him about the sun and the moon, and about persons out of and in the world, and he answered with wisdom and prudence.

"What a man that must be who has so wise a shadow!" thought she; "it will be a real blessing for my people and kingdom if I choose him for my consort—I will do it!"

They were soon agreed, both the Princess and the Shadow; but no one was to know about it before she arrived in her own kingdom.

"No one—not even my shadow!" said the Shadow; and he had his own thoughts about it!

Now they were in the country where the Princess lived when she was at home.

"Listen, my good friend!" said the Shadow to the Learned Man. "I have now become as happy and mighty as any one can be; I will, therefore, do something particular for thee! Thou shalt always live with me in the palace, drive with me in my royal carriage, and have ten thousand pounds a year; but then thou must submit to be called *shadow* by all and every one; thou must not say that thou hast ever been a man; and once a year, when I sit on the balcony in the sunshine, thou must lie at my feet, as a shadow shall do! I must tell thee: I am going to marry the king's daughter, and the nuptials are to take place this evening!"

"Nay, this is going too far!" said the Learned Man; "I will not have it; I will not do it. It is to deceive the whole comtry and the Princess too! I will tell everything!—that I am a man and that thou art a shadow—thou art only dressed up!"

"There is no one who will believe it!" said the Shadow; "be reasonable, or I will call the guard!"

"I will go directly to the Princess!" said the Learned Man.

"But I will go first!" said the Shadow, "and thou wilt go to prison!" and that he was obliged to do—for the sentinels obeyed him whom they knew the king's daughter was to marry.

"You tremble!" said the Princess, as the Shadow came into her chamber; "has anything happened? You must not be unwell this evening, now that we are to have our nuptials celebrated."

"I have lived to see the most cruel thing that any one can live to see!" said the Shadow. "Only imagine—yes, it is true, such a poor shadow-skull cannot bear much—only think, my shadow has become mad: he thinks that he is a man, and that I—now only think—that I am his shadow!"

"It is terrible!" said the Princess; "but he is confined, is he not?"

"That he is. I am afraid that he will never recover."

"Poor shadow!" said the Princess, "he is very unfortunate; it would be a real work of charity to deliver him from the little life he has, and when I think properly over the matter, I am of opinion that it will be necessary to do away with him in all stillness!"

"It is certainly hard!" said the Shadow, "for he was a faithful servant!" and then he gave a sort of sigh.

"You are a noble character!" said the Princess.

The whole city was illuminated in the evening, and the cannons went off with a bum! bum! and the soldiers presented arms. That was a marriage! The Princess and the Shadow went out on the balcony to show themselves, and get another hurrah!

The Learned Man heard nothing of all this—for they had deprived him of life.

THE RED SHOES

THERE was once a little girl,—a very nice, pretty little girl. But in summer she had to go barefoot, because she was poor, and in winter she wore thick wooden shoes, so that her little instep became quite red, altogether red.

In the middle of the village lived an old shoemaker's wife; she sat and sewed, as well as she could a pair of little shoes, of old strips of red cloth; they were clumsy enough, but well meant, and the little girl was to have them. The little girl's name was Karen.

On the day when her mother was buried she received the red shoes and wore them for the first time. They were certainly not suited for mourning; but she had no others, and therefore thrust her little bare feet into them and walked behind the plain deal coffin.

Suddenly a great carriage came by, and in the carriage sat an old lady: she looked at the little girl and felt pity for her, and said to the clergyman,—

"Give me the little girl, and I will provide for her."

Karen thought this was for the sake of the shoes; but the Old Lady declared they were hideous; and they were burned. But Karen herself was clothed neatly and properly: she was taught to read and to sew, and the people said she was agreeable. But her mirror said, "You are much more than agreeable; you are beautiful."

Once the Queen travelled through the country, and had her

little daughter with her; and the daughter was a Princess. And the people flocked toward the castle, and Karen too was among them; and the little Princess stood in a fine white dress at a window, and let herself be gazed at. She had neither train nor golden crown, but she wore splendid red morocco shoes; they were certainly far handsomer than those the shoemaker's wife had made for little Karen. Nothing in the world can compare with red shoes!

Now Karen was old enough to be confirmed: new clothes were made for her, and she was to have new shoes. The rich shoemaker in the town took the measure of her little feet; this was done in his own house, in his little room, and there stood great glass cases with neat shoes and shining boots. It had quite a charming appearance, but the Old Lady could not see well, and therefore took no pleasure in it. Among the shoes stood a red pair, just like those which the Princess had worn. How beautiful they were! The shoemaker also said they had been made for a count's child, but they had not fitted.

"That must be patent leather," observed the Old Lady, "the shoes shine so!"

"Yes, they shine!" replied Karen; and they fitted her, and were bought. But the Old Lady did not know that they were red; for she would never have allowed Karen to go to her Confirmation in red shoes; and that is what Karen did.

Every one was looking at her shoes. And when she went across the church porch, toward the door of the choir, it seemed to her as if the old pictures on the tombstones, the portraits of clergymen and clergymen's wives, in their stiff collars and long black garments, fixed their eyes upon her red shoes. And she thought of her shoes only, when the priest laid his hand upon her head and spoke holy words. And the organ pealed solemnly, the children sang with their fresh sweet voices, and the old precentor sang too; but Karen thought only of her red shoes.

In the afternoon the Old Lady was informed by every one that the shoes were red; and she said it was naughty and unsuitable, and that when Karen went to church in future, she should always go in black shoes, even if they were old.

Next Sunday was Sacrament Sunday. And Karen looked

at the black shoes, and she looked at the red ones—looked at them again—and put on the red ones.

The sun shone gloriously; Karen and the Old Lady went along the foot-path through the fields, and it was rather dusty.

By the church door stood an old invalid soldier with a crutch and a long beard; the beard was rather red than white, for it was red altogether; and he bowed down almost to the ground, and asked the Old Lady if he might dust her shoes. And Karen also stretched out her little foot.

"Look what pretty dancing shoes!" said the Old Soldier. "Fit so tightly when you dance!"

And he tapped the soles with his hand. And the Old Lady gave the Soldier an alms, and went into the church with Karen.

And every one in the church looked at Karen's red shoes, and all the pictures looked at them. And while Karen knelt in the church she only thought of her red shoes; and she forgot to sing her psalm, and forgot to say her prayer.

Now all the people went out of church, and the Old Lady stepped into her carriage. Karen lifted up her foot to step in too; then the Old Soldier said,—

"Look, what beautiful dancing shoes!"

And Karen could not resist: she was obliged to dance a few steps; and when she once began, her legs went on dancing. It was just as though the shoes had obtained power over her. She danced round the corner of the church—she could not help it; the coachman was obliged to run behind her and seize her: he lifted her into the carriage, but her feet went on dancing, so that she kicked the good Old Lady violently. At last they took off her shoes and her legs became quiet.

At home the shoes were put away in a cupboard; but Karen could not resist looking at them.

Now the Old Lady became very ill, and it was said she would not recover. She had to be nursed and waited on; and this was no one's duty so much as Karen's. But there was to be a great ball in the town, and Karen was invited. She looked at the Old Lady who could not recover; she looked at the red shoes, and thought there would be no harm in it. She put on the shoes, and that she might do very well; but they went to the ball and began to dance.

But when she wished to go to the right hand, the shoes danced to the left, and when she wanted to go up-stairs, the shoes danced downward, down into the street and out at the town gate. She danced, and was obliged to dance, straight out into the dark wood.

There was something glistening up among the trees, and she thought it was the moon, for she saw a face. But it was the Old Soldier with the red beard: he sat and nodded, and said,—

"Look, what beautiful dancing shoes!"

Then she was frightened, and wanted to throw away the red shoes; but they clung fast to her. And she tore off her stockings: but the shoes had grown fast to her feet. And she danced and was compelled to go dancing over field and meadow, in rain and sunshine, by night and by day; but it was most dreadful at night.

She danced out into the open church-yard; but the dead there do not dance; they have far better things to do. She wished to sit down on the poor man's grave, where the bitter fern grows; but there was no peace nor rest for her. And when she danced toward the open church door, she saw there an angel in long white garments, with wings that reached from his shoulders to his feet; his countenance was serious and stern, and in his hand he held a sword that was broad and gleaming.

"Thou shalt dance!" he said—"dance on thy red shoes, till thou art pale and cold, and till thy body shrivels to a skeleton. Thou shalt dance from door to door; and where proud, haughty children dwell, shalt thou knock, that they may hear thee, and be afraid of thee! Thou shalt dance, dance!"

"Mercy!" cried Karen.

But she did not hear what the Angel answered, for the shoes carried her away—carried her through the door on to the field, over stock and stone, and she was always obliged to dance.

One morning she danced past a door which she knew well. There was a sound of psalm-singing within, and a coffin was carried out, adorned with flowers. Then she knew that the

Old Lady was dead, and she felt that she was deserted by all, and condemned by the Angel of heaven.

She danced, and was compelled to dance—to dance in the dark night. The shoes carried her on over thorn and brier; she scratched herself till she bled; she danced away across the heath to a little lonely house. Here she knew the executioner dwelt; and she tapped with her fingers on the panes, and called,—

"Come out, come out! I cannot come in, for I must dance!"

And the Executioner said,—

"You probably don't know who I am? I cut off the bad people's heads with my axe, and mark how my axe rings!"

"Do not strike off my head," said Karen, "for if you do I cannot repent of my sin. But strike off my feet with the red shoes!"

And then she confessed all her sin, and the Executioner cut off her feet with the red shoes; but the shoes danced away with the little feet over the fields and into the deep forest.

And he cut her a pair of wooden feet, with crutches, and taught her a psalm, which the criminals always sing; and she kissed the hand that had held the axe, and went away across the heath.

"Now I have suffered pain enough for the red shoes," said she. "Now I will go into the church that they may see me." And she went quickly toward the church door; but when she came there the red shoes danced before her, so that she was frightened and turned back.

The whole week through she was sorrowful, and wept many bitter tears; but when Sunday came, she said,—

"Now I have suffered and striven enough! I think that I am just as good as many of those who sit in the church and carry their heads high."

And then she went boldly on; but she did not get farther than the church-yard gate before she saw the red shoes dancing along before her: then she was seized with terror, and turned back, and repented of her sin right heartily.

And she went to the parsonage, and begged to be taken there as a servant. She promised to be industrious, and to do all she could: she did not care for wages, and only wished to be under a roof and with good people. The clergyman's wife pitied her, and took her into her service. And she was industrious and thoughtful. Silently she sat and listened when in the evening the pastor read the Bible aloud. All the little ones were very fond of her; but when they spoke of dress and splendor and beauty she would shake her head.

Next Sunday they all went to church, and she was asked if she wished to go too; but she looked sadly, with tears in her eyes, at her crutches. And then the others went to hear God's word; but she went alone into her little room, which was only large enough to contain her bed and a chair. And here she sat with her hymn-book; and as she read it with a pious mind, the wind bore the notes of the organ over to her from the church; and she lifted up her face, wet with tears, and said,—

"O Lord, help me!"

Then the sun shone so brightly; and before her stood the Angel in the white garments, the same she had seen that night at the church door. But he no longer grasped the sharp sword: he held a green branch covered with roses; and he touched the ceiling, and it rose up high and wherever he touched it a golden star gleamed forth; and he touched the walls, and they spread forth widely, and she saw the organ which was pealing its rich sounds; and she saw the old pictures of clergymen and their wives; and the congregation sat in the decorated seats, and sang from their hymn-books. The church had come to the poor girl in her narrow room, or her chamber had become a church. She sat in the chair with the rest of the clergyman's people; and when they had finished the psalm, and looked up, they nodded and said,—

"That was right, that you came here, Karen."

"It was mercy!" said she.

And the organ sounded its glorious notes; and the children's voices singing in chorus sounded sweet and lovely; the clear sunshine streamed so warm through the window upon the chair in which Karen sat; and her heart became so filled with sunshine, peace, and joy that it broke. Her soul flew on the sunbeams to heaven; and there was nobody who asked after the RED SHOES.

LITTLE IDA'S FLOWERS

"My poor flowers are quite dead!" said little Ida. "They were so pretty yesterday, and now all the leaves hang withered. Why do they do that?" she asked the student, who sat on the sofa; for she liked him very much. He knew the prettiest stories, and could cut out the most amusing pictures: hearts, with little ladies in them who danced; flowers, and great castles in which one could open the doors; he was a merry student. "Why do the flowers look so faded to-day?" she asked again, and showed him a nosegay, which was quite withered.

"Do you know what's the matter with them?" said the Student. "The flowers have been at a ball last night, and that's why they hang their heads."

"But flowers cannot dance!" cried little Ida.

"O yes," said the Student, "when it grows dark, and we are asleep, they jump about merrily. Almost every night they have a ball."

"Can children go to this ball?"

"Yes," said the Student, "quite little daisies, and lilies of the valley."

"Where do the beautiful flowers dance?" asked Ida.

"Have you not often been outside the town gate, by the great castle, where the king lives in summer, and where the beautiful garden is with all the flowers? You have seen the swans, which swim up to you when you want to give them bread crumbs? There are capital balls there, believe me."

"I was out there in the garden yesterday, with my mother," said Ida; "but all the leaves were off the trees, and there was not one flower left. Where are they? In the summer I saw so many."

"They are within, in the castle," replied the Student. "You must know, as soon as the king and all the court go to town, the flowers run out of the garden into the castle and are merry. You should see that. The two most beautiful roses seat themselves on the throne, and then they are king and queen; all the red coxcombs range themselves on either side, and stand and bow; they are the chamberlains. Then all the pretty flowers come, and there is a great ball. The blue violets represent little naval cadets; they dance with hyacinths and crocuses, which they call young ladies; the tulips and great tiger-lilies are old ladies who keep watch that the dancing is well done, and that everything goes on with propriety."

"But," asked little Ida, "is nobody there who hurts the flowers, for dancing in the king's castle?"

There is nobody who really knows about it," answered the Student. "Sometimes, certainly, the old steward of the castle comes at night, and he has to watch there. He has a great bunch of keys with him; but as soon as the flowers hear the keys rattle they are quite quiet, hide behind the long curtains, and only poke their heads out. Then the old steward says, "I smell that there are flowers here, but he cannot see them."

"That is famous!" cried little Ida, clapping her hands. "But should not I be able to see the flowers?"

"Yes," said the student: "only remember, when you go out again, to peep through the window; then you will see them. That is what I did to-day. There was a long yellow lily lying on the sofa and stretching herself. She was a court lady."

"Can the flowers out of the Botanical Garden get there? Can they go the long distance?"

"Yes, certainly," replied the Student; "if they like they can fly. Have you not seen the beautiful butterflies—red, yellow, and white? They almost look like flowers; and that is what they have been. They have flown off their stalks high into the air, and have beaten it with their leaves, as if these leaves were little wings, and thus they flew. And because they behaved themselves well, they got leave to fly about in the day-time too, and were not obliged to sit still upon their stalks at home; and thus at last the leaves became real wings. That you have seen yourself. It may be, however, that the flowers in the Botanical Garden have never been in the king's castle, or that they don't know of the merry proceedings there at night. Therefore I will tell you something: he will be very much surprised, the botanical professor, who lives close by here. You know him, do you not? When you come into his garden, you must tell one of the flowers that there is a great ball yonder in the castle. Then that flower will tell it to all the rest, and then they will fly away: when the professor comes out into the garden, there will not be a single flower left, and he won't be able to make out where they are gone."

"But how can one flower tell it to another? For, you know, flowers cannot speak."

"That they cannot, certainly," replied the Student; "but then they make signs. Have you not noticed that when the wind blows a little, the flowers nod at one another, and move all their green leaves? They can understand that just as well as we when we speak together."

"Can the professor understand these signs?" asked Ida.

"Yes, certainly. He came one morning into his garden, and saw a great stinging-nettle standing there, and making signs to a beautiful red carnation with its leaves. It was saying, 'You are so pretty, and I love you with all my heart.' But the professor does not like that kind of thing, and he directly slapped the stinging-nettle upon its leaves, for those are its fingers; but he stung himself, and since that time he has not dared to touch a stinging-nettle."

"That is funny," cried little Ida; and she laughed.

"How can any one put such notions into a child's head?" said the tiresome Privy Councilor, who had come to pay a visit, and was sitting on the sofa. He did not like the Student, and always grumbled when he saw him cutting out the merry, funny pictures—sometimes a man hanging on a gibbet and holding a heart in his hand, to show that he stole hearts; sometimes an old witch riding on a broom, and carrying her husband on her nose. The Councilor could not bear this, and then he said, just as he did now, "How can any one put such notions into a child's head? Those are stupid fancies!"

But to little Ida, what the Student told about her flowers seemed very droll; and she thought much about it. The flowers hung their heads, for they were tired because they had danced all night; they were certainly ill. Then she went with them to her other toys, which stood on a pretty little table, and the whole drawer was full of beautiful things. In the doll's bed lay her doll Sophy, asleep; but little Ida said to her,—

"You must really get up, Sophy, and manage to lie in the drawer for to-night. The poor flowers are ill, and they must lie in your bed; perhaps they will then get well again."

And she at once took the doll out; but the doll looked cross, and did not say a single word; for she was cross because she could not keep her own bed.

Then Ida laid the flowers in the doll's bed, pulled the little coverlet quite up over them, and said they were to lie still and be good, and she would make them some tea, so that they might get well again, and be able to get up to-morrow. And she drew the curtains closely round the little bed, so that the sun should not shine in their eyes. The whole evening through she could not help thinking of what the Student had told her. And when she was going to bed herself she was obliged first to look behind the curtains which hung before the windows where her mother's beautiful flowers stood—hyacinths as well as tulips; then she whispered, "I know you are going to the ball to-night!" But the flowers made as if they did not understand a word, and did not stir a leaf; but still little Ida knew what she knew.

When she was in bed she lay for a long time thinking how pretty it must be to see the beautiful flowers dancing out in the king's castle. "I wonder if my flowers have really been there?" And then she fell asleep. In the night she woke up again: she had dreamed of the flowers, and of the Student with whom the Councilor found fault. It was quite quiet in the bedroom where Ida lay; the night-lamp burned on the table, and father and mother were asleep.

"I wonder if my flowers are still lying in Sophy's bed?" she thought to herself. "How I should like to know it!" She raised herself a little, and looked at the door, which stood ajar: within lay the flowers and all her playthings. She listened, and then it seemed to her as if she heard some one playing on the piano in the next room, but quite softly and prettily, as she had never heard it before.

"Now all the flowers are certainly dancing in there!"

thought she. "O, how glad I should be to see it!" But she dared not get up, for she would have disturbed her father and mother.

"If they would only come in!" thought she. But the flowers did not come, and the music continued to play beautifully; then she could not bear it any longer, for it was too pretty; she crept out of her little bed, and went quietly to the door, and looked into the room.

O, how splendid it was, what she saw!

There was no night-lamp burning, but still it was quite light: the moon shone through the window into the middle of the floor; it was almost like day. All the hyacinths and tulips stood in two long rows in the room; there were none at all left at the window—there stood the empty flower-pots. On the floor all the flowers were dancing very gracefully round each other, making perfect turns, and holding each other by the long green leaves as they swung round. But at the piano sat a great yellow lily, which little Ida had certainly seen in summer; for she remembered how the Student had said, "How like that one is to Miss Lina." Then he had been laughed at by all; but now it seemed really to little Ida as if the long, yellow flower looked like the young lady; and it had just her manners in playing —sometimes bending its long, yellow face to one side, sometimes to the other, and nodding in tune to the charming music! No one noticed little Ida. Then she saw a great blue crocus hop into the middle of the table, where the toys stood, and go to the doll's bed and pull the curtains aside; there lay the sick flowers, but they got up directly, and nodded to the others, to say that they wanted to dance too. The old Chimney-sweep doll, whose underlip was broken off, stood up and bowed to the pretty flowers: these did not look at all ill now; they jumped down to the others, and were very merry.

Then it seemed as if something fell down from the table. Ida looked that way. It was the birch rod which was jumping down! it seemed almost as if it belonged to the flowers. At any rate it was very neat; and a little wax doll, with just such a broad hat on its head as the Councilor wore, sat upon it. The birch rod hopped about among the flowers on its three legs, and stamped quite loud, for it was dancing the mazourka; and the other flowers could not manage that dance, because they were too light, and unable to stamp like that.

The wax doll on the birch rod all at once became quite great and long, turned itself over the paper flowers, and said, " How can one put such things in a child's head? those are stupid fancies ! " and then the wax doll was exactly like the Councilor with the broad hat, and looked just as yellow and cross as he. But the paper flowers hit him on his thin legs, and then he shrank up again, and became quite a little wax doll. That was very amusing to see; and little Ida could not restrain her laughter. The birch rod went on dancing, and the Councilor was obliged to dance too; it was no use, he might make himself great and long, or remain the little yellow wax doll with the big black hat. Then the other flowers put in a good word for him, especially those who had lain in the doll's bed, and then the birch rod gave over. At the same moment there was a loud knocking at the drawer, inside where Ida's doll, Sophy, lay with many other toys. The Chimney-sweep ran to the edge of the table, lay flat down on his stomach, and began to pull the drawer out a little. Then Sophy raised herself, and looked round quite astonished.

" There must be a ball here," said she; " why did nobody tell me?"

" Will you dance with me ? " asked the Chimney-sweep.

" You are a nice sort of fellow to dance ! " she replied, and turned her back upon him.

Then she seated herself upon the drawer, and thought that one of the flowers would come and ask her; but not one of them came. Then she coughed, " Hem! hem! hem!" but for all that not one came. The Chimney-sweep now danced all alone, and that was not at all so bad.

As none of the flowers seemed to notice Sophy, she let herself fall down from the drawer straight upon the floor, so that there was a great noise. The flowers now all came running up, to ask if she had not hurt herself; and they were all very polite to her, especially the flowers that had lain in her bed. But she had not hurt herself at all; and

Ida's flowers all thanked her for the nice bed, and were kind to her, took her into the middle of the room, where the moon shone in, and danced with her; and all the other flowers formed a circle round her. Now Sophy was glad, and said they might keep her bed, she did not at all mind lying in the drawer.

But the flowers said, " We thank you heartily, but in any way we cannot live long. To-morrow we shall be quite dead. But tell little Ida she is to bury us out in the garden, where the canary lies; then we shall wake up again in summer, and be far more beautiful."

" No, you must not die," said Sophy; and she kissed the flowers.

Then the room door opened, and a great number of splendid flowers came dancing in. Ida could not imagine whence they had come; these must certainly all be flowers from the king's castle yonder. First of all came two glorious roses, and they had little gold crowns on; they were a king and a queen. Then came the prettiest stocks and carnations; and they bowed in all directions. They had music with them. Great poppies and peonies blew upon pea-pods till they were quite red in the face. The blue hyacinths and the little white snow-drops rang just as if they had been bells. That was wonderful music! Then came many other flowers, and danced all together; the blue violets and the pink primroses, daisies and the lilies of the valley. And all the flowers kissed one another. It was beautiful to look at!

At last the flowers wished one another good-night; then little Ida, too, crept to bed, where she dreamed of all she had seen.

When she rose next morning, she went quickly to the little table, to see if the pretty flowers were still there. She drew aside the curtains of the little bed; there were they all, but they were quite faded, far more than yesterday. Sophy was lying in the drawer where Ida laid her; she looked very sleepy.

" Do you remember what you were to say to me? " asked little Ida.

But Sophy looked quite stupid, and did not say a single word.

"You are not good at all!" said Ida. "And yet they all danced with you."

Then she took a little paper box, on which were painted beautiful birds, and opened it, and laid the dead flowers in it.

"That shall be your pretty coffin," said she, "and when my cousins come to visit me by and by they shall help me to bury you outside in the garden, so that you may grow again in summer, and become more beautiful than ever."

These cousins were two merry boys. Their names were Gustave and Adolphe; their father had given them two new cross-bows, and they brought these with them to show to Ida. She told them about the poor flowers which had died, and then they got leave to bury them. The two boys went first, with their cross-bows on their shoulders, and little Ida followed with the dead flowers in the pretty box. Out in the garden a little grave was dug. Ida first kissed the flowers, and then laid them in the earth in the box, and Adolphe and Gustave shot with their cross-bows over the grave, for they had neither guns nor cannons.

THE ANGEL

WHENEVER a good child dies, an angel from heaven comes down to earth and takes the dead child in his arms, spreads out his great white wings, and flies away over all the places the child has loved, and picks quite a handful of flowers, which he carries up to the Almighty, that they may bloom in heaven more brightly than on earth. And the Father presses all the flowers to His heart; but He kisses the flower that pleases Him best, and the flower is then endowed with a voice, and can join in the great chorus of praise!

"See"—this is what an Angel said, as he carried a dead child up to heaven, and the Child heard, as if in a dream; and they went on over the regions of home where the little Child had played, and came through gardens with beautiful flowers—"which of these shall we take with us to plant in heaven?" asked the Angel.

Now, there stood near them a slender, beautiful rose-bush; but a wicked hand had broken the stem, so that all the branches, covered with half-opened buds, were hanging around, quite withered.

"The poor rose-bush!" said the Child. "Take it, that it may bloom up yonder."

And the Angel took it, and kissed the Child, and the little one half opened his eyes. They plucked some of the rich flowers, but also took with them the wild pansy and the despised buttercup.

"Now we have flowers," said the Child.

And the Angel nodded, but he did not yet fly upward to heaven. It was night and quite silent. They remained in the great city; they floated about there in a small street, where lay whole heaps of straw, ashes, and sweepings, for it had been removal day. There lay fragments of plates, bits of plaster, rags, and old hats, and all this did not look well. And the Angel pointed amid all this confusion to a few fragments of a flower-pot, and to a lump of earth which had fallen out, and which was kept together by the roots of a great dried field flower, which was of no use, and had therefore been thrown out into the street.

"We will take that with us," said the Angel. "I will tell you why, as we fly onward."

"Down yonder in the narrow lane, in the low cellar, lived a poor sick boy; from his childhood he had been bedridden. When he was at his best he could go up and down the room a few times, leaning on crutches; that was the utmost he could do. For a few days in summer the sunbeams would penetrate for a few hours to the ground of the cellar, and when the poor boy sat there and the sun shone on him, and he looked at the red blood in his three fingers, as he held them up before his face, he would say, 'Yes, to-day he has been out!' He knew the forest with its beautiful vernal green only from the fact that the neighbor's little son brought him the first green branch of a beech-tree, and he held that up over his head, and dreamed he was in the beech wood, where the sun shone and the birds sang. On a spring day the neighbor's boy brought him also field flowers, and among them was, by chance, one to which the root was still hanging; and so it was planted in a flower-pot, and placed by the bed, close to the window. And the flower had been planted by a fortunate hand; and it grew, threw out new shoots, and bore flowers every year. It became a splendid flower garden to the sickly boy—his little treasure here on earth. He watered it, and tended it, and took care that it had the benefit of every ray of sunlight, down to the latest that struggled in through the narrow window; and the flower itself was woven into his dreams, for it grew for him and gladdened his eyes, and spread its fragrance about him; and toward it he turned in death, when the Father called him. He has now been with the Almighty for a year; for a year the flower has stood forgotten in the window, and is withered; and thus, at the removal, it has been thrown out into the dust of the street. And this is the poor flower which we have taken into our nosegay; for this flower has given more joy than the richest in a queen's garden."

" But how do you know all this? " asked the Child.

" I know it," said the Angel, " for I myself was that boy who walked on crutches. I know my flower well."

And the Child opened his eyes and looked into the glorious, happy face of the Angel; and at the same moment they entered the regions where there is peace and joy. And the Father pressed the dead Child to His bosom, and then it received wings like the Angel, and flew hand in hand with him. And the Almighty kissed the dry withered field flower, and it received a voice and sang with all the angels hovering around—some near, and some in wider circles, and some in infinite distance, but all equally happy. And they all sang— little and great, the good, happy Child, and the poor field flower that had lain there withered, thrown among the dust, in the rubbish of the removal day, in the dark narrow lane.

THE FLYING TRUNK

THERE was once a merchant, who was so rich that he could pave the whole street with gold, and almost have enough left for a little lane. But he did not do that; he knew how to employ his money differently. When he spent a shilling he got back a crown, such a clever merchant was he; and this continued till he died.

His son now got all this money; and he lived merrily, going to the masquerade every evening, making kites out of dollar notes, and playing at ducks and drakes on the sea-coast with gold pieces instead of pebbles. In this way the money might soon be spent, and indeed it was so. At last he had no more than four shillings left, and no clothes to wear but a pair of slippers and an old dressing-gown. Now his friends did not trouble themselves any more about him, as they could not walk with him in the street, but one of them, who was good-natured, sent him an old trunk, with the remark, "Pack up!" Yes, that was all very well, but he had nothing to pack, therefore he seated himself in the trunk.

That was a wonderful trunk. So soon as any one pressed the lock the trunk could fly. He pressed it, and *whirr!* away flew the trunk with him through the chimney and over the clouds, farther and farther away. But as often as the bottom of the trunk cracked a little he was in great fear lest it might go to pieces, and then he would have flung a fine somersault! In that way he came to the land of the Turks. He hid the trunk in a wood under some dry leaves, and then went into the town. He could do that very well, for among the Turks all the people went about dressed like himself in dressing-gown and slippers. Then he met a nurse with a little child.

"Here, you Turkish nurse," he began, "what kind of a great castle is that close by the town, in which the windows are so high up?"

"There dwells the Sultan's daughter," replied she. "It is prophesied that she will be very unhappy respecting a lover; and therefore nobody may go near her, unless the Sultan and Sultana are there too."

"Thank you!" said the Merchant's Son; and he went out into the forest, seated himself in his trunk, flew on the roof, and crept through the window into the Princess's room.

She was lying asleep on the sofa, and she was so beautiful that the Merchant's Son was compelled to kiss her. Then she awoke, and was startled very much; but he said he was a Turkish angel who had come down to her through the air, and that pleased her.

They sat down side by side, and he told her stories about
her eyes; and he told her they were the most glorious dark
lakes, and that thoughts were swimming about in them like
mermaids. And he told her about her forehead; that it was
a snowy mountain with the most splendid halls and pictures.
And he told her about the stork who brings the lovely little
children.

Yes, those were fine histories ! Then he asked the Princess
if she would marry him, and she said " Yes," directly.

" But you must come here on Saturday," said she. " Then
the Sultan and Sultana will be here to tea. They will be very
proud that I am to marry a Turkish angel. But take care
that you know a very pretty story, for both my parents are
very fond indeed of stories. My mother likes them high-
flown and moral, but my father likes them merry, so that
one can laugh."

" Yes, I shall bring no marriage gift but a story," said he;
and so they parted. But the Princess gave him a sabre, the
sheath embroidered with gold pieces, and that was very useful to him.

Now he flew away, bought a new dressing-gown, and sat
in the forest and made up a story; it was to be ready by
Saturday, and that was not an easy thing.

By the time he had finished it Saturday had come. The
Sultan and his wife and all the court were at the Princess's
to tea. He was received very graciously.

" Will you relate us a story? " said the Sultana; " one that
is deep and edifying."

" Yes, but one that we can laugh at," said the Sultan.

" Certainly," he replied; and so began. And now listen
well.

" There was once a bundle of Matches, and these Matches
were particularly proud of their high descent. Their genea-
logical tree, that is to say, the great fir-tree of which each of
them was a little splinter, had been a great old tree out in the
forest. The Matches now lay between a Tinder-box and an
old Iron Pot; and they were telling about the days of their
youth. ' Yes, when we were upon the green boughs,' they
said, ' then we really were upon the green boughs! Every
morning and evening there was diamond tea for us,—I mean

dew; we had sunshine all day long whenever the sun shone, and all the little birds had to tell stories. We could see very well that we were rich, for the other trees were only dressed out in summer, while our family had the means to wear green dresses in the winter as well. But then the wood-cutter came, like a great revolution, and our family was broken up. The head of the family got an appointment as mainmast in a first-rate ship, which could sail round the world if necessary; the other branches went to other places, and now we have the office of kindling a light for the vulgar herd. That's how we grand people came to be in the kitchen.'

"'My fate was of different kind,' said the Iron Pot, which stood next to the Matches. 'From the beginning, ever since I came into the world, there has been a great deal of scouring and cooking done in me. I look after the practical part, and am the first here in the house. My only pleasure is to sit in my place after dinner, very clean and neat, and to carry on a sensible conversation with my comrades. But except the Water-pot, which is sometimes taken down into the court-yard, we always live within our four walls. Our only newsmonger is the Market Basket; but he speaks very uneasily about the government and the people. Yes, the other day there was an old pot that fell down, from fright, and burst. He's liberal, I can tell you!'—'Now you're talking too much,' the Tinder-box interrupted, and the steel struck against the flint, so that sparks flew out. 'Shall we not have a merry evening?'

"'Yes, let us talk about who is the grandest,' said the Matches.

"'No, I don't like to talk about myself,' retorted the Pot. 'Let us get up an evening entertainment. I will begin. I will tell a story from real life, something that every one has experienced, so that we can easily imagine the situation, and take pleasure in it. On the Baltic, by the Danish shore'—

"'That's a pretty beginning!' cried all the Plates. 'That will be a story we shall like.'

"'Yes, it happened to me in my youth, when I lived in a family where the furniture was polished, the floors scoured, and new curtains were put up every fortnight.'

"'What an interesting way you have of telling a story!'

said the Carpet Broom. 'One can tell directly that a man is speaking who has been in woman's society. There's something pure runs through it.'

"And the Pot went on telling his story, and the end was as good as the beginning.

"All the Plates rattled with joy, and the Carpet Broom brought some green parsley out of the dust-hole, and put it like a wreath on the Pot, for he knew that it would vex the others. 'If I crown him to-day,' it thought, 'he will crown me to-morrow.'

"'Now I'll dance,' said the Fire Tongs; and they danced. Preserve us! how that implement could lift up one leg! The old chair-cushion burst to see it. 'Shall I be crowned too?' thought the Tongs; and indeed a wreath was awarded.

"'They're only common people, after all!' thought the Matches.

"Now the Tea-urn was to sing; but she said she had taken cold, and could not sing unless she felt boiling within. But that was only affectation: she did not want to sing, except when she was in the parlor with the grand people.

"In the window sat an old Quill Pen, with which the maid generally wrote: there was nothing remarkable about this pen, except that it had been dipped too deep into the ink, but she was proud of that. 'If the Tea-urn won't sing,' she said, 'she may leave it alone. Outside hangs a nightingale in a cage, and he can sing. He hasn't had any education, but this evening we'll say nothing about that.'

"'I think it very wrong,' said the Tea-kettle—he was the kitchen singer, and half-brother to the Tea-urn—'that that rich and foreign bird should be listened to! Is that patriotic? Let the Market Basket decide.'

"'I am vexed,' said the Market Basket. 'No one can imagine how much I am secretly vexed. Is that a proper way of spending the evening? Would it not be more sensible to put the house in order? Let each one go to his own place, and I will arrange the whole game. That would be quite another thing.'

"'Yes, let us make a disturbance,' cried they all. Then the door opened, and the maid came in, and they all stood still; not one stirred. But there was not one pot among

them who did not know what he could do, and how grand
he was. 'Yes, if I had liked,' each one thought, 'it might
have been a very merry evening.'

"The servant girl took the Matches and lighted the fire
with them. Mercy! how they sputtered and burst out into
flame! 'Now every one can see,' thought they, 'that we are
the first. How we shine! what a light!'—and they burned
out."

"That was a capital story," said the Sultana. "I feel myself quite carried away to the kitchen, to the Matches. Yes,
now thou shalt marry our daughter."

"Yes, certainly," said the Sultan, "thou shalt marry our
daughter on Monday."

And they called him *thou,* because he was to belong to the
family.

The wedding was decided on, and on the evening before
it the whole city was illuminated. Biscuits and cakes were
thrown among the people, the street boys stood on their toes,
called out "Hurrah!" and whistled on their fingers. It was
uncommonly splendid.

"Yes, I shall have to give something as a treat," thought
the Merchant's Son. So he bought rockets and crackers, and
every imaginable sort of fire-work, put them all into his
trunk, and flew up into the air.

"Crack!" how they went, and how they went off! All
the Turks hopped up with such a start that their slippers flew
about their ears; such a meteor they had never yet seen.
Now they could understand that it must be a Turkish angel
who was going to marry the Princess.

What stories people tell! Every one whom he asked about
it had seen it in a separate way; but one and all thought it
fine.

"I saw the Turkish angel himself," said one. "He had
eyes like glowing stars, and a beard like foaming water."

"He flew up in a fiery mantle," said another; "the most
lovely little cherub peeped forth from among the folds."

Yes, they were wonderful things that he heard; and on the
following day he was to be married.

Now he went back to the forest to rest himself in his
trunk. But what had become of that? A spark from the

fire-works had set fire to it, and the trunk was burned to ashes. He could not fly any more, and could not get to his bride.

She stood all day on the roof waiting; and most likely she is waiting still. But he wanders through the world, telling fairy tales; but they are not so merry as that one he told about the Matches.

THE TINDER-BOX

THERE came a Soldier marching along the high road —*one, two! one, two!* He had his knapsack on his back and a sabre by his side, for he had been in the wars, and now he wanted to go home. And on the way he met with an old Witch: she was very hideous, and her under lip hung down upon her breast. She said, " Good evening, Soldier. What a fine sword you have, and what a big knapsack! You're a proper soldier! Now you shall have as much money as you like to have."

" I thank you, you old Witch! " said the Soldier.

" Do you see that great tree? " quoth the Witch; and she pointed to a tree which stood beside them. " It's quite hollow inside. You must climb to the top and then you'll see a hole, through which you can let yourself down and get deep into the tree. I'll tie a rope round your body, so that I can pull you up again when you call me."

" What am I to do down in the tree? " asked the Soldier.

" Get money," replied the Witch. " Listen to me. When you come down to the earth under the tree, you will find yourself in a great hall: it is quite light, for above three hundred lamps are burning there. Then you will see three doors; these you can open, for the keys are hanging there. If you go into the first chamber, you'll see a great chest in the middle of the floor; on this chest sits a dog, and he's got a pair of eyes as big as two tea-cups. But you need not care for that. I'll give you my blue checked apron, and you can spread it out upon the floor; then go up quickly and take the dog, and set him on my apron; then open the chest, and take as many shillings as you like. They are of copper: if you prefer silver, you must go into the second chamber. But there sits a dog with a pair of eyes as big as mill-wheels. But do not care for that. Set him upon my apron, and take some of the money. And if you want gold, you can have that too—in fact, as much as you can carry—if you go into the third chamber. But the dog that sits on the money-chest there has two eyes as big as round towers. He is a fierce dog, you may be sure; but you needn't be afraid, for all that. Only set him on my apron, and he won't hurt you; and take out of the chest as much gold as you like."

"That's not so bad," said the Soldier. "But what am I to give you, you old Witch? for you will not do it for nothing, I fancy."

"No," replied the Witch, "not a single shilling will I have. You shall only bring me an old Tinder-box which my grandmother forgot when she was down there last."

"Then tie the rope round my body," cried the Soldier.

"Here it is," said the Witch, "and here's my blue checked apron."

Then the Soldier climbed up into the tree, let himself slip down into the hole, and stood, as the Witch had said, in the great hall where the three hundred lamps were burning.

Now he opened the first door. Ugh! there sat the dog with eyes as big as tea-cups, staring at him. "You're a nice fellow!" exclaimed the Soldier; and he set him on the Witch's apron, and took as many copper shillings as his pockets would hold, and then locked the chest, set the dog on it again, and went into the second chamber. Aha! there sat the dog with eyes as big as mill-wheels.

"You should not stare so hard at me," said the Soldier; "you might strain your eyes." And he set the dog upon the Witch's apron. And when he saw the silver money in the chest, he threw away all the copper money he had, and filled his pockets and his knapsack with silver only. Then he went into the third chamber. O, but that was horrid! The dog there really had eyes as big as towers, and they turned round and round in his head like wheels.

"Good evening!" said the Soldier; and he touched his cap, for he had never seen such a dog as that before.

When he had looked at him a little more closely, he thought, "That will do," and lifted him down to the floor, and opened the chest. Mercy! what a quantity of gold was there! He could buy with it the whole town, and the sugar sucking-pigs of the cake woman, and all the tin soldiers, whips, and rocking-horses in the whole world. Yes, that was a quantity of money! Now the Soldier threw away all the silver coin with which he had filled his pockets and his knapsack, and took gold instead: yes, all his pockets, his knapsack, his boots, and his cap were filled, so that he could scarcely walk. Now indeed he had plenty of money. He put the dog on the chest, shut the door, and then called up through the tree, "Now pull me up, you old Witch."

"Have you the Tinder-box?" asked the Witch.

"Plague on it!" exclaimed the Soldier, "I had clean forgotten that." And he went and brought it.

The Witch drew him up, and he stood on the high road again, with pockets, boots, knapsack, and cap full of gold.

"What are you going to do with the Tinder-box?" asked the Soldier.

"That's nothing to you," retorted the Witch. "You've had your money; just give me the Tinder-box."

"Nonsense!" said the Soldier. "Tell me directly what you're going to do with it or I'll draw my sword and cut off your head."

"No!" cried the Witch.

So the Soldier cut off her head. There she lay! But he tied up all his money in her apron, took it on his back like a bundle, put the Tinder-box in his pocket, and went straight off toward the town.

That was a splendid town! And he put up at the very best inn, and asked for the finest rooms, and ordered his favorite dishes, for now he was rich, as he had so much money. The servant who had to clean his boots certainly thought them a remarkably old pair for such a rich gentleman; but he had not bought any new ones yet. The next day he procured proper boots and handsome clothes. Now our Soldier had become a fine gentleman; and the people told him of all the splendid things which were in their city, and about the King, and what a pretty Princess the King's daughter was.

"Where can one get to see her?" asked the Soldier.

"She is not to be seen at all," said they all together; "she lives in a great copper castle, with a great many walls and towers round about it: no one but the king may go in and out there, for it has been prophesied that she shall marry a common soldier, and the King can't bear that."

"I should like to see her," thought the Soldier; but he could not get leave to do so. Now he lived merrily, went to the theatre, drove in the King's garden, and gave much money to the poor; and this was very kind of him, for he knew from old times how hard it is when one has not a shilling. Now he was rich, had fine clothes, and gained many friends, who all said he was a rare one, a true cavalier; and that pleased the Soldier well. But as he spent money every day and never earned any, he had at last only two shillings left; and he was obliged to turn out of the fine rooms in which he had dwelt, and had to live in a little garret under the roof, and clean his boots for himself, and mend them with a darning needle. None of his friends came to see him, for there were too many stairs to climb.

It was quite dark one evening, and he could not even buy himself a candle, when it occurred to him that there was a candle-end in the Tinder-box which he had taken out of the hollow tree into which the Witch had helped him. He brought out the Tinder-box and the candle end; but as soon as he struck fire and the sparks rose up from the flint, the door flew open, and the dog who had eyes as big as a couple of tea-cups, and whom he had seen in the tree, stood before him, and said,—

"What are my lord's commands?"

"What is this?" said the Soldier. "That's a famous Tinder-box, if I can get everything with it that I want! Bring me some money," said he to the dog; and *whisk!* the done was gone, and *whisk!* he was back again, with a great bag full of shillings in his mouth.

Now the Soldier knew what a capital Tinder-box this was. If he struck it once, the dog came who sat upon the chest of copper money; if he struck it twice, the dog who had the silver; and if he struck it three times, then appeared the dog who had the gold. Now the Soldier moved back into the fine rooms, and appeared again in handsome clothes; and all his friends knew him again, and cared very much for him indeed.

Once he thought to himself, "It is a very strange thing that one cannot get to see the Princess. They all say she is very beautiful; but what is the use of that, if she has always to sit in the great copper castle with the many towers? Can I not get to see her at all? Where is my Tinder-box?" And so he struck a light, and *whisk!* came the dog with eyes as big as tea-cups.

"It is midnight, certainly," said the Soldier, "but I should very much like to see the Princess, only for one little moment."

And the dog was outside the door directly, and, before the Soldier thought it, came back with the Princess. She sat upon the dog's back and slept; and every one could see she was a real princess, for she was so lovely. The Soldier could not refrain from kissing her, for he was a thorough soldier. Then the dog ran back again with the Princess. But when morning came, and the King and Queen were drinking tea, the Princess said she had had a strange dream the night before, about a dog and a soldier—that she had ridden upon the dog, and the soldier had kissed her.

"That would be a fine history!" said the Queen.

So one of the old court ladies had to watch the next night by the Princess's bed, to see if this was really a dream, or what it might be.

The Soldier had a great longing to see the lovely Princess again; so the dog came in the night, took her away, and ran as fast as he could. But the old lady put on water-boots, and ran just as fast after him. When she saw that they both entered a great house, she thought, "Now I know where it is;" and with a bit of chalk she drew a great cross on the door. Then she went home and lay down, and the dog came up with the Princess; but when he saw that there was a cross drawn on the door where the Soldier lived, he took a piece of chalk too, and drew crosses on all the doors in the town. And that was cleverly done, for now the lady could not find the right door, because all the doors had crosses upon them.

In the morning early came the King and Queen, the old court lady and all the officers, to see where it was the Princess had been. "Here it is!" said the King, when he saw the first door with a cross upon it. "No, my dear husband, it is there!" said the Queen, who descried another door which also showed a cross. "But there is one, and there is one!" said all, for wherever they looked there were crosses on the doors. So they saw that it would avail them nothing if they searched on.

But the Queen was an exceedingly clever woman, who could do more than ride in a coach. She took her great gold scissors, cut a piece of silk into pieces, and made a neat little bag; this bag she filled with fine wheat flour, and tied it on the Princess's back; and when that was done, she cut a little hole in the bag, so that the flour would be scattered along all the way which the Princess should take.

In the night the dog came again, took the Princess on his back, and ran with her to the Soldier, who loved her very much, and would gladly have been a prince, so that he might have her for his wife. The dog did not notice at all how the flour ran out in a stream from the castle to the windows of the Soldier's house, where he ran up the wall with the Princess. In the morning the King and the Queen saw well enough where their daughter had been, and they took the Soldier and put him in prison.

There he sat. O, but it was dark and disagreeable there! And they said to him, "To-morrow you shall be hanged." That was not amusing to hear, and he had left his Tinderbox at the inn. In the morning he could see, through the iron grating of the window, how the people were hurrying out of the town to see him hanged. He heard the drums beat and saw the soldiers marching. All the people were running out, and among them was a shoemaker's boy with leather apron and slippers, and he galloped so fast that one of his slippers flew off, and came right against the wall where the Soldier sat looking through the iron grating.

"Halloo, you shoemaker's boy! you needn't be in such a hurry," cried the Soldier to him: "it will not begin till

I come. But if you will run to where I lived, and bring me my Tinder-box, you shall have four shillings: but you must put your best leg foremost."

The shoemaker's boy wanted to get the four shillings, so he went and brought the Tinder-box, and—well, we shall hear now what happened.

Outside the town a great gallows had been built, and round it stood the soldiers and many hundred thousand people. The King and Queen sat or a splendid throne, opposite to the judges and the whole council. The Soldier already stood upon the ladder; but as they were about to put the rope round his neck, he said that before a poor criminal suffered his punishment an innocent request was always granted to him. He wanted very much to smoke a pipe of tobacco, and it would be the last pipe he should smoke in the world. The King would not say " No " to this; so the Soldier took his Tinder-box, and struck fire. One—two,—three!—and there suddenly stood all the dogs—the one with the eyes as big as tea-cups, the one with eyes as large as mill-wheels, and the one whose eyes were as big as round towers.

"Help me now, so that I may not be hanged," said the Soldier.

And the dogs fell upon the judges and all the council, seized one by the leg and another by the nose, and tossed them all many feet into the air, so that they fell down and were all broken to pieces.

" I won't! " cried the King; but the biggest dog took him and the Queen, and threw them after the others. Then the soldiers were afraid, and the people cried, " Little Soldier, you shall be our king, and marry the beautiful Princess! "

So they put the Soldier into the King's coach, and all the three dogs darted on in front and cried " Hurrah! " and the boys whistled through their fingers, and the soldiers presented arms. The Princess came out of the copper castle, and became Queen, and she liked that well enough. The wedding lasted a week, and the three dogs sat at the table too, and opened their eyes wider than ever at all they saw.

THE BUCKWHEAT

OFTEN after a thunder-storm, when one passes a field in which buckwheat is growing, it appears quite blackened and singed. It is just as if a flame of fire had passed across it; and then the countryman says, " It got that from lightning." But whence has it received that? I will tell you what the sparrow told me about it, and the sparrow heard it from an old willow-tree which stood by a buckwheat field, and still stands there. It is quite a great venerable Willow-tree, but crippled and old: it is burst in the middle, and grass and brambles grow out of the cleft; the tree bends forward, and the branches hang quite down to the ground, as if they were long green hair.

On all the fields round about corn was growing, not only rye and barley, but also oats; yes, the most capital oats, which when ripe, looks like a number of little yellow canary birds sitting upon a spray. The corn stood smiling, and the richer an ear was the deeper did it bend in pious humility.

But there was also a field of buckwheat, and this field was exactly opposite to the old Willow-tree. The Buckwheat did not bend at all like the rest of the grain, but stood up proudly and stiffly.

" I'm as rich as any corn-ear," said he. " Moreover, I'm very much handsomer: my flowers are beautiful as the blossoms of the apple-tree: it's quite a delight to look upon me and mine. Do you know anything more splendid than we are, you old Willow-tree? "

And the old Willow-tree nodded his head, just as if he would have said, " Yes, that's true enough! "

But the Buckwheat spread itself out from mere vainglory, and said,

" The stupid tree! he's so old that the grass grows in his body."

Now a terrible storm came on: all the field flowers folded their leaves together or bowed their little heads while the storm passed over them, but the Buckwheat stood erect in its pride.

" Bend your head like us," said the Flowers.

"I've not the slightest cause to do so," replied the Buckwheat.

"Bend your head as we do," cried the various Crops. "Now the Storm comes flying on. He has wings that reach from the clouds just down to the earth, and he'll beat you in halves before you can cry for mercy."

"Yes, but I won't bend," quoth the Buckwheat.

"Shut up your flowers and bend your leaves," said the old Willow-tree. "Don't look up at the lightning when the cloud bursts: even men do not do that, for in the lightning one may look into heaven, but the light dazzles even men; and what would happen to us, if we dared do so—we, the plants of the field, that are much less worthy than they?"

"Much less worthy!" cried the Buckwheat. "Now I'll just look straight up into heaven."

And it did so, in its pride and vainglory. It was as if the whole world were on fire, so vivid was the lightning.

When afterward the bad weather had passed by, the flowers and the crops stood in the still, pure air, quite refreshed by the rain; but the Buckwheat was burned coal-black by the lightning, and it was now like a dead weed upon the field.

And the old Willow-tree waved its branches in the wind, and great drops of water fell down out of the green leaves, just as if the tree wept.

And the Sparrows asked, "Why do you weep? Here everything is so cheerful: see how the sun shines: see how the clouds sail on. Do you not breathe the scent of flowers and bushes? Why do you weep, Willow-tree?"

And the Willow-tree told them of the pride of the Buckwheat, of its vainglory, and of the punishment which always follows such sin.

I, who tell you this tale, have heard it from the sparrows. They told it me one evening when I begged them to give me a story.

THE BELL

PEOPLE said, "The evening-bell is sounding, the sun is setting." A strange wondrous tone was heard in the narrow streets of a large town. It was like the sound of a church-bell: but it was only heard for a moment, for the rolling of the carriages, and the voices of the multitude made too great a noise.

Those persons who were walking about the town, where the houses were further apart, with gardens or little fields between them, could see the evening sky still better, and heard the sound of the bell much more distinctly. It was as if the tones came from a church in the still forest; people looked thitherward, and felt their minds attuned most solemnly.

A long time passed, and people said to each other,—"I wonder if there is a church out in the wood? The bell has a tone that is wondrous sweet; let us stroll thither, and examine the matter nearer." And the rich people drove out, and the poor walked, but the way seemed strangely long to them; and when they came to a clump of willows which grew on the skirts of the forest, they sat down, and looked up at the long branches, and fancied they were now in the depth of the green wood. The confectioner of the town came out, and set up his booth there; and soon after came another confectioner, who hung a bell over his stand, as a sign or ornament, but it had no clapper, and it was tarred over to preserve it from the rain. When all the people returned home, they said it had been very romantic, and that it was quite a different sort of thing to a picnic or tea-party. There were three persons who asserted they had penetrated to the end of the forest, and that they had always heard the wonderful sounds of the bell, but it had seemed to them as if it had come from the town. One wrote a whole poem about it, and said the bell sounded like the voice of a mother to a good dear child, and that no melody was sweeter than the tones of the bell. The king of the country was also observant of it, and vowed that he who could discover whence the sounds proceeded should have the title of "Universal Bell-ringer," even if it were not really a bell.

Many persons now went to the wood, for the sake of getting the place, but one only returned with a sort of explanation; for nobody went far enough, that one not farther than the others. However, he said that the sound proceeded from a very large owl, in a hollow tree; a sort of learned owl, that continually knocked its head against the branches.

But whether the sound came from his head or from the hollow tree, that, no one could say with certainty. So now he got the place of Universal Bell-ringer," and wrote yearly a short treatise "On the Owl;" but everybody was just as wise as before.

It was the day of Confirmation. The clergyman had spoken so touchingly, the children who were confirmed had been greatly moved; it was an eventful day for them; from children they became all at once grown-up persons; it was as if their infant souls were now to fly all at once into persons with more understanding. The sun was shining gloriously; the children that had been confirmed went out of the town, and from the wood was borne toward them the sounds of the unknown bell with wonderful distinctness. They all immediately felt a wish to go thither; all except three. One of them had to go home to try on a ball-dress, for it was just the dress and the ball which had caused her to be confirmed this time, for otherwise she would not have come; the other was a poor boy who had borrowed his coat and boots to be confirmed in from the innkeeper's son, and he was to give them back by a certain hour; the third said that he never went to a strange place if his parents were not with him; that he had always been a good boy hitherto, and would still be so now that he was confirmed, and that one ought not to laugh at him for it: the others, however, did make fun of him, after all.

There were three, therefore, that did not go; the others hastened on. The sun shone, the birds sang, and the children sang too, and each held the other by the hand; for as yet they had none of them any high office, and were all of equal rank in the eye of God.

But two of the youngest soon grew tired, and both returned to town; two little girls sat down, and twined garlands, so they did not go either; and when the others reached the willow-tree, where the confectioner was, they said, "Now we are there! In reality the bell does not exist; it is only a fancy that people have taken into their heads!"

At the same moment the bell sounded deep in the wood, so clear and solemnly that five or six determined to penetrate somewhat further. It was so thick, and the foliage so dense that it was quite fatiguing to proceed. Woodroof and anemones grew almost too high; blooming convolvuluses and blackberry-bushes hung in long garlands from tree to tree, where the nightingale sang and the sunbeams were playing: it was very beautiful, but it was no place for girls to go; their clothes would get so torn. Large blocks of stone lay there, overgrown with moss of every color; the fresh spring bubbled forth, and made a strange gurgling sound.

"That surely cannot be the bell," said one of the children, lying down and listening; "this must be looked to." So he remained, and let the others go on without him.

They afterwards came to a little house, made of branches and the bark of trees; a large wild apple-tree bent over it, as if it would shower down all its blessings on the roof, where roses were blooming. The long stems twined round the gable, on which there hung a small bell.

Was it that which people had heard? Yes: everybody was unanimous on the subject, except one, who said that the bell was too small and too fine to be heard at so great a distance, and besides, it had very different tones from those that could move a human heart in such a manner. It was a king's son who spoke; whereon the others said, "Such people always want to be wiser than everybody else."

They now let him go on alone; and as he went, his breast was filled more and more with the forest solitude; but he still heard the little bell with which the others were so satisfied, and now and then, when the wind blew, he could also hear the people singing who were sitting at tea where the confectioner had his tent; but the deep sound of the bell rose louder; it was almost as if an organ were accompanying it, and the tones came from the left hand, the side where the heart is placed. A rustling was heard in the bushes, and a little boy stood before the King's Son; a boy in wooden shoes, and with so short a jacket that one could see what long wrists he had. Both knew each other; the boy was that one among the children who could not come because he had to go home and return his jacket and boots to the innkeeper's son. This he had done, and was now going on in wooden shoes and in his humbler dress, for the bell sounded with so deep a tone, and with such strange power, that proceed he must.

"Why, then, we can go together," said the King's Son.

But the poor child that had been confirmed was quite ashamed; he looked at his wooden shoes, pulled at the short sleeves of his jacket, and said, "He was afraid he could not walk so fast; besides, he thought that the bell must be looked for to the right; for that was the place where all sorts of beautiful things were to be found."

"But there we shall not meet," said the King's Son, nodding at the same time to the Poor Boy, who went into the darkest, thickest part of the wood, where the thorns tore his humble dress, and scratched his face, and hands, and feet, till they bled. The King's Son got some scratches, too; but the sun shone on his path, and it is him that we will follow, for he was an excellent and resolute youth.

"I must and will find the bell," said he, "even if I am obliged to go to the end of the world."

The ugly apes sat upon the trees, and grinned. "Shall we thrash him?" said they; "shall we thrash him? He is the son of a king!"

But on he went, without being disheartened, deeper and deeper into the wood, where the most wonderful flowers were growing. There stood white lilies with blood-red stamens; sky-blue tulips, which shone as they waved in the winds; and apple-trees, the apples of which looked exactly like large soap-bubbles: so only think how the trees must have sparkled in the sunshine! Around the nicest green meads, where the deer were playing in the grass, grew magnificent oaks and beeches; and if the bark of one of the trees was cracked, there grass and long creeping plants grew in the crevices. And there were large, calm lakes there too, in which white swans were swimming, and beat the air with their wings. The King's Son often stood still and listened. He thought the bell sounded from the depths of these still lakes; but then he remarked again that the tone proceeded not from there, but farther off, from out the depths of the forest.

The sun now set; the atmosphere glowed like fire. It was still in the woods, so very still; and he fell on his knees, sung his evening hymn, and said: "I cannot find what I seek; the sun is going down, and night is coming—the dark, dark night. Yet perhaps I may be able once more to see the round, red sun before he entirely disappears. I will climb up yonder rock.

And he seized hold of the creeping-plants, and the roots of trees,—climbed up the moist stones where the water-snakes were writhing and the toads were croaking—and he gained the summit before the sun had quite gone down. How magnificent was the sight from this height! The sea—the great, the glorious sea, that dashed its long waves against the coast —was stretched out before him. And yonder, where sea and sky meet, stood the sun, like a large, shining altar, all melted together in the most glowing colors. And the wood and the sea sang a song of rejoicing, and his heart sang with the rest: all nature was a vast, holy church, in which the trees and the buoyant clouds were the pillars, flowers and grass the velvet carpeting, and heaven itself the large cupola. The red colors above faded away as the sun vanished, but a million stars were lighted, a million lamps shone; and the King's Son spread out his arms toward heaven, and wood, and sea; when at the same moment, coming by a path to the right, appeared, in his wooden shoes and jacket, the Poor Boy who had been confirmed with him. He had followed his own path, and had reached the spot just as soon as the Son of the King had done. They ran toward each other, and stood together, hand in hand, in the vast church of nature and of poetry, while over them sounded the invisible, holy bell; blessed spirits floated around them, and lifted up their voices in a rejoicing hallelujah!

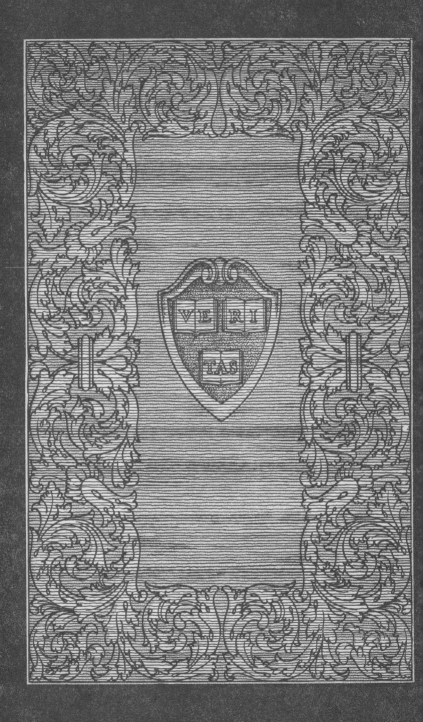